Rocky Mountain Tales

Rocky Mountain
Tales

Edited by

Levette J. Davidson

and Forrester Blake

with drawings by

Skelly

UNIVERSITY OF OKLAHOMA PRESS

NORMAN, 1947

TO *The Innumerable Story Tellers of
the Old West—the Forgotten Homers and
Munchausens—Whose Works Are
Represented in This Volume*

The Chapters

The Illustrations

The Rocky Mountain West

N OT long ago, in England, a few Americans from the Rocky Mountain West sat together in a Nissen hut. Overhead, in thick night, the noise of engines—the power pulse of enemy bombers winging inland from the North Sea—was irregular, lifting and dying away as craft infiltrated the searchlight zones. Batteries in greenwood copses crashed out defensive fire; occasionally, from alerted fighter bases, interceptors roared upward to lose themselves in the furry black. There was danger in the night, a chilling tale of death and of the destruction of cities. But, strangely, in the Nissen hut the Americans sat unheeding. Hard-rock miners from the Colorado high country, cowpunchers from New Mexico and Montana, dry farmers and construction men, clerks from the growing Front Range centers —all had passed such nights before. Fatalists, yet stubborn and determined to yield neither faith, memories, nor way of life, they talked quietly among themselves, with a deep and abiding longing, of the great plains and valleys and of the far American mountains from which they had come.

What is there in this Rocky Mountain land, that it should grip men's hearts in spite of distance and the blackest times of war? Why should most Americans—men native to the Western country, as well as travelers, chance visitors soon moving on their way—so steadfastly cherish it, finding in it solace, humor, strength, that secret vision which has possessed Americans since America's beginning?

In the south, perhaps, it is color, the canyon red and mountain green, the yellow of the valley malpais, the blue of a fathomless sky. There the Rio Grande, Pecos, and Chama roll down from peak sources, meeting first the mesa country below Jemez and Sangre de Cristo ranges, flowing through lava gates and coming at last to desert and the straight New Mexican plateaus spiked with solitary mountain masses, which lead out to Texas plains. Along these rivers are Indian pueblos, dun-colored, blending naturally with the earth; Spanish towns, bright with pepper strings and blue windows and doorways; American towns, of brick and white stone, rising above their more ancient neighbors. On tributaries beyond sight of main routes are ranches, some of adobe, others of knotty pine clapboard, where men and buildings have acquired a leather hue. All there is color, brilliance in great blocks and splashes, color shifting like cloud forms with each day and season, flaring upward, falling swiftly, filling the eyes of all who encounter it.

In the north, perhaps, it is shadow and whiteness, the dark of montane forests, the quartz gleam of snow fields below peaks. Winds of the north are snow-winds; waters of the north are snow-waters, swift in stream beds, mica clear, shining like golden arrows in the sun. Valleys here are tall-grass valleys; meadows are park-land, quiet sub-alpine places marked with crystal pools; ridges are spur lines, evergreen juts, sanctuary for the shyest living thing. For, of all wide regions of America, this country of the northern Rocky Mountains is game country, haunt still of mountain sheep and grizzly, antlered elk and black-tailed deer, coyote and the shaggy, padding timber wolf. In the Yellowstone and the broad valleys below Bitterroot and Bear Tooth ranges, below the Tetons, the Big Horns, and the Medicine Bow, herds have their feeding grounds. When snow flies, and the leaves of cottonwoods and aspens spin like bird flocks in the meadows, game is seen, winding down from the tundra line. It is then that elk calls echo shrill and wild across the parks. It is then that coyotes come in close, slinking about settled places, deer choose forage spots, beavers strengthen dams and lodges, cougars roam more lonesomely at night, and geese and other migratory fowl wing fast away from wintertime.

Between desert and the northern snows lies Colorado, Rocky Mountain core. Here no South Pass shows an even way to Salt Lake and the Oregon. Here no valley of the Rio Grande leads to Mexico and the border California trails. In this red central land, range on range the Colorado Rockies rise, bastioned, tumultuous, massive granite fists allied with storm and space to beat the traveler back. Fremont, striking up the Arkansas, following the trapper Bill Williams into the silver San Juan, felt the cold and hunger of its peaks. Gunnison, seeking Utah, saw the lightning in its skies, heard its thunder rumbles and the roar of hidden waters in its gorges. Pike, climbing heights which bear his name; Long, staring at gray Front Range slopes; old Preacher Dyer, wandering through the mining camps:—each, in his time, pierced its trails and measured icy beauties by the terror they inspired. An American Frontier, lived in, now known but never wholly conquered, Colorado is the mountain heart from which a region's life and history have sprung, the matrix stone in which they rest, in modern years, unshakably imbedded.

So stands the Rocky Mountain West. Like smoke drifting through canyons, leaving traces only here and there among the crevices, the earliest history of the Western country has been lost. Spaniards and the American trapper vanguard, facing lands unknown to white men, had neither time nor wish to write long treatises. Exploring parties, officially sanctioned, made compilations—journals of botanical and geological fact, tables of astronomical and meteorological observation—which quickly found their way to archive shelves. Only after the first informal travelers, the boomers, and editors of gold rush days arrived, was Rocky Mountain life described in all its fulness. Then presses left their current records; files grew, though it appears haphazardly; diaries lengthened; letters went out by pony express; and new stories, native to the region, made the rounds of camp and range. It is in such ways that history—at least the fragmentary record of a frontier land—is saved. And it is from sources such as these—from old letters and personal documents, as well as from yellowed newspaper pages and the lips of old-timers who now look far down the years to early days—that this book of Rocky Mountain tales has come.

The sources of these tales are indicated in footnotes. Editorial license has been taken in minor instances in altering spelling and supplementing punctuation for the sake of clearness.

In preparing this book, the editors rest under heavy obligation not only to the authors and publishers mentioned, but also to the many anonymous or forgotten storytellers whose efforts were rewarded only by the brief interest of some circle of listeners and by their own personal satisfaction in artistic creation.

To the collectors and the librarians who have built up the Western History Collection of the Denver Public Library and the library of the State Historical Society of Colorado, we wish to express our great appreciation and gratitude. Miss Ina T. Aulls, in charge of the former, and Miss Frances Shay, of the latter, have been especially helpful. Our colleagues on the faculty of the University of Denver, Dr. LeRoy R. Hafen and the directors of the State Historical Society of Colorado, and others too numerous to mention, have co-operated in various ways to make this work possible.

LEVETTE J. DAVIDSON
FORRESTER BLAKE

University of Denver
Denver, Colorado
January 9, 1947

Rocky Mountain Tales

Old Jim Bridger

IN the vicinity of U. S. Highway 30, where today it crosses southwestern Wyoming grasslands on its way to Great Salt Lake, stands a cluster of ancient cabins. Over these rough structures, remnants of Jim Bridger's fort and trading post in the Green River country, cottonwoods have spread their branches far, bringing welcome coolness in the hottest summer hours. Among these cabins, too, life has become slow and quiet, like that of an old frontiersman, beaten by the storms and heat and dust of the Rocky Mountain West, who has come at last to peace and deep-eyed meditation upon his younger days.

One hundred years ago there was a different tempo here. Then, in the Rocky Mountain spring trappers appeared, coming out of the Yellowstone or Snake River, or out of the fabulous Uinta Range to the south, with their packs of beaver pelts. Throughout the summer months dust clouds hung in the east, wagon trains rolled one after another into Bridger's Fort to refit and replenish supplies, the post forge flared, anvils were noisy day and night, and there was endless talk of Salt Lake, California, and the distant Willamette. Then again, with the last of the wagon trains gone and the first snow lighting Uinta peaks, the trappers came in, making fall rendezvous, repairing traps and overhauling their guns, casting fresh ball ammunition, buying fresh powder, seeing to it that knives were given the keenest of edges, and, with all, keeping an eye on the weather. It was at such times, in the loveliest of Rocky Mountain seasons, that business was talked. And it was then, beneath stars of a brilliance known to no other land, that the great log fires were built, men laughed and sang and fought, and tales born of the wild Western country—stories of timber and sage, of canyon and tall granite peak—were spun by those who had been there, by white men who before all other white men had sought space and freedom and, in doing so, had freely ranged their spirits with the spirit of a continent.

Among frontiersmen old Jim Bridger, wandering much alone in the American West, perhaps was best known. Certainly as time went on his reputation as a storyteller increased. Year after year he reappeared on Green River, always bringing new tales, holding fascinated not only trappers of the mountain brigades but travelers from the farthest sections of the nation, many of them men of shrewd and educated mind, who listened, laughed with the others, and, in quieter moments, set down for later generations of Americans what had been said around the great rendezvous fires.

BRIDGER'S PERSONALITY[1]

In private correspondence both Captain J. Lee Humfreville, Indian fighter who came to know Jim Bridger under many trying circumstances, and John Hunton, who lived with Bridger at the sutler's store, Fort Laramie, Wyoming, from October, 1867, to April, 1868, have left excellent short characterizations of the old frontiersman.

James Bridger, or, as he was familiarly spoken of in that country, "Old Jim Bridger," was the most efficient guide, mountaineer, plainsman, trapper, and Indian fighter that ever lived in the Far West. He knew more of that country and all things within its borders than anyone who ever lived. . . . Although Bridger had little or no education, he could, with a piece of charcoal or a stick, scratch on the ground or any smooth surface a map of the whole Western country that was much more correct than those made at that time by skilled topographical engineers, with all their scientific instruments. I have seen Bridger look at a printed map and point out its defects at sight. His experience in that country was not confined to a few nations and tribes of Indians. He knew more about them, their habits, customs, and characters than any man who ever lived in all that nation.

[1] J. Lee Humfreville, *Twenty Years Among Our Hostile Indians* (New York, 1899), 462–63, 467; Grace Raymond Hebard and E. A. Brininstool, *The Bozeman Trail* (Cleveland, 1922), II, 233.

4

Old Jim Bridger

On no occasion would he trust an Indian. His disgust for them knew no bounds. He called them "sarpints," "varmints," and "pizen." He maintained that a rattlesnake was of some good, but that an Indian was good for nothing. He prided himself on the fact that in anything the "sarpints" (meaning the Indians, not the rattlesnakes) did, he (Bridger) could outdo them. He was a marvelous trailer . . . unquestionably the most expert that ever lived. Even when old, and with dimmed eyesight, he could run a trail, when mounted, as fast as his horse could carry him. . . .

I occupied the same quarters with him one whole winter, where I had ample opportunity to study his character and learn his peculiar ways and manner of living. He never did anything until he felt so inclined. For instance, if he grew sleepy in the afternoon, say by three or four or five o'clock, he went to bed, and when he awoke, say in four or five or six hours afterward, he would rise, make a fire, roast meat, eat it, and sing "Injun," to use his own term, the rest of the night. If he had a tin pan, he turned it bottom-side up, and with a stick beat on the bottom, making a noise like an Indian tom-tom. He never ate until he was hungry, and, as he lived largely on meats, he was thin and spare, although strong and wiry.—HUMFREVILLE.

He [Jim Bridger] made two or three trips to Cheyenne and Fort D. A. Russell during the time he was here, but I do not think he was absent at any time to exceed ten days. He seemed to prefer to be around here, and to be alone, or with some one or two persons who did not annoy him by constant questioning. Sometimes he seemed to like to talk, and always made a good listener when the subject of conversation interested or pleased him. When it did not, he always curled up his upper lip with a sneer and left the audience. He told me many times he did not like to sacrifice his feelings, intelligence, or personal pleasure, "when it was such an easy matter to walk away from a damn fool talking." I have more than once seen him walk away from a group of army officers in the officers' clubroom (where he was always a welcome guest) because some officer would comment on something or somebody when Bridger would think the comment was made in ignorance or malice.—HEBARD.

5

Rocky Mountain Tales

A DENVER PORTRAIT OF BRIDGER[2]

Supplementing these descriptions of the rugged old scout, a writer in the Rocky Mountain News of frontier times, perhaps famed Editor William N. Byers himself, has recorded his own small, nostalgic bit about Jim Bridger.

This almost last of the old pioneer army is verging on the sere and yellow leaf. His eyesight is much impaired, and with difficulty is he able to recognize the few remaining old companions in the arduous struggles of life on the frontier Plains. He was yesterday the guest of his old acquaintance, Colonel A. G. Boone, and B. D. Spenser, Esq., in Denver. Last evening James Baker, the old Indian hunter, on Clear Creek, visited him, and we should like to have witnessed the meeting of the two old veterans. He left last evening for the East.

GEYSER COUNTRY[3]

To the north of Fort Bridger, beyond Green River, the Grand Tetons, and Jackson Hole, spreads the Yellowstone country, place of mystery throughout the trapper decades. Few Indians would go there. Frontiersmen, spooked by the whispers of ghost smokes and bright red, steaming waters, gave it wide berth. But Jim Bridger went into the Yellowstone. Again and again he packed north, fading for weeks into the silent Wyoming wilderness, then riding forth at some unexpected time with new and far more astonishing tales of that region beyond the Bad Mountains.

Near the source of the river Puante, which empties into the Big Horn, and the sulphurous waters of which have probably the same medicinal qualities as the celebrated Blue Lick Springs of Kentucky, is a place called "Colter's Hell"—from a beaver hunter of that name. This locality is often agitated with sub-

[2] *Rocky Mountain News* (Denver), March 17, 1872.

[3] R. J. DeSmet, *Western Missions and Missionaries* (New York, 1859), 86–88; Nathaniel Pitt Langford, *Diary of the Washburn Expedition to the Yellowstone and Firehole Rivers in the Year 1870* (n. p., 1905), viii; J. W. Gunnison, *The Mormons* (Philadelphia, 1852), 151; Eugene F. Ware, *The Indian War of 1864* (Topeka, 1911), 282–83.

terranean fires. The sulphurous gases which escape in great volumes from the burning soil infect the atmosphere for several miles, and render the earth so barren that even the wild wormwood cannot grow on it. The beaver hunters have assured me that the underground noises and explosions are often frightful.

However, I think that the most extraordinary spot in this respect, and perhaps the most marvelous of all the northern half of this continent, is in the very heart of the Rocky Mountains, between the 43rd and 45th degrees of latitude and the 109th and 111th degrees of longitude, that is, between the sources of the Madison and the Yellowstone. It reaches more than a hundred miles. Bituminous, sulphurous, and boiling springs are very numerous in it. The hot springs contain a large quantity of calcerous matter, and form hills more or less elevated, which resemble in their natures, perhaps, if not their extent, the famous springs of Pemboukkalesi, in Asia Minor, so well described by Chandler. The earth is thrown up very high, and the influence of the elements causes it to take the most varied and most fantastic shapes.

Gases, vapors, and smoke are continually escaping, by a thousand openings, from the base to the summit of the volcanic pile; the noise at times resembles the steam let off by a boat. Strong subterranean explosions occur like those in "Colter's Hell." The hunters and the Indians speak of it with superstitious fear, and consider it the abode of evil spirits, that is to say, a kind of hell. Indians seldom approach it without offering some sacrifice, or, at least, without presenting the calumet of peace to the turbulent spirits, that they may be propitious. They declare that the subterranean noises proceed from the forging of warlike weapons; each eruption of the earth is, in their eyes, the result of a combat between the infernal spirits, and becomes a monument of a new victory or new calamity. Near Gardiner River, a tributary of the Yellowstone, and in the vicinity of the region I have just been describing, there is a mountain of sulphur. I have this report from Captain Bridger, who is familiar with every one of these mounds, having passed thirty years of his life near them.— DeSmet.

[Jim Bridger] told me in Virginia City, Montana, at that time, of the existence of hot, spouting springs in the vicinity of the source of the Yellowstone and Madison rivers, and said that he had seen a column of water as large as his body, spout as high as the flagpole in Virginia City, which was about sixty feet high. The more I pondered upon this statement the more I was impressed with the probability of its truth. If he had told me of the existence of falls one thousand feet high I should have considered his story an exaggeration of a phenomenon he had already beheld; but I did not think his imagination was sufficiently fertile to originate the story of the existence of a spouting geyser, unless he had really seen one, and I therefore was inclined to give credit to his statement, and to believe that such a wonder did really exist.—LANGFORD.

A lake sixty miles long, cold and pellucid, lies enbosomed amid high precipitous mountains. On the west side is a sloping plain several miles wide, with clumps of trees and groves of pines. The ground resounds to the tread of horses. Geysers spout up seventy feet high, with a terrific hissing noise, at regular intervals. Waterfalls are sparkling, leaping, and thundering down the precipices, and collect in the pool below. The river issues from this lake, and for fifteen miles roars through the perpendicular canyon at the outlet. In this section are the Great Springs, so hot that meat is readily cooked in them, and as they descend on the successive terraces, afford at length delightful baths. On the other side is an acid spring, which gushes out in a river torrent; and below is a cave which supplies "vermilion" for the savages in abundance. Bear, elk, deer, wolf, and fox, are among the sporting game, and the feathered tribe yields its share for variety, on the sportsman's table of rock or turf.—GUNNISON.

I can recite accurately only one of [Jim Bridger's] stories, because I took time to put it down, as follows. He said: "That is the greatest country that I ever see. I was up there riding around, and I didn't dare to fire a gun only at long intervals, and then I got right out of the country where I fired it as soon as possible. I would bring down a deer, and cut it up and carry

8

it, and move out. One time I was among some pines, sort of hid in the sidehill along the stream that had a pretty wide valley, and I saw a couple of Injuns coming along down through the grass on their ponies on the other side of the creek. I wanted to watch and wait until they got out of sight, so I kept my eye on them for a long while. I saw them coming for nearly an hour, and they took their time at it, and I was afraid they would cross over, and might run onto some of my tracks. But they didn't, and they went down the valley on the opposite side from where I was.

"They hadn't gone very far before the crust of the earth gave way under them, and they and their ponies went down out of sight, and up came a great powerful lot of flame and smoke. I bet hell was not very far from that place." This story I could never account for, unless [Jim Bridger] had seen some Indians drop through the ground in some part of the hot-spring and geyser country.—WARE.

THE FIREHOLE RIVER[4]

Within the Yellowstone territory are beautiful streams like the Firehole, little snow-water rivers cascading through gorges, coursing in places through broad mountain parks, and in other places becoming heated and discolored among the weird geyser basins of that region. According to Captain W. F. Raynolds and Nathaniel Pitt Langford, both of whom had met Bridger, the old scout crossed many of these streams and gave more than one its name.

I will end these specimen tales by one from Bridger, which partakes so decidedly of a scientific nature that it should not be omitted. He contends that near the headwaters of the Columbia River, in the fastnesses of the mountains, there is a spring gushing forth from the rocks near the top of the mountain. The water when it issues forth is cold as ice, but it runs down over smooth rock so far and so fast that it is *hot at the bottom.*—RAYNOLDS.

[4] W. F. Raynolds, *Report of the Exploration of the Yellowstone River* (Washington, 1868), 77; Langford, *Washburn Expedition,* 112–13.

Mr. Hedges and I forded the Firehole River a short distance below our camp [on September 19, 1870]. The current, as it dashed over the boulders, was swift, and taking off our boots and stockings, we selected for our place of crossing what seemed to be a smooth rock surface in the bottom of the stream, extending from shore to shore. When I reached the middle of the stream I paused a moment and turned around to speak to Mr. Hedges, who was about to enter the stream, when I discovered from the sensation of warmth under my feet I was standing upon an incrustation formed over a hot spring that had its vent in the bed of the stream. I exclaimed to Hedges: "Here is the river which Bridger said was hot at the bottom!"—LANGFORD.

ALUM CREEK[5]

Surprising as the smoky Firehole River must have been to Yellowstone travelers, the presence of heat in a snow-water stream, it appears, was as nothing to the phenomena encountered by Hiram M. Chittenden and A. J. Weikert, also seekers after frontier facts, while unwinding the trails of the eccentric Jim Bridger.

The origin of the name Alum Creek, a tributary of the Yellowstone, was due to an accidental discovery by Bridger. One day he forded the creek and rode out several miles and back. He noticed that the return journey was only a small fraction of the distance going, and that his horse's feet had shrunk to mere points which sank into the solid ground, so that the animal could scarcely hobble along. Seeking the cause he found it to be the astringent quality of the water, which was saturated with alum to such an extent that it had power to pucker distance itself.—CHITTENDEN.

The headwaters of this stream are so strong with alum that one swallow is sufficient to draw one's face into such a shape

[5] Hiram M. Chittenden, *The Yellowstone Park* (Cincinnati, 1895; Stanford University Press, 1940), 44; A. J. Weikert, *Journal*, August 26, 1877. The selections from Chittenden's *The Yellowstone Park*, which are included here and elsewhere, are reprinted by permission of and special arrangement with Stanford University Press, authorized publishers.

that it is almost impossible to get it straightened out again for one hour or so.—WEIKERT.

PETRIFICATION[6]

Of petrification, glass mountains, paint pots, and other strange features of the Yellowstone country many tales have been told, most of them, it seems, based upon the original observations of this same James Bridger.

According to Jim Bridger's account, there exists still in the Park country a mountain which was once cursed by a great medicine man of the Crow nation. Everything upon the mountain at the time of this dire event became instantly petrified and has remained so ever since. All forms of life are standing about in stone where they were suddenly caught by the petrifying influence, even as the inhabitants of ancient Pompeii were surprised by the ashes of Vesuvius. Sagebrush, grass, prairie fowl, antelope, elk, and bear, may there be seen as perfect as in actual life. Dashing torrents and the spray mist from them stand forth in arrested motion as if carved from rock by a sculptor's chisel. Even flowers are blooming in colors of crystal, and birds soar with wings spread in motionless flight, while the air floats with music and perfumes siliceous, and the sun and moon shine with petrified light!—CHITTENDEN.

According to an authority who remains unknown to this day, old Jim Bridger, one evening after a long day's ride, was jogging in to a familiar camping place in the region of petrification. Without warning, he came upon a hidden and precipitous chasm which blocked his way. Exhausted as both he and his horse were from their long march, he was comparatively disheartened by this obstacle, passage of which might well cause him several hours of strenuous exertion and carry him far into the night.

Riding up to the brink to reconnoiter, Bridger found that he could not stop his horse, which kept moving right along as if

[6] Chittenden, *Yellowstone Park*, 45; Raynolds, *Exploration of the Yellowstone River*, 77–78; Nelson A. Miles, *Personal Recollections* (New York, 1896), 187.

by its own momentum out over the edge of the precipice, straight on at a steady gait and on a level line, as if supported by an invisible bridge. Almost before he realized it he was safe on the far side, and in his desired camp. His unbounded amazement at this miracle soon abated, however, when he remembered the strange character of the surrounding country; and he was forced to the conclusion that this chasm, as others in the Yellowstone region, was simply a void in which gravity itself had become petrified.—CHITTENDEN.

Some of [Bridger's] Munchausen tales struck me as altogether too good to be lost. One was to this effect: In many parts of the country petrification and fossils are very numerous; and, as a consequence, it was claimed that in some locality (I was not able to fix it definitely) a large tract of sage is perfectly petrified, with all the leaves and branches in perfect condition, the general appearance of the plain not being unlike that of the rest of the country, but *all in stone*, while the rabbits, sage hens, and other animals usually found in such localities are still there, perfectly petrified, and as natural as when they were living; and more wonderful still, these petrified bushes bear the most wonderful fruit—diamonds, rubies, sapphires, emeralds, etc., etc., as large as black walnuts are found in abundance. "I tell you sir," said one narrator, "it is true, for I gathered a quart myself, and sent them down the country!"—RAYNOLDS.

The story is told that on some such [storytelling] occasion, one night after supper, a comrade who in his travels and explorations had gone as far south as the Zuñi village, New Mexico, and had discovered the famous petrified forest of Arizona, inquired of Bridger:

"Jim, were you ever down to Zuñi?"

"No, thar ain't any beaver down thar."

"But, Jim, there are some things in this world besides beaver. I was down there last winter and saw great trees and limbs and bark and all turned into stone."

"O," returned Jim, "that's petrification. Come with me to the Yellowstone next summer, and I'll show you peetrified trees a-growing, with peetrified birds on 'em a-singing peetrified songs."

Now it so happened that [Bridger] had been to the Yellowstone, and had seen the "peetrified" trees standing but not the "peetrified birds" or the "peetrified songs." The geysers of the Yellowstone at intervals eject hot water, supersaturated with carbonate of lime and geyserite, to a height of from one hundred and fifty to two hundred feet. This water is carried laterally by the wind, sometimes two or three hundred feet, saturating the trees, and gradually covering the nearest side with a crystal formation, while the other side bears living branches. So Jim Bridger's story was in part true.—MILES.

GLASS MOUNTAINS[7]

Deep within the mountainous country of the Yellowstone lies the great Obsidian Cliff, smoky-hued, flint-hard, a shining mass of metamorphic rock. Not without justification, in the old days, did frontiersmen who saw it weave their tales about it.

Coming one day in sight of a magnificent elk, he [Jim Bridger] took careful aim at the unsuspecting animal and fired. To his great amazement, the elk not only was not wounded, but seemed not even to have heard the report of the rifle. Bridger drew considerably nearer and gave the elk the benefit of his most deliberate aim; but with the same result as before. A third and fourth effort met with a similar fate.

Utterly exasperated, he seized the rifle by the barrel, resolved to use it as a club since it had failed as a firearm. He rushed madly toward the elk, but suddenly crashed into an immovable vertical wall which proved to be a mountain of perfectly transparent glass, on the farther side of which, still in peaceful security, the elk was quietly grazing. Stranger still, the mountain was not only of pure glass, but was a perfect telescopic lens, and, whereas the elk seemed but a few hundred yards off, it was in reality twenty-five miles away!—CHITTENDEN.

[7] Chittenden, *Yellowstone Park*, 42–43; Ware, *Indian War*, 283–84; Humfreville, *Hostile Indians*, 464–65; Margaret I. Carrington, *Ab-Sa-Ra-Ka, Land of Massacre* (Philadelphia, 1868 and 1878), 113.

One time I asked [Jim Bridger] what kind of a country it was west of the place where he saw the big lake, and he told me it was a very rocky country. Then he said: "Up there is one of the strangest mountains that I ever did see. It is a diamond mountain, shaped something like a cone. I saw it in the sun for two days before I got to it, and then at night I camped right near it. I hadn't more than got my horse lariated out—it was a little dusky—when I saw a campfire and some Injuns right through the mountain on the other side. So I didn't build any fire, but I could see them just as plain as if there hadn't been anything but air. In the morning I noticed the Injuns were gone, and I thought I would like to see the other side of the mountain. So, I rode around to the other side and it took me half a day."

I said to him, "Might not that have been a mountain of salt?" I put this query to him because the country was entirely unknown, and I wanted to cross-examine him, but he said, "Oh, no. I went up and knocked off a corner of it, a piece of rock as big as my arm, a big, long piece of diamond, and brought it out, and afterwards gave it to a man, and he said it was a diamond all right."—WARE.

"Is there anything remarkable to be seen about here [the Yellowstone country]?" an inquisitive pilgrim asked [Jim Bridger] one day.

"W-a-l-l," he replied, in a peculiar drawling tone which he generally assumed in telling stories in order to gain time to give his imagination fuller play, "there's a cur'ous mountain a few miles off'n the road, to the north of here, but the doggon'd trouble is you can't see the blamed thing."

"A mountain and can't see it—that's curious," interrupted the pilgrim. "How large is it?"

"Wall, I should say it's nigh onto three miles in circumference at the base, but its height is unknown," continued Jim Bridger with imperturbable gravity.

"Is it so high you can't see the top of it?" inquired the puzzled traveler.

"That's what I say, stranger; you can't see the base of it either. Didn't you ever hear of the Crystal Mountain?"

Jim Bridger and the Glass Mountain

"I never did."

"Wall, I'll tell you what it is. It's a mountain of crystal rock, an' so clear that the most powerful field glasses can't see it, much less the naked eye. You'll wonder, p'r'aps, how a thing that can't be seen nohow wus ever discovered. It came about in this way. You see, a lot of bones and the carcasses of animals an' birds wus found scattered all around the base. You see they ran and flew against this invisible rock and jest killed themselves dead. You kin feel the rock an' that's all. You can't see it. It's a good many miles high, for everlastin' quantities of birds' bones are piled up all around the base of it."—HUMFREVILLE.

Many stories are told of Bridger's past history, and he is charged with many of his own manufacture. He is said to have seen a diamond in the Rocky Mountains, by the light of which he traveled thirty miles one stormy night, and to have informed some inquisitive travelers that Scott's Bluffs, nearly four hundred feet high, now stand where there was a deep valley when he first visited that country. When inquired of as to these statements, he quietly intimated that there was no harm in fooling people who pumped him for information and would not even say "Thank ye."—CARRINGTON.

BRIDGER AND BAKER RECOVER THEIR PONIES[8]

Although old Jim Bridger, forever traipsing through the Western country, seemed to possess a secret spot in his heart for the Yellowstone, his travels were by no means confined to that region. Story after story was told about him by men like Jim Baker, trapper and plainsman, who knew him not only in moments of relaxation but also in times of hard and breath-taking action on the Frontier.

I b'leve it was in '46 that this yere scrape happened, and I reckon I can tell purty near the truth about it, as I was thar or thereabouts, I'm purty sure. I was livin' with old Bald Eagle's

[8] *Colorado Transcript* (Golden), February 2, 9, 1876. George West, editor of the *Transcript,* probably got this story direct from his old friend, Jim Baker.

band of Snakes—"Old Bally," us boys uset to call him. I reckon you remember him, don't ye, Jack, fur you was along of old Raven when he riz his har up on the Laramie Plains in '49, when he was goin' fer them Californy pilgrims. Wal, me and Jim Bridger and some of the other boys had bin over in North Park with Old Bally and his Injuns to give the Utes a little turn, and when we got back to the village we found some Blackfeet had run off about thirty of our best ponies. Of course we couldn't stand that, and we started off at once with all the rest of the band to try to catch up to 'em. The Snakes and Blackfeet hadn't been overly hostile, but you know a Injin'll steal horses wharever found.

We rid purty hard on their trail for a couple of days, and struck Chugwater perty far up without gettin' very close to 'em. It was getten' well on to night, and Old Bally ordered us to camp. Me and Jim Bridger rid out over the bluff with a couple of Injuns to reconnoiter a little afore the pickets was sent out. We made up our minds that the Blackfeet had struck out for the Black Hills, and that they were eight or nine hours ahead of us. Old Bally began to be a little skeery about goin' any further, for fear of strikin' the whole Blackfoot outfit, or else a big band of Sioux. The Oghalalas was hot on the Snakes them days, and we was getten' right well into their stampin' grounds.

As I was sayin', me and Jim Bridger and a couple of bucks was sent out to reconnoiter, and afore we'd got two mile from camp we struck fresh Sioux sign in the sand hills. You can bet yer mocassins we didn't stay 'round thar only jest long enough ter make sure of the sign till we made tracks towards camp. After we got over the bluff in sight of camp we concluded we'd better part of us stay and watch while the others rid to camp and give the alarm. Jim's pony was fresher'n mine and I told him to git ter Old Bally as soon as that thar pony'd take him thar. He took one of the bucks along of him and the other stayed with me. This Injin's name in United States lingo was Stag-walkin'-in-the-water, and a faithfuller cuss to me never skinned a head.

Walkee—us white allus called him Walkee for short—thought a heap of me, for he was a brother to my squaw. After Jim had bin gone a spell me and Walkee thought we'd look around a little, so we crep up to the top of the bluff and peeped over. The moon was comin' up, and when we got one good glance to the easterd we didn't have no call to take another. I don't say thar was ten million Sioux right thar within three hundred yards of us, but fer a minit or two I jest thought thar was that many and more too. Me 'nd Walkee hadn't lost them Sioux, and we jest *clum* down that thar bluff to our ponies.

I'm free to say I was skart doggoned near plumb to death, fer that whole band was on the lope, and a-comin' right toward us. When we reached the hosses we could see a big bunch of 'em comin' over the bluff, and as we broke down the hill they made for us. I reckoned Jim hadn't more'n time to git to our camp, and as our band wan't lookin' much for Sioux they'd praps onsaddled, so I didn't expect no help from them for some minits, and made up my mind that our hosses had got to save us if we was goin' to be saved. They was purty wall played from our sixty mile ride, but we had nigh onta a quarter start, and I hoped to git in ahead. Them ponies just jumped their best, but twenty or thirty of the innemy was gainin' on us fast when we reached the bottom.

I was a little ahead of Walkee, and began to think mebby we'd reach our friends anyhow, when all of a suddint I found myself a spinnin' through the air head fust toward the ground. My pony had stuck a foot into a prarry-dog's hole, pitched end over end, and flung me as I have said. Here was a fix now, for a innocent young feller that hadn't got nothin' again them Sioux and who them Sioux had nothin' aginst 'cept only the company he was in. I reckon I thought of purty nigh everything in them two seconds that it took me to light from that hoss. I wan't much hurt, howsomever, and I jumped up and skinned out afoot, hopin' to outwind 'em yet, but that wan't no go, you bet. Walkee tried to haul me up behind him, but two of them cusses was too nigh to us.

"You just git," I said to him, in the expressivist Snake I could use, and lit out towards the timber on Chugwater as fast as these yere legs could travel. It wan't no use, though. 'Bout the fust jump I made I struck into a bed of cactus, which made my mocassins ruther uncomfortable. Them Sioux was comin' up on me fast I knew, but I couldn't stop to look 'round. The whole band was yellin' to the two head bucks, and them bucks was a-yellin' at me. I expected to feel a arrer in my body every jump, but I s'pose they wanted a live Snake for suthin', and they didn't shoot, but in a minnit or two I felt my feet flyin' up behind, and my face strikin' the ground. One of them bucks had flung his lass' under my feet like I ketched that Dock feller out thar, and I found myself a pris'ner o' war. . . .

Wall, fellers, I reckon that thar was a right bad fix to be in. I know'd the Injins didn't hev much time to spare, and I jest consaited they'd raise my har then and thar, and I was bound to show fight whether it done any good or not. The buck that had ketched me jumped off'n his pony and come towards me, making sure to keep the slack of his lass' tight up, so I couldn't help myself. I didn't know no Sioux lingo, and so as he got purty close up I jest flung myself over on my back and grabbed my knife out of my leggings, thinking I'd make the best fight I could fer my har, and at the same time commenced cussin' him fer all that was out in right good United States. I got as fur as callin' him all the white livered, black-an'-tan, lousy niggers I could think of when the feller broke into my discourse with these 'ere plain American words: "The hell's fire! I hope I may be obleeged to eat pisoned kiote fer a month of Sundays if you ain't a white man."

"I've got three pake of the best beaver skins you ever seed that says I ar," says I, and I was now just a tremblin' like a cottonwood leaf in a gale of wind at the discov'ry.

By this time the Sioux was a comin' up purty strong, and as my capter stooped down to cast his lass' off'n my leg he said to me a little low like, "Whoever you be, you'll hev to come along with we'uns now, but I can fix it all right with them. They'll hev to skin back tonight, anyhow, for their village is only an hour's ride from here, over at Holes-in-the-Prary."

Wall, I couldn't raise no fuss about that arrangement, fer I was so glad to find things no wuss that I didn't care much, fer a while anyway. I never knowed adzactly what my friend told the chief of the band, but he fixed it all right fer a time. Some of 'em had ketched my pony, and I was glad to find that his fall hadn't hurt him much. I jumped on'ter his back, and the whole band whirled around and started off at a good lope towards the north-eastard. As we rid along my friend told me all about hisself. His name was Matt Harker, and he told me he had bin to work for the Beauvaises seven or eight year, and was now going with this band for them. He said they was on their way up to the Black Hills after game, and that some of 'em was going to the Bad Lands for buffalo, while the balance would hunt elk and blacktail deer in the hills. Matt was a right good feller, and had bin with the Sioux long enough to understand their lingo and signs purty well.

The night was almost as light as day, and the moon was almost full, and them Injins kep a purty good guard out to the rear, and I couldn't tell whether the Snakes was a follerin' or not, but I was right sure Jim Bridger and Walkee wouldn't rest easy 'thout knowin' how I was fixed. We rid on at a right sharp gallup for a hour or more afore we come in sight of the village. I could see about sixty lodges, and afore we got thar they had bin signaled, and the squaws was jest a husslin' them teepes down, and correlin' the loose ponies. It wan't but a few minutes until they was all packed, and the whole caboodle was on its way to the northerd.

After all, ther wan't mor'n a hundred fightin' bucks in the outfit, but when I seed 'em over the bluff I jest thought there wer a million. They knowd thar wan't morn forty of our band, but we didn't have no squaws nor teepes along, and could have made it powerful hot for 'em.

This was Walkin' Bull's band, and I'd heerd he was a purty good Injin to the whites. I knowd, too, that he had nothin' again me only bein' with the Snakes. He rid back onest or twist to whar I was a ridin' along of Matt, and Matt told him I'd jest as lives go along of him as with the Snakes, and so he jist froze to me to go along of the party. I jest thought that was the best way to fix it, and let things work till I could get away so as they wouldn't suspicion Matt, fer he'd done me a powerful good turn, and I wouldn't have gone back on him if they'd sculped me.

We rid at a purty good lope all night, and struck a branch of Chugwater about sunup. Here we found the balance of Walkin'

Bull's band, which was waitin' fer him. Matt Harker was a right lively talker, and he had told me all about what lay-out he thought he'd got. Ye see Matt uset to be a miner down in Gorgy, but skinned out of thar eight or nine years afore fer some reason I expect best knowd to himself. He had struck St. Joe jest in time to jine Beauvais' cavayard that was a movin' out on the Plains, and he'd bin along of 'em ever since. He'd got in with this band by taking a couple of squaws, and bein' no coward and a right peart hoss thief he made himself all hunky along of 'em.

Durin' that stampede that night I told Matt a good deal of my oterbiogerfy, and we to wonst got to be cronies, so he told me his biggest object in goin' on this tramp to the Black Hills. He said about two year afore he was with a band of Oghalalas when they had a fight with some Pawnees over on White Man's Fork. The Pawnees cleaned 'em out, but most of 'em got away. Matt he rid in and wiped out a Pawnee jest as he was going to raise the har of one of his friends, and then slung him on his hoss and got away with him. The Injin had a arrer broke off in him, and Matt was purty sure he'd go under, but he got him back to camp afore he died. That Injin was so glad Matt had saved his har, that afore he turned up his toes he told him about a place up thar in the Hills whar there was a power of gold. Bein' a Gorgy this waked Matt up, and he'd bin hankerin' to go up thar ever sence. He said the Injin had given him the lay of the land so's he was right sure he could find it, and he wanted me to jine him in huntin' it up after we got up thar.

I didn't go much on this yarn, fer I wan' no miner, but sence they've struck gold here I expect ther might be plenty of it up thar too. I didn't hev a chance to find out about it, as I didn't stay with them Sioux long enough. It's gitten purty late, and I'll jest tell ye how I got back home again, and dry up.

As I said, I jest b'leved Walkee and Jim Bridger'd keep on our trail till they found how I was fixed, and they jest did that too. We made right good time for two or three days, as the band had nothin' to stop fer, and grub was powerful scarce. One after-noon we fell in with that band of Blackfeet that had run off our ponies, and they hed 'em along yet. Thar was seven or eight among 'em as was mine, and the sight of 'em made me feel kinder oneasy like to capter 'em back. I knowd it would be tough to do it alone, but I kept thinkin' about it and plannin' how to do it. I didn't want to go back on Matt, so I told him about it. He tried to coax me to go along of him to the Black Hills, but I jest played it that I was homesick to git back to my squaw, and after a while he told me he hadn't got no love fer them Blackfeet, and if I could play 'em a trick he wouldn't blow on me.

In that thar band of ponies there was a slashin' one of mine that I riz from a colt, and allus found it amusin' to learn him to foller me, and come when I called him. He'd allus jest jump when I give a pecooler whistle I hed teeched him. I knowd ef I could get onter his back ther wan't no Sioux nor Blackfeet pony that was agoin' to ketch me, and I jest thought I'd try it on. We didn't move fur the next day, and camped in a piece of timber on some low bluffs. I knowd the moon wouldn't be up afore ten or 'leven, and laid my plans accordin'. Matt helped me to git some dry buffer to take along, as I didn't expect to have much time to hunt after I got started. When we was a comin' into camp that afternoon Matt and I had rid behind the whole band, and I dropped my robe about a quarter back so's to have a excuse to go back. Wall, it was a gettin' purty wall on to dusk, and I thought it about time to be a gettin'. I was a roomin' in Matt's teepe, and jest then when one of his squaws started in to do up the chamber-work, she diskivered that my robe wan't there. On course Matt and me was astonished. I minded havin' it when we crossed the creek a piece back, and couldn't have lost it on yon side of it. So I sez I'd saddle up and go and hunt for it. I flung the saddle onto my pony right careless like, but you bet I just sinched it tight as I could. I rid out o' that camp quiet enough, but I was jest a shakin' fer fear my plan wouldn't work, but I was goin' to try it if it busted me.

As I rid out I seen three of the Blackfeet herdin' their ponies and ourn in a little bottom down by the creek, and I cast a longin' look at the black skin of that faverit hoss of mine, as he was fillin' himself off'n that tall grass. Wall, I rid out of sight, and when I found my robe I 'lit, fer I wanted to fix everything tight fer a good start. While I was a doin' that I thought I'd better give my pony a drink, and I led him down to a slew for that purpose. I spose I was mor'n a half mile from the Sioux camp, and felt safe enough fer myself, but I wanted them hosses, and was bound to have 'em. Jest then I heerd sumtin' that would a riz most anybody else's har on end, but I happened to know that thar voice.

Right under the bank of the creek not mor'n twenty steps from me I seen a head bobbin' up, and I heerd Jim Bridger's voice a speakin' to me. Do you believe it, that cuss and Walkee had bin follerin' on our trail ever sence that night that Matt ketched me over on Chugwater!

We didn't hev no time to fool away jest then, so I jest told 'em what was up, and I started to open the *baile*. I was right tickled to think I hadn't got to ride that thar journey and herd them ponies alone, you bet, so I jest mounted my hoss and crep back up the creek to git in hearin' of the ponies, while Jim and Walkee started to git theirs. As soon as I could see 'em fairly I peeled out that thar whistle of mine, and you'd a laughed to see that black hoss of mine prick up his ears, and jest as I give another of 'em the pony I was ridin' ketched sight of Jim's and Walkee's hosses, and knowin' 'em he give a screechin' shinner. That thar done the business, fer as that thar black critter come a terin' down the creek to my call the whole band of Snake ponies knowd my hosses voice, and came a tearin' after him like the whole prary was afire behind 'em. Them Blackfeet might as well a tried to stop a Rocky Mountain windstorm as to stop that thar stampede. We never knowd whether they tried to or not, fer me and Jim and Walkee tore down that creek like a streak of greased lightnin', followed by them hosses at full speed.

After we'd rid a hour or so in that way we stopped and saddled some fresh ponies, and in that way we made nigh onto a hundred mile by sunup to the next mornin'. I reckon that's 'bout all you fellers care to hear about that scrape, and I'll jest end up by sayin' that we fetched that whole band of ponies to the Snake village, safe and sound, and hed a little the biggest dogfeast made fer us on account of it you ever seed. Let's turn in.

BRIDGER RESCUES JOE MEEK[9]

A second bad scrape, this time on the Rocky Fork of the Yellowstone, appears to have taken place in the year 1835. Having fallen into the hands of a Crow Indian party under Chief Bold, old Joe Meek, as fabulous a frontier character as ever existed, is reported to have answered questions regarding camp and friends in his own particular fashion.

I said, "Bridger is my captain's name; or, in the Crow tongue, Casapy, the Blanket Chief." At this the chief seemed lost in thought. At last he asked me—

"How many men has he?"

I thought about telling the truth and living; but I said "forty," which was a tremendous lie; for thar war two hundred and forty. At this the Bold laughed:

"We will make them poor," said he; "and you shall live, but they shall die."

I thought to myself, "hardly"; but said nothing. He then asked me whar I war to meet the camp, and I told him:—and then how many days before the camp would be thar; which I answered truly, for I wanted them to find the camp.

It was now late in the afternoon, and there war a great bustle, getting ready for the march to meet Bridger. Two big Indians mounted my mule, but the women made me pack mocassins. The spies started first, and after awhile the main party. Seventy warriors traveled ahead of me; I war placed with the women and boys; and after us the balance of the braves. As we traveled along, the women would prod me with sticks, and laugh, and say, "Masta Sheela" (which means "white man"), "Masta Sheela very poor now." The fair sex were very much amused. . . .

On the afternoon of the fourth day, the spies, who were in advance, looking out from a high hill, made a sign to the main party. In a moment all sat down. Directly they got another sign, and then they got up and moved on. I was as well up in Indian signs as they war; and I knew they had discovered white men. What was worse, I knew they would soon discover that I had been lying to them. All I had to do then war to trust to luck.

[9] Frances F. Victor, *The River of the West* (Hartford, 1870), 190–94.

Soon we came to the top of the hill, which overlooked the Yellowstone, from which I could see the plains below extending as far as the eye could reach, and about three miles off, the camp of my friends. My heart beat double quick about that time; and I once in a while put my hand to my head to feel if my scalp war thar.

While I war watching our camp, I discovered that the horse guard had seen us, for I knew the sign he would make if he discovered Indians. I thought the camp a splendid sight that evening. It made a powerful show to me, who did not expect to ever see it after that day. And it war a fine sight anyhow, from the hill whar I stood. About two hundred and fifty men, and women and children in great numbers, and about a thousand horses and mules. Then the beautiful plain, and the sinking sun; and the herds of buffalo that could not be numbered; and the cedar hills, covered with elk—I never saw so fine a sight as all that looked to me then!

When I turned my eyes on that savage Crow band, and saw the chief standing with his hand on his mouth, lost in amazement, and beheld the warriors' tomahawks and spears glittering in the sun, my heart war very little. Directly the chief turned to me with a horrible scowl. Said he: "I promised that you should live if you told me the truth; but you have told me a great lie."

Then the warriors gathered round, with their tomahawks in their hands; but I war showing off very brave, and kept my eyes fixed on the horse guard who war approaching the hill to drive in the horses. This drew the attention of the chief, and the warriors too. Seeing that the guard war within two hundred yards of us, the chief turned to me and ordered me to tell him to come up. I pretended to do what he said; but instead of that I howled out to him to stay off, or he would be killed; and to tell Bridger to try to treat with them, and get me away.

As quick as he could he ran to the camp, and in a few minutes Bridger appeared, on his large white horse. He came up to within three hundred yards of us, and called out to me, asking who the Indians war. I answered, "Crows." He then told me to say to the chief he wished him to send one of his sub-chiefs to smoke with him.

All this time my heart beat terrible fast. I don't know why they didn't kill me at once; but the head chief seemed overcome with surprise. When I repeated to him what Bridger said, he reflected a moment, and then ordered the second chief, called Little-Gun, to go and smoke with Bridger. But they kept on preparing for war; getting on their paint and feathers, arranging their scalp locks, selecting their arrows, and getting their ammunition ready.

While this was going on, Little-Gun had approached to within about a hundred yards of Bridger; when, according to the Crow laws of war, each war forced to strip himself, and proceed the remaining distance in a state of nudity, and kiss and embrace. While this interesting ceremony war being performed, five of Bridger's men had followed him, keeping in a ravine until they got within shooting distance, when they showed themselves, and cut off the return of Little-Gun, thus making a prisoner of him.

If you think my heart did not jump up when I saw that, you think wrong. I knew it war kill or cure, now. Every Indian snatched a weapon, and fierce threats war howled against me. But all at once about a hundred of our trappers appeared on the scene. At the same time Bridger called to me, to tell me to propose to the chief to exchange me for Little-Gun. I explained to the Bold what Bridger wanted to do, and he sullenly assented: for, he said, he could not afford to give a chief for one white dog's scalp. I war then allowed to go towards my camp, and Little-Gun towards his; and the rescue I hardly hoped for was accomplished.

In the evening the chief, with forty of his braves, visited Bridger and made a treaty of three months.

BRIDGER AS INTERPRETER[10]

The Frontier required of men not only skill in the use of guns and horses, but also a broad knowledge of Indian languages and customs. In the years of treaty making especially, when the interests of white men and red men were being finally adjusted, such knowledge was important.

[10] Percival Lowe, *Five Years a Dragoon* (Kansas City, 1906), 77–82.

Old Jim Bridger

About noon one bright day a long line of dust was seen from our camp, looking west towards Laramie Peak. Soon a long line of Indians came moving slowly down in battle array, arms ready for use and every man apparently expectant, the women and children and baggage bringing up the rear well guarded. It turned out that Major Bridger, the interpreter, had reported to headquarters the approach of the Snakes, and he had been directed to lead them down near to our camp. All the head men of the Sioux and Cheyennes had given assurance that they should not be molested, so down they came, moving very slowly and cautiously, the chief along a short distance in advance. They were dressed in their best, riding fine war horses, and made a grandly savage appearance. In the absence of Major Chilton down at the post, seeing all this caution on the part of the Snakes, Lieutenant Hastings had "boots and saddles" sounded so as to be ready for whatever happened.

Just below us was a large Sioux camp, and the people were showing great interest and some excitement at the approach of their hereditary enemies, and a few squaws howled in anguish for lost friends who had died in battle with these same cautiously moving warriors. When the Snakes reached the brow of the hill overlooking the beautiful Laramie, less than a mile away, and the chief commenced the descent, a Sioux sprang upon his horse, bow and arrows in hand, and rushed toward him. A Frenchman, an interpreter, had been watching this Sioux expecting trouble, and he, too, mounted his horse and was instantly in pursuit. The Snake column stopped and sent up a wild shout of defiance, the chief moved a few steps farther and raised his gun ready to fire just as the intrepid Frenchman reached the reckless Sioux, pulled him from his horse, disarmed and stood over him. Then ensued a harangue between interpreters and chiefs. The wild Sioux, who sought to revenge himself on the Snake chief who had killed his father some time before, was led back to camp while the Snakes held their ground. Their position was a good one; every man had a good gun, plenty of ammunition, besides bows and arrows. Not one out of a hundred Sioux had guns, and the Snakes, though not one to five of the Sioux, would have defended themselves successfully, and the battle would have been the most bloody ever known amongst the wild tribes. They had come prepared for treachery, and with their splendid equipments felt full of confidence in their ability to cope with any band upon the Plains. Having quickly mounted the troop, Hastings took a position where he could overlook the actions of the tribe.

Here I met Bridger the first time. He spoke on behalf of the Snakes, and told Lieutenant Hastings what he already knew, that the Snakes had been assigned a position near his troop and asked where they could camp without interfering with the dragoons. Hastings told him that I knew the ground all about there, and turning to me said: "Corporal Lowe, show Captain Bridger the limits of our camp and give him all the assistance you can." That order was license for me to stay on Bridger's staff until a camp was made. Then and there Lowe became a Snake, and the other tribes were not in it.

I galloped off with the great mountaineer, whose fort I had seen dotted on my atlas at school a few years before. I showed him the finest camp imaginable, and he was pleased. I asked him if he had any objections to my staying with him until the camp was formed. "No, young man, these are the finest Indians on earth; stay with me and I'll show 'um to you." Soon the column was in motion, and they went into camp in their own peculiar way. Every prominent point was dotted by a sentinel, quietly wrapped in his blanket, gun ready for use.

Bridger said: "Well, you seen that fool Sioux made the run, didn't you?" "Yes, sir." "Well, ———," referring to the brave interpreter, whom he knew well, "saved that fellow from hell; my chief would 'er killed him quick, and then the fool Sioux would 'er got their backs up, and there wouldn't have been room to camp 'round here for dead Sioux. You dragoons acted nice, but you wouldn't have had no show if the fight had commenced—no making peace then. And I tell you another thing: the Sioux ain't goin' to try it again. They see how the Snakes are armed. I got them guns for 'um, and they are good ones. It'll be a proud day for the Snakes if any of these prairie tribes pitch into 'em, and they are not a bit afraid. Uncle Sam told 'um to come down here and they'd be safe, but they ain't takin' his word for it altogether. They'll never be caught napping, and they're prepared to travel anywhere. Awful brave fellows, these Snakes; got the nerve; honest, too; can take their word for anything; trust 'em anywhere; they live all about me, and I know all of them.

PUN-NAKS, SIOUX, AND A BAD RIVER CROSSING[11]

In far-flung parts of the West, Bridger played out his adventurous life. On the dusty shores of Salt Lake he met the Pun-nak Indians, wandering far south of their Columbia headwaters range. On Platte River he encountered the Sioux; and on still another occasion, routine to be sure but not without its dangers, he met and surmounted problems created by an inexperienced professional soldier.

On missing our horses the next day, we formed a party of about forty men, and followed their trail on foot—the ground was covered with snow at the time. I [Beckwourth] volunteered with the rest, although fortunately my horses were not among the missing. After a pursuit of five days we arrived at one of their [Pun-nak] villages, where we saw our own horses among a number of others. We then divided our forces, Fitzpatrick taking command of one party, and James Bridger of the other.

The plan resolved upon was as follows: Fitzpatrick was to charge the Indians, and cover Bridger's party, while they stampeded all the horses they could get away with. I formed one of Captain Bridger's party, this being the first affair of the kind I had ever witnessed. Everything being in readiness, we rushed in upon the horses, and stampeded from two to three hundred, Fitzpatrick at the same time engaging the Indians, who numbered from three to four hundred. The Indians recovered a great number of horses from us, but we succeeded in getting off with the number of our own missing, and forty head besides. In the engagement, six of the enemy were killed and scalped, while not one of our party received a scratch. The horses we had captured

[11] T. D. Bonner, *The Life and Adventures of James P. Beckwourth* (New York, 1856), 93–94; Frank Triplett, *Conquering the Wilderness* (Minneapolis, 1888), 266–67; A. J. Shotwell, article in Freeport, Ohio, *Press*, May 3, 1916, quoted by J. Cecil Alter, *James Bridger* (Salt Lake City, 1925), 369.

were very fine ones, and our return to the camp was greeted with the liveliest demonstrations.—BONNER.

When Jackson, Sublette, and Smith bought out Ashley's [fur] company, Bridger was one of the partners of the new firm, and like the others continued trapping, hunting and managing their men, and in this way contributed greatly to the success of the business. His exploits during this period were many and wonderful. At one time, entrenched on an open plain on the Platte River, he and five comrades fought off a large war party of the Sioux, every one of the trappers being wounded, but none killed.

Of the savages, twenty-five were killed and a large number wounded. Toward the close of this fight, which lasted for two days and nights, it became necessary for someone to endeavor to get through the surrounding lines and bring up aid, and as it was a duty requiring not only daring but coolness and judgment, Bridger was selected. Starting out about twelve at night he crawled along for over two hundred yards before encountering any difficulty, but here he came upon a warrior who had been lying down beside his horse.

Bridger's course had been perfectly noiseless, but the horse, which had been feeding in a deep ravine, scented his approach and gave a snort that aroused the master. Seeing that he was discovered, Bridger now arose and rushed on the Indian, intending to strangle him so as to prevent an alarm, but before he could reach the brave, his shrill whoop had been given. Now that nothing was to be gained by further silence on his part, and hearing the rush of the Indian horses, Bridger drew his pistol and with its muzzle almost against his enemy, fired.

The Sioux fell dead and Bridger mounted in haste and dashed off toward a camp of his comrades lower down the river. It was a close chase, the savages pouring along in his rear, but Bridger's chance choice of a steed proved a good one, and by two he had reached his destination. The trappers were aroused, and in a few minutes were in the saddle. Making a detour to gain the sand hills in the rear of the besiegers, they waited till morning, and as the attack on the little fortification began they poured a deadly volley into the thickly clustering savages. This was enough to dispirit the Sioux, who, gathering up their dead and wounded, made all haste to get out of range. So frightened were they that they did not even take time to drive off the Flathead horses of the trappers.—TRIPLETT.

Another laughable incident was related to me by Bridger himself. Soon after he was employed as official guide by the government, he was sent with an exploring party into the Big Horn Mountains. There was quite a party of wagons, pack animals, and a squad of cavalry, all under the command of a young officer fresh from West Point. All went well until the expedition reached the Big Horn River, swollen at the time from melting snows. When Bridger suggested the plan for crossing the turbulent stream, he was curtly told that he was only employed as a guide. With this, the fresh young West Pointer ordered two of the mounted men to ride in and fasten a line to the opposite shore. The horses lost their footing in the swift current and one of the men was drowned. Then, in humiliation, the West Point youth appealed to Bridger, and implored him to take the crossing in hand. This Bridger agreed to do, but admonished the youngster to retire to his tent and remain there until called for.

To describe in detail the provisions made for crossing the stream, while interesting, would prove a long story. First, a crude boat was constructed of poles and willows. This was covered with some heavy canvas, and made waterproof by a liberal application of pitch, prepared from gum gathered from the spruce and pine trees. The men then stripped, and on horseback, succeeded in crossing with a line, and with this, dragged the cable ashore, which was made fast to a large tree. All hands then stretched the cable and made it fast on the side where the party awaited; with the boat secured to the cable by a slip noose all were safely carried across the river, the young officer being last of all.

And here comes the laughable part of the story: The first thing the youngster did on being restored to his command was to call on the chaplain to assemble the expedition and return thanks to Providence for the safe crossing. Here Bridger's eyes sparkled as he told how that chaplain had fallen on his knees, and in a loud voice thanked the Lord God of Hosts for bringing the troops over in safety. "And darn his sanctimonious skin," Old Jim concluded to me in recounting the story, "he never mentioned Bridger once, and I felt as if I had had something to do with the plan myself."—SHOTWELL.

BRIDGER AS A NATURALIST[12]

Old Jim Bridger, Western horseman ranging restlessly, shaping his course always to fit that of weather and country, came to be a great judge of the elements. At particular times strangers, themselves bound by the moods of mountains and plains, noticed this about him.

Bridger came out and invited us in, and introduced us to his Indian wife, and showed us his half-breed children—keen, bright-eyed little things. Everything was rude and primitive. This man strongly attracted my attention; there was more than civility about him—there was native politeness. He is the oldest trapper in the Rocky Mountains; his language is very graphic and descriptive, and he is evidently a man of great shrewdness.

He alarmed us in regard to our prospect of getting through; said the season had arrived when a heavy snow might be looked for any day; urged us to stay with him all winter; showed us where we could lodge, guarded against the cold with plenty of buffalo skins; and assured us that he could make the benefit of our society and the assistance of Mr. Ferris, in his business, more than compensate for the expense of living. This was a delicate way of offering the hospitality of his establishment without remuneration.—FERRIS.

The wagon trains crossing the Plains at that time were very numerous and usually before leaving the starting points along the Missouri River, the emigrants bought little guidebooks for

12 B. G. Ferris, *The Mormons at Home* (New York, 1856), 84; Humfreville, *Hostile Indians*, 467; Chittenden, *Yellowstone Park*, 43–44; H. E. Palmer, "History of the Powder River Expedition of 1865," Nebraska State Historical Society Transactions (Lincoln, 1887), Vol. II, 220; oral tradition.

ten cents, giving the location of good water and grass along the road. Hence it frequently happened that camp was made at night where not a spear of grass was to be found for the horses or cattle, it having been consumed by the thousands that had camped there before.

Then the travelers called on Bridger and asked him where the next camping place was. The information was cheerfully given, and the travelers immediately turned to their guidebooks, and not finding mention of the locality would accuse Bridger of deceiving them, which was very annoying, and did not increase his regard for the pilgrims. Sometimes he would sit for hours and act as if deaf and dumb, in order to put a stop to the silly questions of travelers.—HUMFREVILLE.

Opposite a certain camping ground where [Bridger] frequently stopped, there arose the bald, flat face of a mountain, but so distant that the echo from any sound which originated in camp did not return for the space of about six hours. Bridger converted this circumstance into an ideal alarm clock. Upon his retiring for the night he would call out lustily, "Time to get up!" and, true to his calculation, the alarm would roll back at the precise hour next morning when it was necessary for the camp to bestir itself.—CHITTENDEN.

Sept. 2, 1865—Ever since we left Fort Laramie our camp has been surrounded with thousands of wolves, that made the night hideous with their infernal howlings, but not until tonight have we heard the "medicine wolf," which Old Bridger claims to be a supernatural sort of an animal whose howling is sure to bring trouble to camp. Bridger, Nick Janisse, and Rulo, being very superstitious, were so frightened by this peculiar howling that they took up their blankets and struck for a new camp, which, according to their theory, was the only way of escaping from the impending danger. They went down the river about half a mile and camped in the timber by themselves.—PALMER.

It is said that Bridger, like many another frontiersman, became an expert judge of signs, camp sites and so forth. Yet, he was known to have made mistakes. When he floated down the Bear River in 1824, for example, to discover the Great Salt Lake, he is said to have tasted those Utah waters and to have muttered in some amazement, "Hell, we're on the shore of the Pacific Ocean." And when asked as to the best method of determining the altitude of a place, he is said to have once humorously recommended boring down until salt water was reached and then measuring the depth of the hole.—ORAL TRADITION.

JIM BRIDGER'S EYESIGHT[13]

A story in which other professional soldiers encounter Old Bridger.

As the Major [Jim Bridger] and myself reached the top of the hill, we involuntarily halted our steeds; I raised my field glasses to my eyes and took in the grandest view that I have ever seen. . . . As I lowered my glass the Major said: "Do you see those 'ere columns of smoke over yonder?" I replied: "Where, Major?" To which he answered, "Over by that saddle," meaning a depression in the hills not unlike the shape of a saddle, pointing at the same time to a point fully fifty miles away. I again raised my glass to my eyes and took a long, earnest look, and for the life of me could not see any columns of smoke even with a strong field glass. The Major was looking without any artificial help. The atmosphere appeared to be slightly hazy in the long distance, like smoke, but there were no distinct columns of smoke in sight. Yet, knowing the peculiarities of my frontier friend, I agreed with him that there were columns of smoke, and suggested that we had better get off our animals and let them feed until the General came up. This we did, and as soon as the General and his staff arrived, I called his attention to Major Bridger's discovery. The General raised his field glass and scanned the horizon closely, but after a long look he remarked that there were no columns of smoke to be seen.

The Major quietly mounted his horse and rode on. I asked the General to look again, that the Major was very confident that he could see columns of smoke, which, of course, indicated

[13] Palmer, "Powder River Expedition," 466–67.

an Indian village. The General made another examination and again asserted that there were no columns of smoke. However, to satisfy curiosity, and to give our guides no chance to claim that they had shown us an Indian village and we would not attack it, he suggested to Capt. Frank North, who was riding with the staff, that he go with seven of his Indians in the direction indicated, to reconnoiter, and to report to us on Peno Creek or Tongue River, down which we were to march.

I galloped on and overtook the Major, and as I came up to him, overheard him remark about "these damn paper collar soldiers' telling him there were no columns of smoke." The old man was very indignant at our doubting his ability to outsee us, with the aid of field glasses even. The joke was too good to keep and I had to report it to the General. In fact, I don't believe the Major saw any columns of smoke, although it afterward transpired that there was an Indian village in the immediate locality designated. Bridger understood well enough that that was a favorite locality for Indians to camp, and that at most any time there could be found a village there; hence his declaration that he saw columns of smoke.

BRIDGER'S REMINISCENCES[14]

On one of these [Rocky Mountain] excursions he [Bridger] headed north into the British Possessions, and with the North Star for a guide, continued on his way down the valley of the Mackenzie River to the Arctic Ocean. Here at the threshold of the polar night he could go no farther, and turning back, made his way safely to his starting place, which he reached after an absence of eighteen months, during which time he had not tasted bread nor looked into the face of a white man. . . .

Some time [also] during these years, I can't recall the date, Bridger was taken with a longing to see the old home and having an extra accumulation of pelts, concluded to take charge of the shipment. The most valuable part of the cargo was five thousand beaver skins, which he expected to sell at $4 each. What was his surprise and gratification on arrival at St. Joe to find beaver in

[14] Shotwell, quoted by Alter, *James Bridger*, 429.

demand at $7. He easily disposed of his beaver at this figure, totaling $35,000. This was further augmented $5,000 by the proceeds from other pelts, putting into his hands $40,000, a princely sum of money at that time for a young man almost born to the wilderness. His people, still living, were of course overjoyed at the return of the wanderer whom, while heard of at times, they never expected to see again, so hazardous was life in the wild West.

Bridger himself was pleased with the quiet life and having abundant ready money bought a tract of land, married, and as he supposed, settled down to the quiet life of a farmer. But this was only for a short time. The call of the wilds was not to be hushed and in a few years he was back among his life's familiar scenes, returning at times for short intervals to visit his family, but not remaining long.

JIM BRIDGER AND GOLD[15]

In the early days of Western settlement, Clear Creek and Cherry Creek communities in Colorado Territory enjoyed a boom in the gold-mining business. There, it seems, Old Jim Bridger paused long enough to reflect upon the nuggets he had missed.

Captain Bridger arrived here this morning by coach, and will proceed at once to lay out and locate a government road passing through Denver and on northwest through Bridger Pass towards the Pacific. . . . The Captain says they found gold everywhere in this country in [the old] trapper days, but thought it unworthy of their notice to mine for it, as beaver (then worth $8 per pound) was the best paying gold they wanted to mine for in the creeks and rivers.—*Rocky Mountain News.*

Another cause of more than ordinary importance which operated to the diversion of our own and other migratory peoples, and consequently to the disadvantage of Colorado in 1874, was the reported discovery of very rich gold mines in the Black

[15] *Rocky Mountain News,* May 8, 1861; Frank Hall, *History of Colorado* (Chicago, 1890), II, 221–22.

Hills of Dakota. The impelling cause of the interest excited, and which soon induced an extensive movement in that direction, was a report made by General George A. Custer, who by order of the government traversed and examined the country in 1874, and gave a glowing account of its resources in gold, timber, etc., which was emphasized and made infinitely more attractive by the floating rumor that the famous old mountaineer, trapper and hunter, Jim Bridger, had found gold there in 1859, while acting as guide and interpreter to a military exploring party commanded by Captain Raynolds.

As the story ran, he discovered it in a brook where he stopped to slake his thirst, and carried the specimens to the officer in charge, who ordered him to conceal them or throw them away, as, if the story came to the knowledge of the soldiers, it would cause a stampede. At that time Bridger was an old man but still hearty and vigorous, residing on a farm in Jackson County, Missouri. Traced to its source, it was found that Captain Raynolds' expedition had been ordered to explore the headwaters of the Yellowstone, Missouri, and Columbia rivers, and passing through the Black Hills en route, one day having traveled a long distance, Bridger dismounted from his horse at a small, clear stream, and stooped to drink of its crystal water. While in this position his attention was attracted by the curious appearance of what seemed to be a lot of small yellow pebbles. Though familiar with the color of gold, it had never occurred to him that the precious metal existed in that locality; but his curiosity impelled him to scoop out a handful of the stuff, which he exhibited to Dr. Hayden and Captain Raynolds. Both at once pronounced it pure gold, and inquired where he found it. When told, Raynolds became greatly excited, and fearing the effect upon his men, insisted that Bridger should throw it away and under no circumstances permit the discovery to be known, as the knowledge that gold existed there in such abundance and so easy of access, would cause the soldiers to desert.

Bridger, in relating the circumstance, stated that since his first discovery of gold in the Black Hills, he had found it at other places in the same region. But he cautioned people against going there except in strong, well-armed parties for defense against the Sioux, to whom the Hills belonged, and who were very numerous and would naturally resist the invasion of their territory. But the fires had been lighted, and all warnings of danger produced no effect other than to stimulate emigration.—HALL.

BRIDGER, SHAKESPEARE, AND THE ENGLISH[16]

To Jim Bridger's campfires came many a Western stranger, attracted by the brightness and cheer, the promise of food and soft buffalo robes on which to sleep, and by the assurance of safety at least for one night. Some of these strangers, like the old scout, were content for the most part to keep thoughts and questions to themselves. Others, however, were like the little owls of the prairie, sharp-eyed and curious. Such visitors were inclined, all too frequently, to impose not only habits and customs but personal literary tastes upon a too generous host.

Sir George's habit was to sleep until about ten or eleven o'clock in the morning, when he took his bath, ate his breakfast, and set out generally alone for the day's hunt; and Bridger says it was not unusual for him to remain out until ten o'clock at night, and he seldom returned to camp without augmenting the catalogue of his exploits.

His dinner was then ordered, to partake of which he generally extended an invitation to my friend Bridger, and after the repast was concluded, and a few glasses had been drunk, he was in the habit of reading from some book, and eliciting from Bridger his comments thereon. His favorite author was Shakespeare, which Bridger "reckon'd was a leetle too highfalutin' for him"; moreover, he remarked that he "rayther calculated that thar Dutchman, Mr. Full-stuff, was a leetle bit too fond of lager beer," and suggested that probably it might have been better for the old man if he had imbibed the same amount of alcohol in the more condensed medium of good old Bourbon whisky.

Bridger seemed deeply interested in the adventures of Baron Munchausen, but admitted, after the reading was finished, that "he be dogond ef he swallered everything that thar *Baren*

[16] R. B. Marcy, *Thirty Years of Army Life* (New York, 1874), 403–404; Carrington, *Ab-Sa-Ra-Ka*, 114; Humfreville, *Hostile Indians*, 467–68.

Mountchawson said, and he thought he was a durn'd liar." Yet, upon further reflection, he acknowledged that some of his own experiences among the Blackfeet would be equally marvelous "ef writ down in a book."

One evening Sir George entertained his auditor by reading to him Sir Walter Scott's account of the battle of Waterloo, and afterward asked him if he did not regard that as the most sanguinary battle he had ever heard of. To which Bridger replied, "Wall, now, Mr. Gore, that thar must 'a bin a considdible of a skrimmage, dogon my skin ef it mustn't; them Britishers must 'a fit better thar than they did down to Horleans, whar old Hickry gin um the forkedest sort o' chain-lightnin' that perhaps you ever did see in all yer born days!" And upon Sir George's expressing a little incredulity in regard to the estimate Bridger placed upon this battle, the latter added, "You can jist go yer pile on it, Mr. Gore—*you can*, as sure as yer born."—Marcy.

[Jim Bridger] cannot read, but he enjoys reading. He was charmed by Shakespeare; but doubted the Bible story of Samson's tying foxes by the tails, and with firebrands burning the wheat of the Philistines. At last he sent for a good copy of Shakespeare's plays, and would hear them read until midnight with unfeigned pleasure. The murder of the two princes in the tower startled him to indignation. He desired it to be read a second and a third time. Upon positive conviction that the text was properly read to him, he burned the whole set, convinced that "Shakespeare must have had a bad heart and been as de——h mean as a Sioux, to have written such scoundrelism as that."— Carrington.

His [Jim Bridger's] manner of living during this winter did not coincide with my habits or ideas, by any means, so I tried to entertain him every afternoon and keep him awake until nine or ten o'clock in the evening. My first effort was in reading to him. A copy of "Hiawatha" was found among the troops, which I read to him as long as he permitted it. He would sit bent over, his long legs crossed, his gaunt hands and arms clasping his knees, and listen to the reading attentively, until a passage was reached in which Longfellow portrayed an imaginary Indian, when Bridger, after a period of uneasy wriggling on his seat, arose very wrathy, and swearing that the whole story was a lie, that he would listen to no more of it, and that "no such Injun ever lived." This happened over and over again. After a while I quieted him, and began reading again, but after a short time he was sure to stop me, swearing that he would not listen any longer to such infernal lies. However, I managed to entertain him in this way for two or three weeks, during which time I secured a reasonable amount of sleep out of each twenty-four hours.

Bridger became very much interested in this reading, and asked which was the best book that had ever been written. I told him that Shakespeare's was supposed to be the greatest book. Thereupon he made a journey to the main road, and lay in wait for a wagon train, and bought a copy from some emigrants, paying for it with a yoke of cattle, which at that time could have been sold for one hundred and twenty-five dollars. He hired a German boy, from one of the wagon trains, at forty dollars a month, to read to him. The boy was a good reader, and Bridger took great interest in the reading, listening most attentively for hours at a time. Occasionally he got the thread of the story so mixed up that he would swear a blue streak, then compel the young man to stop, turn back, and reread a page or two, until he could get the story straightened out. This continued until he became so hopelessly involved in reading "Richard the Third" that he declared he "wouldn't listen any more to the talk of a man who was mean enough to kill his mother." That ended our reading of Shakespeare, much to my disgust, for I was again doomed to be kept awake at all hours of the night by his aboriginal habits. After that it was amusing to hear Bridger quote Shakespeare. He could give quotation after quotation, and was always ready to do so. Sometimes he seasoned them with a broad oath, so ingeniously inserted as to make it appear to the listener that Shakespeare himself had used the same language.— HUMFREVILLE.

Fandango and Fofarraw

AWAY from old Jim Bridger's fort, beyond the Flaming Gorge of Green River, Brown's Park, and the weird cliffs of the Yampa, lies the country of the Colorado Western Slope, rugged and big and hard-boned, a land today of few roads and few towns, striking its rainbow mesas westward into the Utah desert and running its mountain lines, cracked with canyons, black river gorges, and glinting granite peaks, far into New Mexico in the south. Here, in the present time, ranchers of the Gunnison and Uncompahgre pitch sub-alpine camps in summer, when the mountain grass is tall and brilliant green, and bring their stock to valleys before the autumn storms. On San Juan ridges, miners blast the gold and silver veins. Railroadmen, riding high and lonely narrow guages, push their trains through slanting drifts of snow. And still farther toward the summits, in the depth of wintertime, trappers set their steel traps and their deadfalls, coming out in spring with fur, just as Bridger, Beckwourth, and Kit Carson did a hundred years ago.

This Colorado and New Mexico borderland—region of the Continental Divide, encompassing virtually one hundred thousand square miles of mountain, forest, and valley—is known today to but a handful of Americans. It stands remote from the great American cities. Continental routes swerve to north or south around it; even aircraft, loftiest fliers of the Western skies, see danger in it and avoid it. Yet for centuries certain kinds of men have known this land. From the north, in the earliest times, Indians infiltrated its Mesa Verde section, building the community houses which may be seen there to this day. From the south came the Spaniards, carrying with them Iberian customs and habits of thought; while from the east came still other men, Frenchmen up the prairie rivers from Louisiana, Americans across the middle buffalo grounds, Britishers and Frenchmen out from the shores of Superior.

In the minds of the Spaniards, clanking shrewd of face and obsidian-eyed out of their deep monarchical past, lay visions of the legendary New World cities of gold, the Seven Cities of Cibola, whispered to lie somewhere far within the continent. Reaching the Taos Plateau in the fifteenth century, spreading ever to the north and east, from the old valley of San Luis to Spanish Peaks and the Plains, these piked and armored conquerors searched closely among the mountains and the cap-rock canyons of the prairies, found not cities of gold but heat, thirst, and hostile Indian nations, and retreated, leaving few marks of their passage except the rumors, new seeds of old ways, which through long generations have grown into the Spanish-American tales of the present.

THE SEVEN CITIES OF CIBOLA[1]

A few of the tales told by these earliest and most daring of Spaniards, to whom the Seven Cities came to be, at last, no more than mirages in the Great American Desert.

In the year 1530 Nunó de Guzmán, governor of New Spain, at that time owned an Indian, one of the natives of the valley or the valleys of Oxitipar, whom the Spaniards called Tejos. The Indian told him that he was the son of a trader deceased long ago, who, while his son was still a child, was wont to travel over the interior of the country in order to sell the handsome plumes that are used for headdresses by the Indians. In exchange he brought home a large quantity of gold and silver, both metals being very common in that region. He added that once or twice he himself had accompanied his father, and had seen towns so large that he could compare them in size to Mexico and its suburbs. There were seven of these towns, and there were whole rows of streets inhabited by gold- and silver-workers. He said besides, that in order to reach these seven cities it was necessary to cross a desert for forty days, and there was no vegetation except for short grass about five inches in height, and that the

[1] Translations from the Spanish journals, published in A. F. Bandelier's "Contributions to the History of the Southwestern Portion of the United States," papers of the Archaeological Institute of America, American Series, Vol. V (Cambridge University Press, 1890), 11–13, 144–46, 153–54.

direction was to the north between both oceans.—PEDRO DE
CASTANEDA.

The Lord of those cities lives and resides in one of them called
Ahacus, and has placed others in the other cities to command
them for him; . . . and he told me that Cibola was a big city, in
which there are many people, streets, and squares, and that in
some parts of the city there are very large houses, as high as
eleven stories, in which the principal men come together on certain days of the year. They say that the houses are of stone and
lime, as others had already told me, and that the entrances and
fronts of the principal buildings are of turquoises. He also said
to me that the other Seven Cities are like this one, and some of
them larger, and that the principal one of all is Ahacus. He says
that toward the southeast there is a kingdom called Marata, in
which there used to be many and large settlements, all of which
are houses of stone and many-storied, and that this kingdom was
and still is at war with the lord of the Seven Cities, through which
warfare the kingdom of Marata has declined greatly, although it
still holds it own, and is at war with the others. And he also
stated that toward the southeast there is the kingdom called
Totonteac, which he mentions as being the largest in the world,
the most populous, the wealthiest, and that there they dress in
cloth made of the material out of which is manufactured the
gown I wear, and others of a thinner kind, and that it is taken
from the animals mentioned previously; and that the people are
highly civilized, different from those I have yet seen. He also
said that there is another large province and kingdom named
Acus. There is also Ahacus, and that word, with aspiration, is
the name of one of the Seven Cities, the largest of them all; and
Acus, without aspiration, is a province by itself. He said that the
costume of Cibola was as it has been described to me; that all
those who dwell in that city sleep in elevated beds above the
floor, covered with sheets and bedding. He offered to go with
me to Cibola and beyond, if I would take him along.—FRAY
MARCOS DE NIZA.

As Estevan arrived within a day's journey of Cibola he sent
his messengers to the lord of the place, informing him of his

coming, and that he intended to treat for peace with him and cure the sick. When they gave the gourd to the chief, and he saw the rattles, he threw down the gourd angrily and said, "I know these people, for these rattles are not of the make of my own. Tell them to return at once, else not one of them shall remain alive." And the messengers returned to Estevan sorrowfully, hardly venturing to tell him. But at last they informed him of what had happened, and he said to them that they should not be afraid, that he would go there, for whenever the Indians, on his previous travels, gave him evil words at the outset, it was a sure sign that he would be well received by them. So he went on and reached the city of Cibola about sundown, with all the people of his escort, of whom there were about three hundred men and many women. But they refused to let him enter the city, and quartered him in a large and good house outside. Besides, they took away from Estevan all he carried, saying that the chief thus ordained it, and all that night they gave them nothing to eat or to drink. The next day, after the sun had risen to the height of a lance, Estevan went out of the house and had some of the principal men of his escort with him. Forthwith there came many people from the city, and as soon as he saw them he fled, and we with him. Then it was that they gave us these wounds with their arrows, and we fell. Others fell on top of us dead, and so we remained until night, afraid to move. We heard a great uproar in the city, and we saw on the flat roofs many men and women who were looking; but we saw nothing of Estevan, and believe that he was killed with arrows, like the rest of those who came with him, and that we alone escaped.—FRAY MARCOS DE NIZA.

UNEXPLORED MARVELS[2]

More literal and therefore perhaps more reliable in their descriptions of the middle Plains were the men who came later, those American trappers and frontiersmen who, in first exploring the river courses of the Louisiana Territory, crisscrossed the old Spanish trails.

[2] William Dunbar and Dr. George Hunter, *American State Papers*, class II, *Indian Affairs* (Washington, 1832) Vol. IV, No. 113, 740–41. An-

Fandango and Fofarraw

The Red and Arkansas rivers, whose courses are very long, pass through portions of . . . fine country; they are both navigable to an unknown distance by boats of proper construction; the Arkansas River is, however, understood to have greatly the advantage with respect to the facility of navigation. Some difficult places are met with in the Red River below the Natchitoches, after which it is good for one hundred and fifty leagues. . . . There the voyager meets with a very serious obstacle—the commencement of the "raft" as it is called; that is, a natural covering which conceals the whole river for an extent of seventeen leagues, continually augmented by the driftwood brought down by every considerable stream. This covering, which for a considerable time was only driftwood, now supports a vegetation of everything abounding in the neighboring forest, not excepting trees of considerable size, and the river may be passed without any knowledge of its existence. . . .

About two hundred leagues up the Arkansas is an interesting place called the Salt Prairie. There is a considerable fork in the river there and a kind of savanna where the salt water is continually oozing out and spreading over the surface of the plain. During the dry summer season, the salt may be raked up in large heaps; and a natural crust of a handbreadth in thickness is formed at this season. This place is not often frequented on account of the danger from the Osage Indians; much less dare the white hunter venture to ascend higher where it is generally believed that silver is to be found. It is further said that high up the Arkansas River salt is found in form of solid rock and may be dug out with the crowbar. . . . Every account seems to prove that immense natural magazines of salt must exist in the great chain of mountains to the westward; as all the rivers, in the summer season, which flow from them are strongly impregnated with that mineral and are only rendered palatable after receiving the numerous streams of fresh water which join them in their course.

other good story, on pages 723–24, tells of the Spanish governor's daughter who was captured by the Comanches, tattooed, and married to an Indian. When ransom arrived she decided that she could not return to her own people, choosing to stay with her Comanche husband.

The great Western prairies, besides the herds of wild cattle (bison, commonly called buffalo), are also stocked with vast numbers of a wild goat (not resembling the domestic goat) which is extremely swift-footed. As the description given of this goat is not perfect, it may, from its swiftness, prove to be the antelope; or it may possibly be a goat which has escaped from the Spanish settlements of New Mexico. A Canadian, who had been much with the Indians to the westward, speaks of a wool-bearing animal, larger than a sheep, the wool much mixed with hair, which he had seen in large flocks; he pretends, also, to have seen the unicorn, the single horn of which he says rises out of the forehead and curls back, conveying the idea of the fossil *cornu ammonis*.

This man says he has traveled beyond the great dividing ridge so far as to have seen a large river flowing to the westward. The great dividing mountain is so lofty that it requires two days to ascend from the base to its top; other ranges of inferior mountains lie before and behind it; they are all rocky and sandy. Large lakes and valleys lie between the mountains. Some of the lakes are so large as to contain islands, and rivers flow from some of them. Great numbers of fossil bones of very large dimensions are seen among the mountains, which the Canadian supposed to be of the elephant. He does not pretend to have seen any of the precious metals, but he has seen a mineral which he supposed must yield copper.

From the top of the high mountain the view is bounded by a curve, as upon the ocean, and extends over the most beautiful prairies which seem to be unbounded, particularly towards the east. The finest of lands he has seen are on the Missouri; no other can compare in richness and fertility with them. This Canadian, as well as Le Fevre, speaks of the Osages, of the tribe of White Hairs, as lawless and unprincipled; the other Indian tribes hold them in abhorrence as a barbarous and uncivilized race; and the different natives who hunt in their neighborhood have been concerting plans for their destruction.

Fandango and Fofarraw

Land of the Rio Grande, as mysterious to American trappers and hunters looking westward from the Mississippi Valley as were the Cities of Cibola to the Spaniards themselves.

In the historical anecdotes of New Mexico it may not be improper to record the name of James Pursley [Purcell], the first American who ever penetrated the immense wilds of Louisiana and shewed the Spaniards of New Mexico that neither the savages who surround the desert which divides them from the habitable world, nor the jealous tyranny of their rulers was sufficient to prevent the enterprising spirit of the Americans from penetrating the arcanum of their rich establishments in the New World. Pursley was from near Baird's Town, Kentucky, which he left in 1799. In 1802, with two companions, he left St. Louis and traveled west on the head of the Osage River, where they made a hunt; from thence they struck for the White River of the Arkansas and intended to descend it to Orleans, but while making preparations the Kanses stole their horses: having secured their peltries they pursued them into the village.

The horses were there, but the Indians refused to give them up; Pursley saw his horse with an Indian on him going to the water at the edge of the town. He pursued him, and with his knife ripped open the horse's bowels. The Indian returned to the village, got his gun and snapped it at Pursley, who followed him into the village with his knife; the Indian took refuge in a lodge surrounded by women and children. This conduct struck the chiefs with astonishment and admiration of the "mad Americans," as they termed them, and they returned the other horses to the hunters. Pursley and his companions now returned to the place where they had buried their peltries, and determined to pursue the route by land to St. Louis; but some persons stole their horses a second time, when they were no great distance from the Osage River, on which they formed a rough canoe and descended that stream nearly to its junction with the Missouri. Here they overset their canoe and lost their whole year's hunt,

[3] Zebulon Pike, *Exploratory Travels through the Western Territories of North America* (Denver, 1889; a reprint of the London edition of 1811), 314–16.

but saved their arms and ammunition, which are always the primary objects in a desert.

On the Missouri they met Monsieur——in his barge, bound to the Mandanes. Pursley embarked with him for the voyage, his two companions preferring to return to their homes. On the arrival of the former at the point of destination, his employer despatched him on a hunting and trading tour, with some bands of the Paducas and Kyaways, with a small quantity of merchandise. In the ensuing spring they were driven by the Sioux from the plains into the mountains which give rise to the Platte, Arkansas, &c., and it was their sign which we saw in such amazing abundance on the headwaters of the Platte, their party consisting of nearly two thousand souls with ten thousand beasts. The Indians, knowing they were approximate to New Mexico, determined to send Pursley with his companions and two of their body into Santa Fe, to know of the Spaniards if they would receive them amicably and enter into a trade with them. This being acceded to by the governor (Allencaster) the Indian deputies returned for their bands; but Pursley thought proper to remain with a civilized people, among whom a fortuitous event had thrown him, a circumstance which he assured me he had at one time entirely despaired of.

He arrived at Santa Fe in June, 1805, and had been following his trade (a carpenter) ever since, at which he made a great deal of money, except when working for officers, who paid him little or nothing. He was a man of strong natural sense, and of undaunted intrepidity; and entertained me with numerous interesting anecdotes of his adventures with the Indians, and of the jealousy of the Spanish government. He was once nearly being hanged for making a few pounds of powder, which he innocently did, as he was accustomed to do in Kentucky, but which is a capital crime in these provinces. He still retained his gun, which he had with him during his whole tour, and spoke confidently that if he had two hours' start, not all the province could take him. He was forbidden to write, but was assured he should have a passport whenever demanded; he was obliged, however, to give security that he would not leave the country without the permission of the government. I brought letters out for him.

He assured me that he had found gold on the head of the Platte, and had carried some of the virgin mineral in his shot pouch for months, but that being in doubt whether he should ever again behold the civilized world, and losing in his mind all the ideal value which mankind has stamped on that metal, he threw his sample away; that he imprudently mentioned it to the Spaniards, who had frequently solicited him to go and shew a detachment of cavalry the place, but conceiving it to be in our territory he had refused, and was fearful that the circumstance might create a great obstacle to his leaving the country.

GUADALUPE[4]

Cupped between the granite lines of the San Juan and Sangre de Cristo, flanked on the south by Taos lava plains and northward by the lifting grassy slopes of Poncha Pass, the valley of San Luis, in southern Colorado, holds itself aloof. Sagebrush, sand dunes, grey alkali; cottonwoods, clear streams, piedmont pastures and good land—all these are here. Alamosa, Conejos, Monte Vista; Cochetopa, Saguache, Guadalupe—these are the ancient names, the names of Spanish and Indian origin. On the sage flats and in the pine timber are farms and the log houses and corrals of stock ranches. For people have lived long in the San Luis, seeing the sun flame on its bordering peaks, listening to the sighs of its winds, keeping deep in their minds the mysteries, the hard actions, the old, old tales of tragedy which overshadow that country.

North, across the river from Conejos, Colorado, is the site of Guadalupe, the original settlement of this vicinity. According to legend, this settlement was founded because a mule in the pack train of a Spanish traveler balked here. The animal was bearing a small image of the Virgin of Guadalupe, and when threats, beatings and cajolings failed to budge him, the traveler decided that the image was in some way concerned and vowed to erect a church upon that spot. The mule, apparently satisfied, moved on. As good as his word, the traveler returned with some of his

[4] *Colorado, A Guide to the Highest State*, compiled by Workers of the Writers' Project in Colorado (New York, 1941), 400.

countrymen, and a church and settlement were reared to bear witness to the miracle. Major Head fortified the town against the threat of the Tabeguache Utes who claimed this territory, and the fort was attacked soon after its completion, in 1855, by a large force under Chief Kanakache, who carried a shield of buffalo hide so thick that it deflected bullets. During the fight Kanakache lowered his shield for a moment and was severely wounded by Major Head. The Utes withdrew and did not again attack the settlement. Guadalupe was finally abandoned because of the threat of floods. Cloudbursts have obliterated all traces of the early town.

A MYSTERIOUS HAPPENING AT SAGUACHE LAKE[5]

A legend of the Spanish settlers of the western San Luis, beautiful region lying close under Cochetopa Pass and ridges of the San Juan.

Having been interviewed lately by a number of persons curious to learn something definite in regard to the old Mexican and Ute legend of the Saguache, and thinking the story, as I obtained it from an old Mexican who seemed to be familiar with the legend as told and believed by his neighbors, would be interesting to many, I have concluded to give it to the public through the *Review*. I will not vouch for its truth, but simply relate it as told to me by Pedro Condalaro.

It was in December, 1874, that I found myself in company with a number of persons en route for the Gunnison country from Trinidad. In the company were John Trimble, Will Graham, the Tinguely family and Mr. and Mrs. Dixon, and while our little train was moving slowly between Fort Garland and Saguache we were joined by Pedro Condalaro, who was going to Saguache with an ox team on some business. One evening we camped on the Canero and the next on the Largaretto, and Pedro camped with us. It was there and from him that I learned the following story:

As long ago as 1840 one Emanuel Juárez, a wealthy middle-

5 This story, by S. Richardson, was found in a clipping from the *Gunnison Review*, 1882, in the files of the State Historical Society of Colorado, Denver.

aged Spaniard, lived near where Fort Garland has since been built, on the Sangre de Cristo Creek. He possessed large herds of cattle, sheep, and horses, which ranged in the foothills north toward Sierra Blanca. He was wealthy and had one of the finest ranches in the San Luis Valley. He was a widower, having lost his wife some years previous, but still had in his family, whom he almost idolized, three lovely daughters and one son who were all grown, except the youngest daughter, and she, above all, the old man idolized and petted. The daughters were very beautiful, being of pure Castilian blood. The son was a noble specimen of the race, very much attached to his home, and was a great favorite with all the Spaniards and Mexicans throughout the whole Saguache Valley. He was considered a model young man by all the people for miles around among the Mexican settlements.

One day while Emanuel Juárez was returning from Ojo Caliente, where he had been to look after some interests, the Indians attacked the ranch in an unlucky hour when the peons were away with the herds, and no one was at home but the son and three daughters. The Utes made the attack. The young man made as good a defense as possible but was soon killed, the ranch was burned, and the three girls were taken captive. As soon as the horses belonging to the ranch could be corraled and supplies gathered, the Indians decamped, taking a westerly direction, stopping for a short time at Washington Springs, and then passed on to the Rio Grande and camped for the night on the banks of the river.

Meantime the elder Juárez arrived home and found his ranch burned, and in it the body of his murdered son. The peons in his service, who had observed the smoke and flames, rallied round the smoking ruins as their master arrived. Emanuel Juárez buried the charred and disfigured remains of his son as soon as possible, and then took an oath, which all his subjects endorsed, that he would recover his daughters or perish in the attempt.

He did not become insane, but without shedding a solitary tear he went to work and prepared for pursuit.

Gathering his peons together, and finding that they all had their arms and saddle horses with them which they used in herding, and calling in a few neighboring herders from the Sangre de Cristo, he commenced pursuit, determined to recapture his daughters or die with them. The pursuing party, well-armed and well-mounted, rode fast and in good order. The Indians discovered their pursuers while advancing in the vicinity of Washington Springs, some nine or ten miles distant, and believing that they could not fight Juárez, although they were forty strong, broke camp and struck out for the Cochetopa Pass, taking the old road toward Saguache. The pursuing party pressed them hard, and, when between the Canero and the Largaretto, the Indians, finding they could not escape in the direction of Cochetopa, deployed to the right for Saguache Lake and rode into it on the northern edge, while Juárez and his party were riding fast and close behind.

The Indians rushed into the lake at a point where the water was shallow and had advanced into the water some three hundred yards when the pursuing party arrived at the edge of the lake. As Juárez rushed forward he and his host saw the Indians and the girls disappear beneath the surface of the water. Awestruck and confused, the peons held up while appealing to the Holy Mother of Christ and petitioning Her for safety and protection; but not so with the brave and frantic Juárez. He never stopped, but driving his enormous spurs into the flanks of his foaming broncho, rushed forward only to disappear where his daughters had gone down. The last of that noble family of Castilians disappeared beneath the surface of Saguache Lake. The peons and servitors remained mounted on the edge of the lake for some time but could not discover anything upon the glassy and unruffled surface of the water.

They had long been of the opinion that the lake, which had no visible outlet upon the surface of the earth around it, must have some underground outlet and that the Indians, Juárez, and his three daughters had been engulfed in it. There are on the west side of the lake three large streams running into it, the Carnero, the Largaretto, and the Saguache. From the north San Luis Creek, and from the east several small streams, but it would seem that evaporation could not be sufficient to carry off all the water continually flowing into the lake from all these sources.

Fandango and Fofarraw

The Mexicans believe to this day that the Indians, Juárez and his daughters fell into the maelstrom and went to parts unknown; and it is a fact that whenever the Utes or Mexicans pass by the lake they speak of the event narrated with a great deal of superstitious awe and verily believe that the ghosts of the brave Juárez and his beautiful daughters may be seen riding on horseback over the surface of the lake during the night.

TRAGEDY AT THE FOOT OF MOSCA PASS[6]

This story, also given to a local newspaper by Mr. S. Richardson, was told to him and his companions in the year 1874 while they were sitting around a campfire on the Canero, south of Saguache, by the same Pedro Condalaro who had joined their train on the Rio Grande and who had recited the legend of Saguache Lake.

A long time ago, before the Mexican War, and while a portion of our state belonged to Mexico, there lived in the south end of the San Luis Valley several wealthy Castilian families. They were descendants of the early Spanish gentry of Santa Fe and vicinity. Among them, living on the Rio Grande, were the Martínez and García families, who were neighbors. They were wealthy and well to do, and their chief occupation was sheep and cattle raising, or general stock raising. In those days the wealthy Spaniards employed the native Mexicans, who were often peons. A peon is a slave to all intents and purposes, and once a Mexican is bound up in service for debt, or any other cause, he seldom, under the laws of the country, gains his entire freedom.

This class of labor was employed by the Spaniards in those days, and upon it they mostly depended for herders of sheep, horses, and neat cattle. It was said that these two families were wealthy, and of course that being the case, they lived luxuriously, and were the aristocracy of the immediate neighborhood. In the García family there was a bright young man, who was, at the time of the event of which we wish to speak, about twenty-five years old. He was fine looking, of fair complexion, a good scholar

[6] S. Richardson, in an unidentified newspaper clipping in the files of the State Historical Society of Colorado.

in his native tongue, and had acquired some knowledge of the English language.

This young man, Pedro García, was a noble specimen of his race. He was apt in all the acquirements considered necessary in those days. As a rider he had no peer throughout the entire valley; and, taken altogether, he was considered very promising, and had already amassed a considerable fortune, which consisted mainly of sheep.

In the Martínez family there was one daughter about twenty years of age, and one little boy about twelve years.

María Martínez was a very remarkable girl but delicate in health. She had been reared under the most tender solicitude of her parents. To say that she was beautiful, would not be saying much, from the description I received. She was well up in all the accomplishments thought necessary for a young lady to acquire in that day.

As the parents lived near, the young people were often in each other's society, and in fact, there was very little to attract the young people from each other.

María would frequently ride her pony over and visit Mrs. García, and Pedro would as often ride back with her to the Martínez ranch.

As might be expected, it was not long before the young people found out that they could not live separately. Their love for each other was of such an extreme nature as to emerge almost into idolatry, and they were married under the rites of the Catholic church. Pedro still lived with his parents, while María alternated between both families, and the young people were quite as much at home at one place as at the other.

Their lives seemed to be one perpetual sunshine. María fairly worshipped her husband, who in turn loved her as only a devoted husband can love a pure and noble woman.

One day a trader from the vicinity of Pueblo came over the Sangre de Cristo Range and purchased ten thousand sheep of Pedro García, paying down a few thousand dollars. Pedro was to deliver the sheep at Pueblo and receive the balance of the money. When the time came for delivery, Pedro rounded up the flock and prepared to start. His wife then insisted on taking a few servants with her and accompanying him as far as the foot of Mosca Pass. To this Pedro objected, but when a beautiful woman pleads as she did, she usually gets her own way, and so at last he consented and they set out for Saguache Creek and the Mosca Pass. They traveled slowly on account of the sheep; but at due time arrived at the intersection of Saguache and San Luis creeks. Here Pedro fixed a comfortable camp for his wife to remain in for a couple of days while he assisted the herders in reaching the foot of the pass, at the sand hills, planning to return as soon as the summit was reached and let the herders go on down the mountain to the Arkansas River; thus he could spend a few days with his wife, who would then return to the Rio Grande, and he would cross over and overtake the herders and go with them to Pueblo.

Pedro started out with nine herders after a very affectionate parting, the first since they were married. María waited three days, and Pedro did not return.

"Man proposes, but God disposes," is an old saying that was but too clearly verified in the plans of Pedro.

After waiting three days María sent one of her servants to see what had become of her husband. He left in the morning, early, and returned in the evening, and told the following story to the nearly distracted wife. He said that he went as far as the sand hills, and there he found some of the pack animals and Pedro's saddle mule, also a few sheep, but no sign of any of the men, that they had not passed up the ravine above the sand hills, and that it was his opinion all of the men had perished, along with most of the sheep, by being drifted under the sand the night after their arrival there, as the wind had blown quite hard that night where María was camped, but must have been fearful at the sand hills, as they were so much exposed.

María immediately ordered her horse saddled, and all her company to prepare for traveling. She would not wait until morning, but go at once to the sand hills. The little party arrived there towards morning, and it was not long before María was convinced that all had perished. During the morning, while she was walking over the loose dry sand, moaning and calling for Pedro, she was followed by her favorite shepherd dog. Suddenly the dog stopped and commenced to howl; putting his nose to the ground he commenced digging away the sand; and soon was trying to pull out a blanket. The servants coming up discovered that there must be more than a blanket there, and scraping away the sand, pulled out the dead body of Pedro García.

María never uttered a single cry, nor shed a tear. She fell on her knees beside the corpse of her husband, and with her handkerchief brushed the sand from his face, kissed him, and talked to him, entreating him to wake up and speak to her, his María. She was as pale as the face of the corpse she was kissing. The servants stood back awe-stricken, and uttered broken prayers to the Holy Virgin, the Mother of Christ. María merely moaned, she could not weep. After a while, the servants prevailed upon her to return to camp, and led her away. Afterwards they brought in the body of her husband. Again did she kneel beside the body and talk to him, entreating him to speak to her but once more, and tell her that he was not dead.

They prepared shelter as best they could, and also the evening meal, but María could neither eat nor drink. They made up for her a couch of blankets and prevailed upon her to lie down, which she did, and seemed to rest. The servants then fell asleep, and did not waken till morning. When they looked for María, she was not where they had left her. They found her lying upon the body of her husband—dead.

Their bodies were taken to the Rio Grande and buried in the same grave, under the direction of the Catholic priest. But according to [the story], they can still be seen walking lovingly arm in arm, during the nighttime, over the sand hills, at the foot of Mosca Pass.

WITCH-FIRE, AND A BURRO STRANGELY MARKED[7]

In which superstition, storm, and blue peak lightning have their parts to play.

[7] Levette J. Davidson collected these while visiting the San Luis Valley in the summer of 1941; Charles Hayden, of Walsenburg, Colorado, a story as he heard it from his Spanish-speaking neighbors.

An old gentleman graciously recalled for me his boyhood experience with a haunted house, abandoned by a Mr. Brown, the agent for Lafayette Head, who had been prominent in the founding of the little [San Luis Valley] colony of Conejos, in 1854. One night when Simeon and his boy friend went near, attracted by the glowing windows, the house burst into flame. They started to run away, for they did not want to be blamed for it; but curiosity got the better of them, and they went back to investigate. The flames had disappeared and the wood was not even burned. But when they opened the door, they saw a big bowlful of fire in the middle of the floor of the front room. This flame jumped over their heads and landed on the roof of a small, abandoned adobe house near by. It then sparkled from all corners, as it had often done before. Evidently the witches haunted this place frequently; but for special purposes they went over to the big frame house.

Another time, on the way to a dance, Simeon had to pass a big grove of cottonwoods, along the creek. He saw flames in the branches, and they jumped along from tree to tree, keeping up with him. When he got to the dance, he told the others; they all went outside to see. Then the flames burst into a thousand sparks and disappeared high overhead. When I repeated this and the preceding story to a learned friend, expecting him to reject them as superstitions, he assured me that he had seen fireballs on tree tops when conditions had been right. But he attributed them to static electricity, not to witches. Simeon also remembered stories of Indian raids on the community, and the wild funeral rites which the savages held over Chief Bonito, who had been killed near there.—DAVIDSON.

All burros carry crosses consisting of a stripe down the back and one across the shoulders. The only tender spot there is upon a burro and the only place where it is susceptible to punishment is in the center of the cross. The tradition is that when Joseph took Mary and Jesus to Egypt to escape the wrath of Herod, Joseph walked and Mary rode on the back of a burro, holding the infant Jesus in her arms. On the way the burro was startled by a couple of doves that suddenly flew up under its feet. The burro side-stepped and caused Mary and Jesus to fall to the ground. Since then all burros have carried crosses, and the doves have never ceased to mourn.—HAYDEN.

THE MOUNTAIN OF THE HOLY CROSS[8]

Not only in the San Luis, bordering even more ancient Spanish lands to the south, has life revealed its loneliness and tragedy, and the strange solace which sometimes comes out of them.

The half-legendary story concerning the naming of Holy Cross is that a Franciscan friar for past sins banished himself from Spain to Mexico. Not finding peace in Mexico, he left for the north with an exploring party. After weeks of rambling, a camp was one day made upon a mountain top to await the clearing of the low-dragging, dark clouds. The friar went a short distance from the camp and knelt down to pray. While he prayed the clouds parted, and when he opened his eyes, before him, gigantic and imposing in the sunlight, was a snowy cross.

THE ANGEL OF SHAVANO[9]

All the Western mountains are tragic in a way, thrusting peaks to sunlight, yet finding darkness at their piedmont lines. Men who live in mountains know such things. They see the bigness, the frosty blue of the firmament light, the stillness of forests casting basal shadows on broad parks. In all this, men sense religious overtones; and in their secret hearts, they are conditioned by them.

[Mount] Shavano, named for a Ute chief, is believed to be a modified spelling of the Ute Che-wa-no, or blue flower. On [Mount Shavano's] slopes, marked by slow-melting snows in deep fissures, a figure with outstretched arms, known as the Angel of Shavano, is seen in spring and early summer. The angel, according to the legend, appeared on the mountain when Shavano, who had been schooled by the Holy Friars of Santa Fe, prayed for the soul of his dying friend, George Beckwith, a member of the Gunnison expedition. Now each spring, which was the season when Shavano made his prayer, the angel reappears on the mountain.

[8] *The Daily News* (Denver), August 15, 1904.
[9] *Colorado Guide*, 311.

Fandango and Fofarraw

A tale of craft and gold, as it is known in the San Luis country.

Salvador Lonar was a rich old man. God had been good to him. His great house and all his lands, the money he had saved—they were all gifts from the Heavenly Father. He thought not of his years of toil, or earthly hardships, his wise dealings with his neighbors. To himself he gave such little credit. He was getting old, he felt his days were numbered and he longed to be with his sainted wife, the mother of his sons and daughters.

Meditating upon these things, he decided to divide his possessions among his children, leaving nothing for himself, for he would be welcome to visit among his children.

So he called them all together. To each, he gave that part of his wealth as best fitted their needs, advising them as to how they should do. Lovingly and carefully, he divided everything he had, keeping naught for himself. The children eagerly took their shares, assuring the father he could stay with them as long as they lived.

To the oldest son he came first, but Juan was a busy man, his family large, and the care of the old man was left to Juan's wife, who immediately fixed a little house in the rear of the big house and promptly forgot him.

Days passed, Juan came not to visit him, nor did the other children send for him. His money gone, he realized that he had done the wrong thing. Perhaps his own children were not to blame so much, but the wives and the sons-in-law. The grandchildren did not have time to include this feeble old man in their busy, happy lives.

One day, as he sat brooding over his unhappy situation, an old friend called. "What is the trouble, Salvador?" asked the old man.

"I am ill, I can not eat. I will be all right," said Salvador.

"Ah, no!" replied his friend. "This is not the reason. Your heart is sad because your children have neglected you. You don't eat because you have nothing to eat, but we will fix that. You

[10] Interview with Mrs. Hake, Alamosa, Colorado, Library of Congress, WPA File–Colo. W 3133.

should have kept your wealth; it is not for you to say how long you will live. Yonder chest, where you keep your clothes, I shall take away with me. I will give you one hundred silver dollars tonight."

"But I cannot repay you," cried Salvador, "and what will you do with my chest?"

"Indeed, you shall not repay me," cried his friend, "and I shall return your chest. Follow my instructions and all shall be well."

Later that day the good friend Pedro returned. The chest was very heavy and it was all the two men could do to carry it in. A new lock fastened it. Drawing the curtain over the window, the old friend deposited the one hundred silver dollars on the table.

"Now," he said, "begin counting when I leave, laying down one dollar at a time, one, two, three, four, up to a hundred. Then start counting over again." Salvador was puzzled but agreed to do as his friend suggested.

Late that night, Juan's wife, seeing the light burning in Grandpa's cabin, crept down to the little house to see what was going on. Hearing the jingle of silver, she crept back to tell Juan that Grandpa was counting hundreds of dollars.

The next morning the old man on arising was surprised to find that the daughter-in-law had brought a nice breakfast.

When Pedro returned, Salvador told of the visit and they laughed together, for now the man was on to Pedro's scheme. "Lest something should happen, I shall leave only fifty silver dollars today, but count just the same," said Pedro. Again the next night, Juan and his wife listened and again they heard the clinking of coins.

Soon the news spread about and the neighborhood sent word to the other children that their father was still a rich man. Was he not counting his gold like a miser? Once again he was in favor of his children. Gleefully, Pedro and Salvador clapped their hands over their little scheme.

Each of the children now begged their father to come and spend some time with them, but the old man knew, in his heart, that it was not he whom they were anxious for but his money.

There were now only two of the silver dollars left but Juan's wife had become very solicitous of the father, and the constant dropping of the silver dollars was sweet music to her ears.

Winter came and the constant desire of Salvador to go to his fathers was soon to be realized. Pedro came and brought with him a lawyer. A will was to be made and the contents of the chest which aroused so much curiosity with its new padlock were to be equally divided among his children.

Doctors were called in, fine foods were brought to the father, tender care was granted this fine old man in his last illness, and when he died they laid him away with all the pomp and style befitting a wealthy man.

In due time the lawyer came; the chest was unlocked and to each was given a package—of what? Nothing. Nothing but stones had filled the chest; but the children, thoughtless of their father, caring only for what he could give them, had visions of bags of gold, more money to spend. They were now getting their just deserts:

> *El quien espera las zapatas de un muerto*
> *Al fin llevara una mala suerte.*
> *(He who waits for a dead man's shoes*
> *Will inherit only bad fortune.)*

LEGENDS OF THE PURGATOIRE[11]

Not far from the San Luis, but on the eastern side of Colorado's magnificent Blood of Christ Range, sprawls the lonely valley of the Purgatoire River. Even today this is a mysterious country, a cattle land known to few, filled with dry creek beds, cactus flats, and strange rock formations, and possessed of many tales of a violent past.

The narrator [of the Purgatoire legend] was a very old Catholic priest who had then been in the northern New Mexico field for forty or fifty years. The priest claimed to have had this tale upon his entry into this field from the lips of old Spanish

---

[11] A. W. McHendrie, "Origin of the Name of the Purgatoire River," *The Colorado Magazine*, Vol. V, No. 1 (February, 1928), 18–22.

priests and inhabitants of New Mexico whose familiarity with local tales and traditions dated back perhaps another forty or fifty years; and these individuals in turn claimed to have received the story from those who were old men at the time of the telling.

The story as told by the priest ran that at some time back in the early explorations of the Spanish, a body of Spanish soldiery left the seat of the Spanish government in what is now known as Old Mexico, to search for the fabled Quivera. This expedition was commanded by a Portuguese officer in the Spanish Army, with a Spaniard as second in command. Several priests accompanied the expedition, which was not only the custom, but a regulation of the government. Somewhere along the route the first and second officers became embroiled in a quarrel, which resulted in the second officer killing his superior. The second officer then assumed command of the expedition and proposed to go on with the enterprise. The priests, however, felt that the slayer of the first in command was guilty of murder and would not proceed further in what they conceived to be an accursed or unhallowed mission. The priests accordingly turned back with several of the soldiers who likewise refused to continue under the command of an individual guilty of so serious an offense. The expedition went on but never returned, and its fate so far as accurate knowledge is concerned, remained a mystery. Some years later another expedition of Spanish explorers went northeast from Santa Fe toward the Quivera country [which lay somewhere along the Arkansas River in what is now western or central Kansas], and in this journey found upon the banks of a tributary to the Arkansas the rusted arms and armor of what had evidently been a considerable force of Spanish soldiery. The position and condition in which these remnants were found led the discoverers to the conclusion that the owners of these weapons and equipment had been surrounded in camp upon the banks of this stream and had been exterminated, presumably by hostile Indians. Doubtless being familiar with the fact that there had been a lost expedition and that there were no priests with it, they gave the river what to them was an exceedingly appropriate name to commemorate the tragedy.

Lost in the Purgatoire River

TALES OF THE SPANISH PEAKS[12]

Northwest of the Purgatoire stand the Spanish Peaks, antlered heights along an ancient piedmont trail. Sweeping up strongly from range land, looking out upon dog-flats, cottonwoods, and cedar-covered ridges, these peaks glow in moonlight like spikes of Spanish silver. Indian and trapper, high-booted dragoon, slouching, easy-talking rider of the Western Plains—all have known them, all have heard strange tales about them.

[This] great mountain, with its treasures of gold and its demon-infested valleys, is mentioned about the year 1541 in connection with the story of three monks who with a few other followers of Coronado were left behind when that explorer, after his fruitless search for the mythical city of Quivera, returned to Mexico.

It is asserted that two of the monks, Fray Luis de Ureda and Fray Juan de Padilla, were sincere in their desire to teach the natives the doctrines of Jesus Christ, and that both died the death of martyrs for their cause.

Of Fray de la Cruz, the third monk, nothing definite is known, but chroniclers of that period had knowledge of widely circulated tales current among the natives of the Rio Grande region, which were narrations of somewhat conflicting character, all of them, however, in substance rendering the same story, namely, that of the reopening by Fray de la Cruz of the demon-infested Huajatolla mine.

He, so it is said, had succeeded in subduing the power of evil spirits manifest on Mountain Huajatolla. He had penetrated the dark fissures and apertures in the deep end of the valley, and had accomplished the exhausting and burdensome task of bringing to light of day a fabulous amount of treasure.

But other Indians from the Pecos region reported that the perfidious monk, by promising rich rewards, had decoyed a number of their companions to those dismal mines, forcing them by fiendish tortures when once there, to enter the subterranean

[12] Louis B. Sporleder, "Legends of the Spanish Peaks," *The Trail,* Vol. XV, No. 1 (June, 1922), 5–8; reprinted from a pamphlet *Huajatolla, Breasts of the World,* published circa 1916, by Louis B. Sporleder, of Walsenburg, Colorado; *Colorado Guide,* 354.

passages, and bring forth the gold that lies loose on the ground, and that, when these forced slaves had served their purpose, all were killed. Of other and subsequent reports, nearly all were agreed that Fray Juan de la Cruz with his followers and a number of pack animals, loaded heavy with treasure, left the valley of evil spirits and proceeded toward the City of Mexico that same year; but that, fearing discovery, they had avoided settlements and taken a route hitherto not traveled.

In history there is no record of what eventually became of these adventurers; they did not arrive in Mexico, and every trace of them was forever lost.

In the year 1811 a Mexican traveler, "Baca" by name, found some distance south of the double mountain what could have been a portion of Fray de la Cruz' treasure—nuggets with lumps of gold scattered by the side of an ancient trail, far away from mines or mineral-bearing ores.

This traveler also reports evidences of recent earthquakes and other seismic disturbances near Huajatolla Peaks. He further mentions that he found open fissures in the valleys of the East Mountain, from which vapors still issued; and that all the country was overhung by a haze like a gloomy dark pall.

About fifty years later a prospector from the Pikes Peak region, animated by rumors common in the camps of Mexican freighters, sought again for Huajatolla's mines of gold, but with no other success than the discovery of a tarnished silver cup—a single name inscribed upon its rim—the name of "Hermione."

He found this cup, beautifully modeled, in a natural grotto at the base of the East Peak by the side of a tiny living spring.— SPORLEDER.

It is a matter of local [Walsenburg and Trinidad, Colorado] history that in the early 60's two old trappers used to come down out of the mountains with their donkeys loaded with very rich silver ore every fall, which they took to Bent's Fort, where they had it smelted. They said this ore came from an old Spanish mine. One of the men died while in the East and when the other man returned alone he was unable to find the mine. At different times men and parties came to Trinidad from widely remote parts of the United States to go out to look for this lost mine, but it still remains hidden.

George S. Simpson, who lived at Bent's Fort before going to Trinidad, knew these men, saw them leave in the spring, saw them return in the fall with the ore, and talked with them about the mine, but, of course, they naturally gave no clue as to the location of it. That the mine was on the regular trail from Bent's Fort to Taos, New Mexico, by way of the Spanish Peaks, was as definite a location as they would give Simpson.

Joseph David was a lover of the sport of hunting and fishing and made the most of opportunities to get out in the Spanish Peaks section where the game was best. On one occasion while sitting around the evening fire he saw, while looking toward the West Peak, indications of what must have been at some remote time a winding road leading up the Peak, and later wanderings on the Peak showed repair work might have been done in days gone by, but the timber growth had obliterated the old trail. The upper part of the Peaks is covered with rock slides and in all probability these slides have covered the much sought lost mine or mines.—SPORLEDER.

Old Spanish legends refer to the Marble Cave as La Caverno del Oro (The Cave of Gold) and have it that the Spanish conquistadores entered it from another opening on the western or San Luis side of the [Sangre de Cristo] range and worked rich mines in its depths. According to another tale, the fabulously rich Three Steps Mine of the Spanish was near the cave. . . .

The cave was discovered in 1919 by Forest Ranger Paul Gilbert, who thus describes it: "I first heard of Marble Cave in 1918 from a Mexican woman who at the time was 105 years old —she died at the age of 110. The woman stated that the Spanish obtained the gold from it, that if one were to descend to a sufficient depth, a set of oak doors would be found, which [when] forced open, would disclose a tunnel leading to the sources of the gold. She said that when she was a child her people used to take a blanket, wrap it around a heavy stone, and throw it down the shaft. In a short time the blanket would be blown back, minus the rock, by the strong winds that come from the hole."

Following the woman's directions, Gilbert found Marble Cave the next spring. The cavern is rather a volcanic fissure than a cave. It is entered by a vent; at ninety feet is a circular shaft twenty feet in diameter. Gilbert failed to interest anyone further in exploration until 1929, when a party of ten from the Colorado Mountain Club and Ranger Truman, of Westcliffe, undertook the most extensive exploration yet made.

The party descended far down the shaft without finding bottom. At seventy feet, on a small offset, they discovered the remains of a crude ladder that scientists in the party judged to be at least 200 years old. At approximately three hundred feet was found a hand-forged hammer, believed to be of seventeenth century manufacture. Two of the party made their ways down the shaft to a depth of some 500 feet, at which level, according to Gilbert, "the hole was little more than a cold and muddy shaft-like cave with dangerous loose rock in the walls." Upon returning from the Marble Cave, the party discovered, some thousand feet below the side of the mountain, the remains of an old log and stone fort, the purpose of which is a matter of conjecture.—*Colorado Guide.*

A FANDANGO IN TAOS[13]

On the southern border of the San Luis the Rocky Mountain country changes, saw-tooth cordilleras, sub-alpine forests of spruce, hemlock and the rare and lovely limber pine, rushing streams in canyon after canyon, and the green, moist reaches of montane peaks giving way sharply to the southwestern desert. It is through this bordering region that roads, paralleling the course of the upper Rio Grande, cross brittle lava plains, lose themselves on eroded cedar plateaus, drop to the depths of black gorges, and come at last to towns—to San Cristobal, Taos, Rancho de Taos, Espanola, and Santa Fe—which have neither the names nor the look of American towns. For to the south of San Luis is New Mexico, gray and green and purple desert country, land of pueblos, land of the Spaniard, and home too, for just a little time, of Carson, the Bents, and the fantastic Taos trapper brigades.

[13] George F. Ruxton, *Life in the Old West* (New York, 1922; first edition, *Life in the Far West*, London, 1848), 289–95.

No sooner was it known that *Los Americanos* had arrived than nearly all the householders of Fernandez de Taos presented themselves to offer the use of their *salas* for the fandango which invariably celebrated their arrival. This was always a profitable event; for as the mountaineers were generally pretty well flush of cash when on their spree, and as open-handed as an Indian could wish, the sale of whisky, with which they regaled all comers, produced a handsome return to the fortunate individual whose room was selected for the fandango. On this occasion the *sala* of the Alcalde Don Cornelio Vegil was selected and put in order; a general invitation was distributed; and all the dusky beauties of Fernandez were soon engaged in arraying themselves for the fete. . . .

Off came the coats of dirt and *alegría* which had bedaubed their faces since the last "function," leaving their cheeks clear and clean. Water was profusely used, and their *cuerpos* were doubtless astonished by the unusual lavation. Their long black hair was washed and combed, plastered behind their ears, and plaited into a long queue, which hung down their backs. *Enaguas* of gaudy colors (red most affected) were donned, fastened round the waist with ornamented belts, and above this a snow-white *camiseta* of fine linen was the only covering, allowing a prodigal display of their charms. Gold and silver ornaments, of antiquated pattern, decorated their ears and necks; and massive crosses of the precious metals, wrought from the gold or silver of their *placeres*, hung pendent on their breasts. The *enagua* or petticoat, reaching about halfway between the knee and the ankle, displayed their well-turned limbs, destitute of stockings, and their tiny feet, thrust into quaint little shoes *(zapatitos)* of Cinderella dimensions. Thus equipped, with the *reboso* drawn over their heads and faces, out of the folds of which their brilliant eyes flashed like lightning, and each pretty mouth armed with its *cigarito*, they coquettishly entered the fandango.

Here, at one end of a long room are seated the musicians, their instruments being generally a species of guitar called *heaca*, a *bandolin*, and an Indian drum called *tombé*—one of each. Round the room groups of New Mexicans lounge, wrapped in the eternal *serape*, and smoking of course, scowling with jealous

eyes at the more favored mountaineers. These, divested of their
hunting coats of buckskins, appear in their brand-new shirts of
gaudy calico, and close-fitting buckskin pantaloons, with long
fringes down the outside seam from the hip to the ankle; with
mocassins, ornamented with bright beads and porcupine quills.
Each, round his waist, wears his mountain belt and scalp knife,
ominous of the company he is in, and some have pistols sticking
in their belts.

The dances—save the mark!—are without form or figure, at
least those in which the white hunters sport the fantastic toe.
Seizing his partner round the waist with the grip of a grisly bear,
each mountaineer whirls and twirls, jumps and stamps; introduces Indian steps used in the "scalp" or "buffalo" dances, whooping occasionally with unearthly cry, and then subsiding into the
jerking step, raising each foot alternately from the ground, so
much in vogue in Indian ballets. The hunters have the floor all
to themselves. The Mexicans have no chance in such physical
force dancing; and if a dancing *Peládo* steps into the ring, a lead-
like thump from a galloping mountaineer quickly sends him
sprawling, with the considerate remark—"Quit, you darned
Spaniard! You can't shine in this crowd."

During a lull, *guages* [cask-shaped gourds] filled with whisky
go the rounds—offered to, and seldom refused by the ladies,
sturdily quaffed by the mountaineers, and freely swallowed by
the *Peládos*, who drown their jealousy and envious hate of their
entertainers in potent *aguardienta*. Now, as the *guages* are oft
refilled and as often drained, and as night advances, so do the
spirits of the mountaineers become more boisterous, while their
attentions to their partners become warmer—the jealousy of the
natives waxes hotter thereat, and they begin to show symptoms
of resenting the endearments which the mountaineers bestow
upon their wives and sweethearts. And now, when the room is
filled to crowding,—with two hundred people swearing, drinking, dancing, and shouting—the half-dozen Americans monop-
olizing the fair, to the evident disadvantage of at least threescore
scowling *Peládos*, it happens that one of these, maddened by
whisky and the green-eyed monster, suddenly seizes a fair one
from the waist-encircling arm of a mountaineer, and pulls her

from her partner. Wagh!—La Bonte—it is he—stands erect as a pillar for a moment, then raises his hand to his mouth and gives a ringing war whoop—jumps upon the rash *Peládo,* seizes him by the body as if he were a child, lifts him over his head, and dashes him with the force of a giant against the wall.

The war, long threatened, has commenced; twenty Mexicans draw their knives and rush upon La Bonte, who stands his ground, and sweeps them down with his ponderous fist, one after another, as they throng around him. "Howgh-owgh-owgh-owgh-h!" the well-known war whoop, bursts from the throats of his companions, and on they rush to the rescue. The women scream, and block the door in their eagerness to escape; and thus the Mexicans are compelled to stand their ground and fight. Knives glitter in the light and quick thrusts are given and parried. In the center of the room the whites stand shoulder to shoulder, covering the floor with Mexicans by their stalwart blows; but the odds are fearful against them, and other assailants crowd up to supply the place of those who fall.

The alarm being given by the shrieking women, reinforcements of *Peládos* rushed to the scene of action, but could not enter the room, which was already full. The odds began to tell against the mountaineers, when Kit Carson's quick eye caught sight of a high stool, supported by three long heavy legs. In a moment he had cleared his way to this, and in another the three legs were broken off and in the hands of himself, Dick Wooton, and La Bonte. Sweeping them round their heads, down came the heavy weapons amongst the Mexicans with wonderful effect. At this the mountaineers gave a hearty whoop, and charged the wavering enemy with such resistless vigor that they gave way and bolted through the door, leaving the floor strewed with wounded, many most dangerously; for, as may be imagined, a thrust from the keen scalp knife by the nervous arm of a mountaineer was no baby blow, and seldom failed to strike home—up to the "Green River" on the blade.

The field being won, the whites, too, beat a quick retreat to the house where they were domiciled, and where they had left their rifles. Without their trusty weapons they felt, indeed, unarmed; and not knowing how the affair just over would be followed up, lost no time in making preparations for defense. However, after great blustering on the part of the *prefecto*, who, accompanied by a *posse comitatus* of "greasers," proceeded to the house, and demanded the surrender of all concerned in the affair —which proposition was received with a yell of derision—the business was compounded by the mountaineers promising to give sundry dollars to the friends of two of the Mexicans who died during the night of their wounds, and to pay for a certain amount of masses to be sung for the repose of their souls in purgatory. Thus the affair blew over; but for several days the mountaineers never showed themselves in the streets of Fernandez without their rifles on their shoulders, and refrained from attending fandangos for the present, and until the excitement had cooled down.

OLD COLONEL PFEIFFER[14]

Hunter, Indian fighter, and feudist par excellence of the southern Rocky Mountain country.

This [southern] section of Colorado has been the "stamping ground" of many an old trapper and explorer, and quite a number of them lie yet where they died, unburied. Campfire tales, that warm ambition or freeze the blood with terror—tales founded on fact, with Kit Carson, the Bents, St. Vrain, Bill Williams, Col. Pfeiffer, the Autobeas, Roubideaux, and other old mountaineers as central figures; or Indian and Mexican atrocities, the Ute and Navajo wars, the Taos massacre, and the fiendish Espinozas—all have additional interest when told near the scene of their enactment. Most of the heroic band of old mountaineers have passed away. Many of them, after carrying life recklessly through the troubles incident to a change of government and continual war with "our red brethren," settled down to a civilized life, ranching, and Mexican wives. None of them ever went back to the States. Col. St. Vrain lives in Taos. Tom Tobin [Autobeas] has a ranch on the Trinchera, near Fort Garland; his brother Charley lives on the Huerfano, and both are extensively engaged in stock raising.

[14]*The Rocky Mountain Directory and Colorado Gazeteer for 1871* (Denver, 1870), 62.

"Old Col. Pfeiffer" (not yet quite forty-five) wanders, almost alone, among the scenes of his warfare and the graves of his comrades. He was a careless boy, fresh from the military institute in Stockholm, Sweden, when he first came to the Far West, in 1847. He was always noted for his cool daring, and soon was distinguished as a good Indian fighter. He took an active part in the long series of wars with the Comanches, Apaches, Utes and Navajos, that have kept back progress in New Mexico, Arizona and Colorado, and are not quite over yet. He was a lieutenant-colonel under General Kit Carson, during the Navajo campaigns of 1863-4-5-6, when eleven thousand of those "lords of New Mexico," who called the Mexicans their herders, were compelled to surrender to a small force, mostly volunteers, and were removed from the San Juan country to the Bosque Redondo Military Reservation.

Many wild stories are told of his exploits. On one occasion in Santa Fe, he wrapped a *serape* around his head, and went into a store that was on fire, and brought out two kegs of powder that were charred and blazing. At another time, with a knife in his right hand, he killed a grizzly bear that was chewing up his left arm. He fought a duel, once, with two Capote Indians. The weapons were camp knives. He killed them both, though badly used up himself. When the Apaches killed his wife and children, at the Ojo del Muerte (Spring of the Dead) in 1863, he was shot through both legs. In fact, there is hardly room for a fresh cut or bullet hole on his body; and he still lives, but lives unhappy.

Since his family were killed his only pleasure has been revenge. It was a bad day for the Apaches when they killed old Pfeiffer's family. He made several trips, alone, into their country, staying sometimes for months, and always seemed pleased, for a few days, on his return. If there was no party going his way, in a few weeks he was off again, with his horse and trusty rifle. He was always accompanied by about half a dozen wolves, in the Apache country. "They like me," he said once, "because they're fond of dead Indian, and I feed them well." Col. Pfeiffer, when not out in the mountains, makes his home at Fort Garland and Conejos. He too will soon be gone.

THE MAN-EATING SERPENT[15]

An old Abiquiu tale which has lingered late in the Chama River country of northern New Mexico, and which, on particularly brilliant desert nights, has seemed to possess more than a comfortable basis in fact.

Many miles from the railroad and not far from the old town of Abiquiu, New Mexico, are hundreds of cliff dwellings. . . . Under these and in the mountains back of them are many caves, and from some of them warm water issues. . . . Tradition has it that when the cliff dwellers first came to this country they brought with them a huge serpent from the south, that they worshiped this serpent, and that the serpent lived in the caves. Further, it is asserted that human sacrifices were offered to this serpent, and that these were dropped down through the hole in the bottom of the dwelling.

Today and for years past many Mexicans who live near these cliff dwellings firmly believe that, although the cliff dwellers have departed, the serpent still lives in these caves, and that from time to time it comes forth and does not return until it has devoured at least one human being. Some few claim to have seen it, but these few are called liars by the many who believe in the existence of the serpent and who also believe that no one can see it and live. Many claim, however, to have seen its trail which, according to common report, resembles the trail of an alligator.

About a year ago a goat herder and his son were tending their flock about fifteen miles from the cliff dwellings. According to Juan Velásquez, a Mexican rancher who lives near Ojo Caliente, the goat herder and his son suddenly heard a noise, like the rushing of winds or like the noise made by a swiftly moving train. The father and son had both heard of the serpent and, believing it was coming toward them, at once rushed for their house, about three miles away. The father was so frightened that he reached home before he noticed that his son was not following close behind him. To this day no trace whatsoever

[15] *The Denver Post*, March 5, 1911, signed "Sam Boardman, Albuquerque, N. M."

has been found of the son, although according to Velásquez and many others, the trail of the serpent was very plain.

JIM BAKER TAMES A DRUNKARD[16]

Fofarraw. That is a word. It has a French tang to it, a slow and easy Spanish tingle in it. It is gusty too, full blown, a Western American word. Trappers like Jim Baker, who told tales and had tales told about him, helped make it; frontiersmen from all the West have used it. Fofarraw means flashy talk, cabin or rendezvous life, high-built, roaring fires and trappers lolling back, stars and a white chalk moon overhead, and Rocky Mountain yarns.

One night in the early part of February, we—Buckskin Jack Fletcher, Rube Marvin, Cal Pratt, and the author [George West] —were seated in the cabin with our friends, the whole quartette being squatted in a half circle upon a buffalo robe spread upon the dirt floor before a blazing fire, and enjoying the pleasure of a smoke—not singly, but after the fashion of the Indians. This had also become a fashion with our friends, and we do not remember ever seeing either of them fill and smoke a pipe by himself. On this occasion Rube had filled the pipe with their favorite mixture—tobacco and kinnikinnick—placed a coal of fire upon it, and passed it from hand to hand until it had reached Jack Fletcher at the other side of the wide fireplace. Jack placed the stem to his lips—drew a long breath through it and passed the pipe to his next neighbor. . . . This continued for perhaps five minutes.

Suddenly the sound of the unshod feet of a horse was heard approaching from the direction of the village. In a moment more the rider was heard to dismount, the wooden latch was raised, and the shaggy yellow head of old Jim Baker protruded through the opening, and his rough voice exclaimed:

"Hullo! What the dognation kind of a teepe do you call this?"

Without the least sign of annoyance at the unceremonious address, Jack welcomed him with, "Wall, you slab-sided, red-

16 George West, "Buckskin Yarns," *Colorado Transcript* (Golden), February 2, 9, 1876.

headed old cuss, you'd better picket yer pony and come in and see."

"I reckon the squaws and papooses of this yer village has nigh about tramped out all yer grass," answered Jim, "and I expect you'd one of yer better come out and picket her yerself."

Without further parley Cal left the circle and went out to perform the task, while Jim Baker stalked into the cabin, and without ceremony deposited his long rifle in a corner. His dress, like that of all the old mountaineers of the day, was made up principally of buckskin. Sticking in his leggings was a huge sheath knife, and attached to his belt by a slipknot was a long lariat, braided from soft buffalo hide of several strands. It was small but heavy and pliable, and it was noticed that he removed neither it nor his knife from his person.

Not a word further was spoken by any of the party until Cal's return, and then the circle was reformed with Jim Baker at the end opposite Buckskin Jack, who again filled and lighted the pipe. This was then passed three or four times around the circle as before, and not until the last vestige of its contents was consumed was it laid aside. Silence was then broken for the first time since the entrance of the visitor, who somewhat excitedly opened the ball:

"What kind of a doggoned set of half-breeds hev ye got around this yer camp, anyhow?"

Upon being asked to explain, he went on:

"I run agin a screechin' cuss out here that seemed to be gittin' on the warpath right lively. He shot off his mouth right sassy like, and I had a notion ter reach over and lift his har jest to learn him manners."

While Jim was yet speaking an unearthly drunken yell reached the inmates of the cabin, followed by a demand for admittance.

"That's the same hell-hound I'm speakin' about," said Jim, and as he jumped to his feet it was noticed that he slipped the knot from the lariat at his side, and sprang for the door.

"That's that howlin' jackass of a Dock Turpin," said Rube Marvin, "and I've a notion to run him into the creek."

By this time old Jim had stepped outside the door, and as he did so he shouted to the intruder:

"Who's a-runnin' this yere teepe, you screechin' son of a Navajo. Git out'n this, or I'll tie ye to that thar pony's tail and set her a flyin' up that kenyon."

His coarse, savage voice seemed to have the desired effect upon Dock, for as old Jim stood in the moonlight he could doubtless see by his appearance that he was in dead earnest, and he at once turned to make his escape. By this time Jim's "mad" was up, and as Turpin started to run he gave his lariat a twirl or two over his head and sent the noose flying after the now fast-retreating cause of the disturbance. As it fell it encircled one of his ankles, and was so suddenly drawn taut that he was thrown heavily upon the frozen ground. Old Jim then coolly dragged him on "all fours" back to the corner of the cabin, threw the lariat over a protruding log, hauled him up until he was compelled to stand upon his hands and the other foot, and made him fast in that uncomfortable position.

Meanwhile Dock was howling at the top of his voice, cursing his tormentors in his drunken frenzy.

"You jest dry that up right now," said Jim, "or I'll make yer do it."

As this warning did not have the desired effect, he stepped back to the door, where his saddle had been deposited, and took from the horn of it his Indian whip. Forcing the thick hickory handle crosswise into the mouth of his victim, he brought the buckskin thong which formed the lash across the back of his neck, and fastened it to the butt of the stock.

Dock was now completely gagged, and incapable of creating any more noise. Telling him to give the logs a kick or two when he thought he could behave himself, Jim coolly left him to sober off in the biting night wind, and walked into the cabin, followed by the whole party, who had witnessed his novel method of taming a wild drunkard.

Fandango and Fofarraw

WHY ONE TRAPPER RETURNED TO THE ROCKIES[17]
A tale duplicated all too often, it is to be suspected, in the grass-roots annals of the Rocky Mountain West.

"See here, boys!" exclaimed a trapper by the name of Rube, "you seem to be all in for tellin' what started you to the Rockies. Now what d'ye s'pose started me? Now you can believe it or not believe it, just as ye please, but, 'honest Injun,' it war a cussed old mule. Tho' mind ye, thar war a gal in it, too! Yer may talk about pretty gals, an' yer spry gals; they war'nt a patchin' to Selina Perkins. She weighed a hundred and sixty pounds, an' she had a face on her like a full moon. She was a rouser, she war. Wall, we war engaged to be married, an' I war to run her daddy's farm, which war about nine miles from St. Louis. The day afore the weddin' I went into town to buy a critter, an' fell in with some of my ole pards, who war out to the Rockies with me the year afore, in Bill Sublett's company. Wall, we took a drink or two together, an' I began to feel like takin' another trip, but I couldn't see how the thing war to be did. Thar war the gal, an' the weddin' war to come off the next night, so I thought I'd take a night to consider on it.

"The next mornin' I bought a mule I had been lookin' at the day before, an' after runnin' around with the boys all day, towards night I started for hum, an' would you believe it, I hadn't made up my mind whether to marry or start for the Rockies. The company would be off the next mornin' an' as I rid along on the mule I kept a studyin', but couldn't come to no conclusion. About eight miles from St. Louis the roads forked—one road led to my gal's an' t'other led to town. Just afore I reached the forks a happy idea struck me. 'By thunder,' says I, 'I'll leave it ter the mule. If she takes the right hand road, it's marry; if she takes the left, it's the Rockies.' So I dropped the bridle on ter her neck, stuck my hands into my pockets and said, 'Go it, Bets' —that war her name. Wall, boys, she took the left an' here I am. I writ a letter to Selina, tellin' her to hold out fathful for two years. I'd be on then with pockets full of dollars, an' we'd hitch sure an' certain, without fail."

[17] James B. Marsh, *Four Years in the Rockies; or the Adventures of Isaac P. Rose* (New Castle, Pennsylvania, 1884), 30–32.

Rocky Mountain Tales

A MASTER TRAPPER MEETS A TENDERFOOT[18]

In which, it seems, more than the traditional tables are turned.

There is one whimsical old genius who is noted particularly among the trapper tribe as the prince of queer ones. He calls himself William S. Williams, M. T., and he is most resolutely determined upon having the title initials ("M. T.") always affixed to his name. He is the oldest man in the mountains, having fully resolved to live and die there, and more droll anecdotes are told about him than would fill a pair of volumes of modern size. "M. T." is meant to signify *Master Trapper*, and the old man has just seized upon the whim of insisting that this distinguishing mark shall on all occasions and under all circumstances be attached to his name. He chanced at one time to fall into a mortal quarrel with a Blackfoot Indian, and upon achieving advantage, he at once seized upon the red fellow's scalp lock.

"Bill Williams!" shouted the Indian, whose whole knowledge of English consisted in the capacity of pronouncing this singular old white man's name.

"William S. Williams, M. T., if you please," said the old man of the mountains, as he coolly darted the point of his knife around the scalp lock and tore it off!

This extraordinary individual is now about fifty-five or sixty years of age, and he has lived more than half his life in the mountains. He declares that he never was anywhere else, but it is remembered that he was once a Methodist preacher in the States, and it is known that he is an educated man, with a critical knowledge of Greek and Latin. By his own words, he was "rolled out of a thunderstorm in the mountains," for he found himself there and doesn't remember anything else. He is quite certain that he is not human, and has a strong persuasion that he was "translated from the Great Bear, or some other luminous celestial animal, for some most particular and especial purpose that is meant to be made known to him hereafter."

[18] Matthew C. Field, "William S. Williams, M. T.," *The Colorado Magazine*, Vol. XV, No. 2 (March, 1938), 73–76; a reprint of an article from the New Orleans *Picayune*, January 4, 1844. Mr. Field obtained material for this sketch while accompanying the Sir William Drummond Stewart and William Sublette expedition to the Rocky Mountains in 1843.

He was never known to wear a hat, but once in the winter, finding his head cold, he shot a wolf, scalped the animal, and drew the warm skin on to his own head! For all such eccentric things this old man is remarkable, but, perhaps, the singularity of his character may be better shown by relating an odd meeting that he once had with a young fellow fresh from the States. Williams was camping alone when the young man accidentally encountered him.

"Hum!" said the old man in soliloquy, "here comes another enormous fool of a young rascal to crowd us here in the mountains! We shan't have an inch of elbow room left! Cook, old cake! cook!" said he, addressing a lump of dough that he was turning over on the coals of his solitary fire with his naked toes, that protruded through his venerable mocassins. "Cook, old cake! here comes a white fool, and he's hungry of course. Now, you miserable young blockhead, do you know me?" said the old man to the stranger.

"I guess I do," said the boy, for he was a wandering sprig of Yankeeland.

"You guess," replied the old eccentric, "you're a pretty sample of a scalp lock to come here guessing! Had you nobody to keep you at home, that you must come strolling out here among the bears and Blackfeet?—How do you know me?"

"I reckon, I guess."

"O, you're a big figure at mathematics! You had better get rid of your guessing and your reckoning, if you want to live among the rocks. Take up that chunk of burnt dough there, and stuff it down your ravenous maw!"

"Thank you—I'm not hungry."

"Don't come here to tell lies, sir; we are honest men in the mountains, and you mustn't come here to contaminate us with your civilization. You are hungry, and you know it, and you must eat that cake; I've got another. Do you take me for an antediluvian, not to share my dinner with you?"

"Ain't you tha man they call Bill Williams?" said the hungry lad, as he greedily devoured the cake.

"What do they call me?" roared Bill, with the growl of a hungry bear.

"William Williams, I think," answered the young aspirant in the trapping trade, with a half-frightened tone of subdued respect.

"William S. Williams, M. T., young buzzard's meat!" replied the trapper, drawing himself up with an air of a Julius Caesar. "Look here, boy, do you see that butte?—There's a hole in it, and there's where I put my bones."

"Bones!" said the boy, greatly bewildered at the words of the old man.

"Yes-wah!" continued Bill, lifting his rifle and imitating a shot, "there's where I bury my dead; that's my bone-house!"

"Why don't you—"

"Don't tell me I don't," interrupted the old man, "or I'll don't you, knock me dead if I don't! How would you like to sleep there tonight? Eat away, and don't be gaping at a natural Christian like a born fool! I always stow away me white bones decently. Eat away, you stupid young blockhead, and stop staring. I dare say you call yourself a gentleman!"

"Ye-es!" stammered the youngster.

"Happy of your acquaintance. If you have done eating, just remember that you have dined with William S. Williams, M. T."

KIT CARSON FOFARRAW[19]

A tale of the northwestern country, embellished with Indian trickery; and a description of Rocky Mountain beaver trapping as that occupation was carried on in the days when prices were right.

Someone referred to [Kit] Carson's intimate knowledge of Indian strategy. "Why yes," he said, "I am up to a good many of their tricks, but they fooled me once—they fooled me pretty bad that time. I'll tell you about it! It was in—let me see—yes, 1835. There were six of us hunters out after buffalo, up in the Snake country. We had made a pretty good hunt, and came into

[19] James F. Meline, *Two Thousand Miles on Horseback* (New York, 1868), 250–51; newspaper clipping dated February 4, 1905, in *Dawson Scrapbooks* (State Historical Society of Colorado), Vol. I, 101.

camp at night, intending to start in next morning. Well, we camped. Had a good many dogs with us, some of them good dogs. They barked a good deal, and we heard wolves. As I lay by the fire, I saw one or two big wolves sneaking about camp— one of them quite in it. Gordon wanted to fire, but I would not let him, for fear of hitting some of the dogs. I had just a little suspicion that the wolves might be Indians, but when I saw them turn short around, and heard the snap of their teeth, as the dogs came too close to one of 'em, I felt easy then, and made sure it was a wolf.

"The Indian fooled me that time. Confound the rascal,"— becoming animated—"confound the rascal, do you think he hadn't two old buffalo bones in his hand that he cracked together every time he turned to snap at the dogs? Well, by and by we dozed off asleep, and it wasn't long before I was awoke by a crash and a blaze. I jumped straight for the mules, and held 'em. If the Indians had been smart, they'd a had us all, but they run as soon as they fired. They killed but one of us—poor Davis. He had five bullets in his body, and eight in his buffalo robe. The Indians were a band of Sioux on the warpath after the Snakes, and came on us by accident. They tried to waylay us next morning, but we killed three of 'em, including their chief."—MELINE.

Kit Carson was probably the most successful hunter who ever piked a buffalo, flogged an antelope or trailed a bear. . . . The greatest catch of beavers ever made in a short time was that of Kit Carson's hunters in 1840 at the northwest end of South Park [Colorado]. In this raid Kit Carson's twenty men caught eighty-four beavers in ten days.

Carson then lived at Fort Bent but had been through the country before and noticing a grove of poplar alive with beavers he organized a party to capture them. . . . [They drained the pond, drove the beavers into the brush with dogs, and then beat them to death, allowing the yearlings to live. At that time a fullgrown hide was worth $8 at St. Joseph; a 2 year old, $4].

The largest season's catch in this Western region is believed to be that made by Carson in 1841 on Wisdom River in Montana. There was a section of the river seventy miles long which had been dammed by beavers, until it spread five miles wide. Carson determined to take his trappers and plenty of Indians to prepare the hides and spend a trapping season there. He took forty-three men accompanied by two hundred Indians. The squaws went along to tan the hides. The Indian warriors went along to eat the meat which the squaws would be given for their labor. The whole Indian encampment was supported by Kit Carson's men, who killed buffalo and deer for them. Traps were used and from three thousand to thirty-five hundred pelts were secured. The laziest of the men got forty or fifty and the energetic ones one hundred each.—*Dawson Scrapbooks.*

THE LIFE AND DEATH OF JIM BECKWOURTH[20]

A description, in brief, of a famous mulatto frontiersman, as presented by a newspaper editor equally famed in the days of first settlement along the Rocky Mountain Front Range.

The career of James P. Beckwourth in Colorado is eminently worthy a place in the pages of history. To say that he had Negro blood in his veins heightens interest in the story, because of the tragedy begotten by that fact on the disputed soil of Kansas, and the singular tragedy of his ending in the Far West, both as a sequence of his origin. Personally he was a unique character and a study. He was born in Virginia of a Negro-slave mother, the son of an Irish overseer. In 1817 his white blood and his intelligence induced him to run away and he came with a caravan to New Mexico over the Santa Fe Trail, and was for some years employed by Louis Vásquez with the American Fur Company.

In later years, when the Kansas slavery question was at the border on the west line of Missouri, Beckwourth joined a party of Kit Carson's men to escort a wagon train to the Missouri River. Arriving at their destination Beckwourth was left to guard the horses and camp, while his comrades made a reconnaissance for game. Suddenly two men, coming from the Missouri side, rushed upon Beckwourth, and, after a struggle, put handcuffs upon him, meanwhile telling him that he was a d——

20 William N. Byers, *Encyclopedia of Biography of Colorado* (Chicago, 1901), 20–21.

nigger; that he had run away and they had come to catch him. At the moment he was about to be led away, Kit Carson's men appeared upon the scene, among them O. P. Wiggins, of Denver, and ordered them to desist. With their guns and a show of authority as fugitive slave catchers, the Missourians defied the mountaineers and declared they would take the "nigger" and that opposition was useless. Wiggins was the first to speak. He cocked his rifle, and instantly four guns were pointed at the breasts of the desperadoes. They unlocked the handcuffs, and the moment he was free Beckwourth picked up a gun and killed the two bloodhounds which the men had brought. This so infuriated the Missourians that one of them recklessly fired upon Beckwourth and missed him. Then they ran. Beckwourth fired and killed his man. Another shot from one of the party killed the other. The United States marshal and his posse followed the party westward for a week, and were finally obliged to give up the chase.

After that time, owing partly it is presumed to his color, and for the most part to his cleverness as an Indian fighter, the Crow Indians prevailed upon Beckwourth to become their head chief, and in this office he is said to have made much trouble for his former friends, the Fur Company, while he endeared himself to the tribe by his intrepid daring and good generalship in their wars with other tribes. After a period of years he severed his connection with the Crows and became interpreter and guide to government expeditions. But after another period of years he was compelled to flee from the vigilantes in a region of the northwest and returned to Missouri. He returned with the tide of immigration to Colorado in 1859, and became a partner of his old employer, Louis Vásquez, who had established himself in connection with his nephew, Pike Vásquez, as a trader in Denver. He soon married a very attractive young Negro woman, whose mother was the first laundress in Denver. His wife lived on the claim which he had located on the Platte, then two miles above the Denver site, and neighbor to the home of W. N. Byers, while Beckwourth was busy with his varied pursuits.

Early in the '60's, while engaged in business and enjoying the comforts of domestic life, one of the most singular circumstances conceivable occurred to Beckwourth. The Crows, who had removed as far north as the headwaters of the Missouri, had not forgotten nor lost their affection for their whilom chief. They had even kept track of him through all these years, and when they were fully appraised of his situation in Denver they sent envoys to persuade him to make them a visit. He yielded to the influence and went to the encampment of the Crows. They entertained him with all the honors an Indian can bestow. He remained many days with them. During the time they used every means and argument to persuade him to again become their chief. Upon his final refusal and his preparation to return to his home, the Indians honored him with a great farewell dog feast. The meat that was served to him was poisoned and he died on the spot. The Crows freely acknowledge the crime, saying: "He has been our good medicine. We have been more successful under him than under any chief." Their excuse was that if they could not have him living it would be good medicine to them to have him dead.

TIMELY AID REPAID[21]

Crisis in the Blackfoot country, with an appropriate hair-lifting ending.

'Bout twenty years ago I was trapping in the Blackfeet country 'way northeast, and, as I wasn't doing much, I concluded to go into the buffalo country and try my hand a bit at shooting, in order to get food for the winter, and a few hides to provide myself with tobacco and powder and shot. While on my way there, I met the band of Injuns commanded by this Jem you've seen; but he had some other name then which I don't recollect. He isn't a real Bannock; his band was then, and is now, made up of renegades from several tribes; and they never count for much, as they won't stop on reservations, and they acknowledge no law but their own. Well, when I struck their camp, I was so mighty hungry that I didn't care what I did, and I'd have fought the whole of the tribe for a piece of meat; for I tell you a man

[21] John M. Murphy, *Sporting Adventurer in the Far West* (New York, 1880), 304–307.

doesn't care much for bullets when he is starving and food is near. So I entered their camp boldly. They were as surprised as Injuns can be when they saw me riding down between their tepees, but they made no effort to injure me, for Injuns always like sand in a man, even if he is their foe; and none of the Injuns were then overfond of the whites.

When I saw the chief's tent, which I knew by its size, I jumped off my mule and walked in. I found this Jem and his whole family—wives, children, and dogs—inside. The women, children, and dogs were all eating together, so I knew he had finished his grub; for the braves never eat with the squaws and the youngsters, and the only company these have are their flea-bitten curs. When they saw me they looked kind of afraid, but they never said anything, nor did I; and walking toward a big iron pot, which they must have stolen from the whites, I looked into it, and, finding it full of meat, helped myself to some; and after I had stuffed myself full—for every person can help himself in an Injun camp to any grub he sees there—I lit my pipe and offered a smoke to this ere Jem, who was lying down on a buffalo hide near the fire, and he took it mighty quick, I tell you, for I think he was out of tobacco. When he finished he gave it back, and knowing by his looks that he wished he could have a few more puffs, I took out my pouch and gave him half I had, and he grabbed it as quickly as a starving man would a piece of venison.

Well, I stopped in camp that night, but not in any tepee, as I had plenty of blankets of my own; so I slept under a tree. Next day I traded some powder and ball for a large chunk of elk, and slinging this on my saddle, I marched out of camp without saying a word to anybody. I traveled about five miles that day, and, seeing beaver signs plenty, I concluded to try my luck there. I made a nice wickiup in a thicket of cottonwoods, and, after that was built, I placed my traps in the creek until I got within two miles, maybe, of the Injun camp; for I saw the Injuns weren't working it, because, perhaps, they were after scalps, not beavers.

I knew they wouldn't hurt me so long as I had made a friend of the chief; and that he was a friend I guessed from the way in which he took some matches from me. He didn't know what they were, except that they would light when struck; and as this seemed to be great medicine to him, I knew he would put them in his medicine bag and worship them ever after, and I, of course, would always be respected by him for giving him the medicine.

Well,—I stayed in camp there two days, but I wasn't idle, for I killed four deer, in order to have plenty of meat for a week or two. On the third day I visited my traps, and when I got to those near the Injun village I heard a tremendous yelling, and, on looking about, saw a dozen of the redskins running out of a piece of woods not seventy yards away from me, and about fifty legging it after them and shooting arrows at them in lively style.

I knew at once that it was a surprise by the Blackfeet; and as I did not care to be jumped by them, I dodged into the sagebrush and threw myself flat on the ground. Very soon after I saw three Injuns running across my front, and, on sitting up a little, found that the first was this Jem, and that the other two were big Blackfeet, who were screaming like the steam whistle of a cotton mill. Now, Jem having been good to me, I didn't care to see him double-banked; and as I had no great love for the thieving Blackfeet, I drew a bead on them and tumbled them both over in two shots as dead as a sardine box.

When Jem heard the report of the firing he turned round; and seeing that the Blackfeet had somehow disappeared, he guessed what had become of them. I jumped up at the same time and beckoned to him to stop, which he did, and we both ran for camp together. I told him by the sign language what I had done, and, though he said nothing, I knew he was mighty thankful; for it was more than likely that if I hadn't been round there his scalp would have gone to the Blackfeet nation, and he knew it.

Fandango and Fofarraw

A southwestern desert tale, wherein, it appears, the gullibilities of a wandering writer tempted old trappers at fofarraw time.

A trapping party from the Gila came in soon after our arrival, bringing with them a rich quantity of beavers, which they had caught during the preceding winter, spring, and summer upon the affluents of that river and the adjacent mountain streams. . . . In narrating the events of their long excursion, an account was given of visiting the Munchies, a tribe of white Indians. What added much to the interest I felt in this part of their story, was the recollection of an article which went the newspaper rounds several years since, stating the existence of such a tribe. I had disbelieved it at the time; but this, and subsequent corroborative evidence, has effectually removed from my mind all doubts upon the subject.

Our trappers had remained with the Munchies for four weeks, and spoke of them in high terms. In reference to their color they were represented as being of a much fairer complexion than Europeans generally, a thing easily explained if we remember this one fact, i.e., my informants must have spoken comparatively, taking themselves as the true representatives of that race, when in reality their own color, by constant exposure to the weather, had acquired a much darker hue than ordinary; then drawing their conclusions from a false standard, they were led to pronounce the fair natives much fairer, as a body, than the whites.

Among the visitors at the Fort were several old trappers who had passed fifteen or twenty years in the Rocky Mountains and neighboring countries. They were what might, with propriety, be termed "hard cases." These veterans of the mountains were very communicative, and fond of relating their adventures, many of which were so vested with the marvelous as to involve in doubt their credibility. . . .

Five or six years since, a party of trappers, in search for beavers, penetrated into an unfrequented part of the mountains

[22] Rufus Sage, *Scenes in the Rocky Mountains* (Dayton, Ohio, n. d.), chapter XV, 250–54. The first edition was published in Philadelphia in 1846.

forming the eastern boundary of Sonora. During their excursion they ascended a lofty peak that overlooked an extensive valley, apparently enclosed upon all sides by impassable mountains. At a long distance down the valley, by aid of a spyglass, they could plainly distinguish houses and people, with every indication of a populous city. At the point from whence this discovery was made, the mountain side facing the valley was a precipitous wall of vertical rock, several hundred feet to the base, rendering a descent impossible. After trying at other places, with like ill success, they were at length compelled to relinquish the design of further investigation for the time being. Subsequently, on visiting Arispie, a town of Sonora, several foreigners were induced to join them in a return expedition, and a company of some twenty or twenty-five repaired to the place for the purpose of prosecuting a research so interesting.

On arriving at the mountain from whence the object of their curiosity had been first seen, there lay before them the valley and city with its domes and palaces, amid which a swarming population was distinctly observed, apparently engaged in the prosecution of their various avocations. There could be no doubt of its reality, but how to reach it was the next question.

A number of days were occupied in vain search for a pass into the valley. The creek upon which it lay was found to emerge from the vast enclosure, through the mountain, by a frightful chasm formed of vertical rocks upon each side, for hundreds and even thousands of feet in altitude. The current was rapid, and interrupted by frequent falls that precluded the possibility of a passage up its bed. They crossed it, and finding a convenient slope, again ascended the mountain. On reaching the summit, a counterscarp was observed, where, by dint of great exertion, a descent could be effected; but not with horses. Arrangements were made accordingly, and one-half of the party remained with the animals and baggage, while the others, continuing the exploration, finally succeeded in entering the valley.

Meanwhile, the movements of the advancing party were viewed with great anxiety by those in reserve. In the course of the succeeding day they were seen to enter the city and mingle among its inhabitants; but, after that, they were never again seen or heard of. Three weeks elapsed and no sign of them appeared. At length their companions were forced by hunger to leave the spot and abandon them to their fate.

MISCELLANY[23]

For the shag end of an evening, when the campfire burns low and men feel sleep heavy in their eyes and the darkest tales have been told.

Poor old Charles Norton, whose death at the county hospital here August 27 was noted in our last issue, was a pioneer of the Salmon River and Custer mining districts; he was essentially a man of nerve. In his early days he was something of a bear hunter and many a cinnamon and silvertip fell before his unerring aim.

It was about ten years ago that he met the bear that chewed him up and left him almost helpless and but the caricature of a man in appearance. He was prospecting in the mountains, with but one companion, some sixty miles from Challis. He noted traces of a bear and followed them into the underbrush. He located bruin, and took aim and brought him down. At the same instant a big silvertip rose up beside him and struck him a blow in the face that broke both his jaws and literally crushed his face in. The bear then chewed him up, mangling and tearing him from head to foot, and finally went off leaving him for dead.

Here his companion found him hours later and finding him still alive fixed him up as best he could and started for Challis for help. It was sixty miles to Challis and by the time Norton's partner got back with help, the flies had gotten at him and blown him and before they took him into town, they took about a quart of maggots from his face and head. A litter was slung between two horses and he was taken to Challis. He still hung onto life and a doctor was sent for, thirty miles away.

It seemed impossible that Norton could recover. The doctor said he couldn't but went ahead and fixed him up as best he could. It was found necessary to take out his whole lower jaw. Norton, however, went right on living and getting better. It developed

[23] *Pocatello* (Idaho) *Tribune*, September 3, 1898; Meline, *Two Thousand Miles on Horseback*, 265.

after a while that his face would not heal because of its being more or less torn open every time he was fed. A hole was then cut in his neck through which he was fed. His face then healed and then it was found impossible to heal the hole in his neck.

Finally Norton was sent to the hospital at Salt Lake City and the hole in his neck was closed with silver wire and finally healed. In the meantime the contraction of the muscles of his face caused his mouth to close so tightly that he could not eat and his mouth had to be cut open time and time again. It always came together again in a short time and the operation had to be repeated. All these operations were performed without ether or other anesthetics.

Eventually Norton left the hospital and went out with a prospecting party. Here his troubles recommenced. His mouth grew shut and he couldn't eat. He begged his companions to cut his mouth open but none of them would do it. Finally he whetted up his knife, pinned a pocket mirror to a stump and cut his mouth open himself—and all went well again.

In the meantime, cancer developed in Norton's face and in the last five years he had it cut out four times. He always insisted on going through the operation without anesthetics. It was just before the last of these operations, a year or more ago, that he met Abe Pierce and was telling him that he was on the way to the hospital for another operation and as he ended his story, he said: "And do you know, Abe, I am getting to be a d——d baby. I kind of flinch when I think of it."

After years of terrible suffering, the old man's nerve was beginning to give away but he went through the operation bravely and his will held to the end. Charles Norton died like thousands of the pioneers of the West—a county charge, long forgotten by the relatives whose addresses he himself had forgotten.—*Pocatello Tribune*.

The canyons are all well known to the Western hunters and trappers from the fact that they are at once roads and passages where no others can be found, and are remarkable natural objects, either from their great size or natural beauty. Kit Carson tells a story of a friend of his, an old trapper, who had not been within the limits of civilization since his childhood, and had never seen a street of brick houses. He went down to St. Louis and was invited to stay at the house of an acquaintance. Sallying forth in the afternoon, he did not return in the evening, nor in fact all night. By daybreak next morning his friend went out to hunt him, and found him asleep in the market-house. He had lost his way, he said, because the "confounded canyons here are all so much alike I couldn't tell one from another."—MELINE.

Overland Trails

LIKE the wind itself, time has blown long and steadily over the American West. In a century unnumbered blizzards and cloudbursts have come; frost and sharp desert heat, following each other in regular cycle, have chipped away mountain gorge walls and the great cap rock cliffs of the Plains; flashfloods, terrible, swift, threatening the very lives of travelers, have swept again and again down the same Western streams. Fords have been washed out, and yet, on the banks of these fords, dust dunes have been raised. Rivers have kept their old courses, but channels within them have dried up or deepened, and the routes of Western travel have shifted.

So some men point to the facts. The solid wagon wheels, they mourn, no longer roll. Trapper travois and Mormon handcarts; high Conestagas with their ox teams, water barrels, and lashed, shining plows; springy Concord coaches fitted with curtains for ladies; Rocky Mountain freight wagons; land agents in their buckboards; the stage stations; the cedar corrals; the flashing Pony Express—all have gone, passed beyond the Divide, these men say. Only relics—a few stage coaches in Santa Fe and Cheyenne; a few freight wagons that once served Central, Leadville, and Idaho Springs; a few Conestagas in Ogden and beyond the Blue Mountains in Pendleton—now stand on display.

But Westerners—the Western people who make their lives in the mountains and far out on the Plains—talking little themselves, listen quietly and wonder sometimes. They know the bigness, the brightness of the Western night. They know where the old trails are. They have their ranches along the Santa Fe Trail in the south, near the Cimarron Cutoff or the pass at Raton. They ride their Platte and Sweetwater ranges; travel Echo Canyon along the Mormon line; herd sheep along the Bozeman Trail to the Bitterroots and farther northwest, on Snake River flats by the Oregon Trail. They have seen the broad ruts. They have camped beside them under white Western stars; and like the fires of frontiersmen, their campfires have lighted the night. They have heard things, these Western people, seen strange shapes in the silvery sage. Living close, feeling free winds and the chill of the mountains, seeking the warmth of a flickering blaze, they know, of this reticent land of the West, what other men cannot know. They could tell much today, if they would, of the old overland trails.

CROSSING THE PLAINS IN '58[1]

In the course of his travels, Daniel Kellogg, prospector and Western pioneer, preserved for his own records impressions of life on the Plains in the days of Pikes Peak-or-Bust.

Being on morning watch I saw at dawn large numbers of buffalo near. I started out alone to get a cow or a calf. The country was level and afforded no cover and I was unable to get a shot, but seeing the valley to the left I made for it. Presently five bulls came feeding up the slope. Lying flat on the ground I got a shot at one that exposed his side. The shot revealed my whereabouts and instantly the tufted tails of the whole band were in the air. Bellowing and pawing the dust they advanced, their wicked eyes glittering through the matted hair of their foreheads. Loading as best I could without getting to my feet, I fired again and then jumped up and waved my hat and rifle and yelled like a Comanche hoping to stampede them. But they seemed less disposed to stampede than I did; I momentarily expected them to charge. I had found five more buffalo than I wanted.

At last one of them wheeled, ran back a short way and lay down; the others turned, went back to their wounded companion, again faced my way, and remained with him for a few minutes, ran back to me again, and turned again and clumsily

---

[1] "Across the Plains in 1858," the diary of Daniel Kellogg, *The Trail*, Vol. V, No. 7 (December, 1912), 1–9 and No. 8 (January, 1913), 1–10. Additional material may be found in LeRoy Hafen, *Pikes Peak Gold Rush Guidebooks of 1859; Colorado Gold Rush: Contemporary Letters and Reports, 1858–1859;* and in *Overland Routes to the Goldfields, 1859, from Contemporary Diaries,* Southwest Historical Series (Glendale, California, 1942).

galloped off down the slope into the valley. Approaching the wounded bull I fired at his forehead, but at the flash he was on his feet in an instant and I realized that I had a mad buffalo on my trail. I ran toward the train, whose dust I could see a long way off. After a close chase for some distance the bull slowed down, spread his forefeet apart and sank to the ground. I then shot him once more under the horns, cut out his tongue and made for the wagons.

All the Indians met lately predict a hard winter on account of the comet. They express themselves quite understandingly to us by the sign language, motioning to us and then pointing to the east whence we came, then to the west where we are going, shrugging their shoulders and pulling their blankets close around them, laying their heads to one side and closing their eyes. This is the Indian way of telling us that we white men have come from under the sun where it is warm and are going to the mountains where it is cold; and that the malign influence of the comet will be the death of us. The Indian on his pony, clad in breech clout and mocassins, his copper-colored skin glistening in the sun, his head shaved except for a scalp lock from which dangles an eagle feather, his face painted, riding up to the train with spear and shield of buffalo hide, sitting on his horse like a statue, straight as an arrow and as haughty as the devil, he is the chief of wonders of this strange land.

We trade sugar or coffee for buffalo robes. Pointing to the sugar or coffee, holding up a tin cup and extending five fingers and pointing to the robe is an offer of five cups of sugar or coffee for the robe. If accepted the Indian says "How, how." The man with the biggest thumb then measures out the required number of cups keeping his thumb inside the cups as he measures. We calculate that one cup in five is gained by the thumb expedient. On the other hand the wily Indian palms off on us his poorest robes. We have been able to get but few good ones. As so many of us want to buy his best robes the Indian decides to keep them.

When an Indian shakes your hand he answers your "How are you?" with a deep, gutteral "How." If he accepts your offer for barter he shows his willingness to deal by an emphatic "How,

how." Before learning this we held out our cup of sugar and
pointed to a robe, asking the Indian "How much?" The Indian
repeated "How much?" in a louder tone. He meant that he understood we wanted to trade and that he was willing. I imagine
that when the first white man met an Indian he said, "How do
you do?" The Indian appropriated the first word and afterward
used it as a salutation and as a sign of approval. The word "how"
seems to be in general use among all the tribes we meet.

INDIANS INTERCEPT A SUPPLY TRAIN[2]

*In February, 1865, during a time of general alarm on the
Plains, the wagon train of H. M. Foster was returning to Denver
City from Leavenworth, Kansas. Why the train, with its sorely
needed supplies, failed to reach the Cherry Creek settlements
is succinctly told by Charles E. Pennock, a member of the party.*

Being anxious to get to the end of their journey while weather permitted and having seen no Indians though constantly hearing them, it was decided to go ahead to Alkali Station, nine miles
to the westward from Julesburg. These stations or roadhouses
were located at convenient distances along the road, where supplies were kept for the convenience of travelers; also all were
fortified as a protection from the attacks of Indians.

It was nearing this station that the first Indians were sighted,
and their actions gave evidence of their hostile intent, by dashing about, yelling and whooping, with purpose of inspiring fear
in the hearts of the little band of freighters, but cowards as they
were, keeping well beyond the range of guns. When arriving at
the station, the corral was hastily formed, the cattle put within,
and the gaps chained; then provisions, bedding and other things
necessary were taken into the house, and preparations made for
a siege, that was felt to be unavoidable, as they were already surrounded by the redskins.

The first act of hostility was stampeding the cattle, which
was accomplished by blood-curdling yells, waving buffalo robes,
and shooting arrows into the already terror-stricken oxen, until

[2] From the manuscript reminiscences of Charles E. Pennock, Bellevue,
Colorado, published in the *Rocky Mountain News*, December 14, 1927.

maddened by fear and pain they broke through the corral, and ran wildly toward the bluffs where they were slaughtered to the last one.

But the Indians were not satisfied with this achievement, they knew the wagons contained many things which they coveted, and which they longed to plunder, and outnumbering the freighters at least thirty to one, they thought it an easy matter to gain possession of them. Above all other considerations, the scalps—that seemed within easy reach—would be the most highly prized of all. A scalp worn in the belt of a warrior gave him a higher standing in the tribe; it was a symbol of heroism and bravery, as a medal of honor bestowed upon the whites for acts of heroism.

With the cattle gone it gave the plainsmen a clearer field for shooting; previously the cattle had served as a protection for the redskins. Now whenever one exposed his body, it became a target for the guns of the plainsmen. In the three days' battle which ensued, it became a battle of wits, in which, as in most cases, intelligence triumphs over ignorance; as an instance: a freighter stuck his head out of the window to see what the Indians were doing, when Spat! came a bullet against the wall barely missing the head of the plainsman. This served to make the men more wary, also it gave Doc Bogard—who was an experienced Indian fighter, and like Colonel Chivington an expreacher—an idea, which worked out on several occasions with tragic results to the Indians. The plan was for one of the men to put his hat on the end of a ramrod and stick it out the window, then when the redskin fired—which he did and was sure to do—Doc stood ready to fire as soon as the way was clear; and before the Indian could get out of the way he was made a good Indian, and several more were made good by the same manner. In all, sixteen Indians were seen to fall, lacking one of the total number of the besieged bullwhackers.

The Indians also set their wits to working with what might have been fatal results to the besieged teamsters. From the protection of the wagons, they shot fired arrows into the roof of the building in spots where the wind had blown off the soil and left the hay exposed, thus setting fire to the roof. Then something had to be done, and done quickly, and the only thing that could be done was for someone to crawl onto the roof at the risk of his life and put the fire out. Volunteers were called for and a slender youth of eighteen years was the first to respond. With the arrows whizzing around him, he succeeded in putting out the fire and, due to the poor marksmanship of the enemy, returned to safety. Twice more he repeated the same feat with success. It was this same Frank Pennock, who from his station, saw an Indian skulking by the wagons that formed the corral. Seeing a clear opening between the spokes of a wagon wheel, which the Indian would have to pass he drew a bead on that point and when darkened on that point by the Indian's body, pulled the trigger and the Indian fell in his tracks, shot through the body. As it proved to be a chief they exhausted all their ingenuity in trying to recover it. Lariats were tied to ox bows, then thrown beyond the body, and when securely caught could be drawn from the danger zone; but this body was beyond their reach. So on the evening of the third day, when the Indians had withdrawn to the bluffs to hold a council, the men went out to view the dying warrior.

The old chief was near death, but when Frank was pointed out to him as his slayer, he raised his hand as a token of forgiveness. Frank took his hand and dropping it turned away, for, as he afterward told the writer, he could not bear to witness his suffering. But there were others among them who were not so tainted with human impulses, especially the Irishman by the name of Pat Sheridan, who scalped him, though it is to be hoped that the chief was first given the mercy shot; but as to that the writer does not know.

At this time the freighters also held a council, at which it was decided to attempt to escape the coming night, as their ammunition was nearly exhausted, with no prospects of relief. Before leaving they buried bolts of dress goods and other things bought for the families in Denver; but the Indians discovered them, and the only thing saved from the whole trainload of merchandise was a rocking horse bought by Frank for his little nephew. This he put on his shoulder and with the others stealthily made their way to the river and walked to Julesburg on the ice.

97

The next morning, the owner of the train and Doc Bogard with a detachment of soldiers went back to the station to see what had been done to the wagons and cargo. The Indians had carried off everything of value and burnt the wagons and station, not a thing left but the irons of the wagons and the walls of the station; so there was nothing that could be done but return to Julesburg. The road led through a ravine, and as they were riding through they were attacked by Indians from ambush. As they were getting away, the mule that Foster was riding fell down, with the rider's leg underneath, leaving him helpless; the soldiers fled and Doc fought the Indians off until the mule was gotten up, when a running fight was kept up until Julesburg was reached, where they both came in laughing.

BUFFALO BILL, PONY EXPRESS RIDER[3]

Many an American, living far from the Plains, laughed at the storied exploits of Buffalo Bill; but among men who knew him on the Frontier, there were as many who saw little reason to laugh.

Among the most noted and daring riders of the Pony Express was Hon. William F. Cody, better known as Buffalo Bill, whose reputation is now established the world over. While engaged in the express service, his route lay between Red Buttes and Three Crossings, a distance of one hundred and sixteen miles. It was a most dangerous, long, and lonely trail, including the perilous crossing of the North Platte River, one-half mile wide and, though generally shallow, in some places twelve feet deep, often much swollen aud turbulent. An average of fifteen miles an hour had to be made, including changes of horses, detours for safety, and time for meals. Once, upon reaching Three Crossings, he found that the rider on the next division, who had a route of seventy-six miles, had been killed during the night before, and he was called on to make the extra trip until another rider could be employed. This was a request the compliance with

[3] Alexander Majors, *Seventy Years on the Frontier* (Chicago, 1893), 176–77; Frank A. Root and William E. Connelley, *The Overland Stage to California* (Topeka, 1901), 123, 277.

which would involve the most taxing labors and an endurance few persons are capable of; nevertheless, young Cody was promptly on hand for the additional journey, and reached Rocky Ridge, the limit of the second route, on time. This round trip of three hundred and eighty-four miles was made without a stop, except for meals and to change horses, and every station on the route was entered on time. This is one of the longest and best ridden pony express journeys ever made.—Majors.

The pay of the pony express riders was fixed at from fifty to one hundred and fifty dollars a month and board. William F. Cody (Buffalo Bill) and a few others, who had extra risks from riding through regions infested by the Cheyennes and Comanches—among the most feared savages roaming the plains of Nebraska and Colorado in those days—were paid one hundred and fifty dollars for their services. To make the ride they were often obliged to take their lives in their own hands. Along the two thousand mile trail, stretching from the "Big Muddy" to the ocean, relay stations were established at regular intervals, and bronchos and a number of men equipped with rifles and revolvers stationed at each.

It was not unexpected that mishaps should occur while making the long journey across the continent. Now and then a rider would lose the road, and, bewildered, wander around for hours in search for the lost trail. Once in a while a rider would be caught in a blinding snowstorm; another would be impeded in his ride by a swollen stream on the plains or in the mountains; and thus considerable valuable time would be lost. Occasionally a horse would drown and the rider, knowing it was a case of life or death with him, would be obliged to swim ashore and, with the mail-pouch of valuable letters on his back, walk to the next station and secure a fresh pony to complete his ride.

The letters in care of the pony express were wrapped in oil-silk as a protection against the weather, being then placed in the four pockets of the leather pouch specially prepared for them. The reason for so many pockets was that the weight might be, as nearly as possible, evenly distributed and that there be little inconvenience to both pony and rider. The pouch was provided with locks, and keys to it were distributed at the various forts along the route and also at Salt Lake City and Carson. Even with the packages of letters wrapped in oil-silk, they were sometimes injured by water when it was necessary for the riders to swim their horses across swollen streams. . . . At times there would be a lively chase for the rider by Indians, but only once has there been mention made when he was overtaken. On this occasion the rider was scalped, but the pony escaped with the letter pouch, which was subsequently recovered out on the plains and the letters promptly forwarded to their destination. . . .

Buffalo Bill was not only one of the best pony express riders, but he was an overland stage driver, and a good one. He drove between Fort Kearney and Plum Creek, in 1865, a handsome gray team, a decided favorite among all the stage boys in that vicinity. He participated, some distance west of Kearney, during the old staging days, in one of the liveliest fights that ever took place with the Indians on the great overland line. The story of the fight in which he took a prominent part is told by John M. Burke, the veteran driver, as follows:

"The condition of the country along the North Platte had become so dangerous that it was almost impossible for the Overland Stage Company to find drivers, although the highest wages were offered. Billy at once decided to turn stage driver, and his services were gladly accepted. While driving a stage between Split Rock and Three Crossings he was set upon by a band of several hundred Sioux. Lieutenant Flowers, assistant division agent, sat on the box beside Billy, and there were half a dozen well-armed passengers inside. Billy gave the horses the reins. Lieutenant Flowers applied the whip, and the passengers defended the stage in a running fight. Arrows fell around and struck the stage like hail, wounding the horses and dealing destruction generally, for two of the passengers were killed and Lieutenant Flowers badly wounded. Billy seized the whip from the wounded officer, applied it savagely, shouted defiance, and drove on to Three Crossings, thus saving the stage."—Root.

THE PHANTOM SCOUT[4]

Legends of hard-riding, faithful messengers, killed while dis-charging some important mission, are still to be heard in the Western country. In Wyoming especially, a high and wind-swept land, such stories find an appropriate setting.

S——, more than thirty years ago, then a young man, lived with his parents in their country home, which was located several miles from the limits of Cheyenne. He rode a fine saddle horse to and from his work in Cheyenne. Usually he would arrive home at night in time for the evening meal, but occasionally he remained in town to enjoy some sort of entertainment, perhaps a show.

It was after one of these performances that S——, riding home-ward alone, was to have an experience which he was never able to explain, even to himself. The hour was near midnight, and a brilliant moon, now and again obscured by scudding clouds, lighted the road and the surrounding prairie. S——, riding swiftly alone, suddenly discovered that he was not the only rider abroad that night. He could see, plainly, another horseman, riding like mad across the near-by plain. This rider, bending low in his saddle, was evidently urging his mount on to all of the speed of which it was capable.

Instantly S—— concluded that here was someone in desperate trouble and riding for help. As he noted that the rider was com-ing at an angle that would bring him into the road at some dis- ·tance ahead of his own position, S——put the spurs to his horse and raced ahead to intercept the other man and offer his aid. He purposely rode some distance beyond the point where he saw that the oncoming rider would have to enter the road; then stopping his horse, he waited for the man to come up to him.

To his surprise, the rider did not slacken his speed as he ap-proached, but passed in a rush of icy wind, while the horse that S—— was riding snorted and reared, plunging into a ditch beside the road where he stood trembling with fear. S—— was finally

[4] Writers' Unit, W 12211, WPA, Library of Congress file. The story was given to Alice C. Guyol, Hartville, Wyoming, by "the man who saw the apparition."

The Phantom Scout

able to urge his frightened horse into the road and to give chase to the other horseman, but he was hopelessly outdistanced and was finally forced to continue on his way home, wondering just what had happened.

S—— was a normal type of young Westerner, not especially imaginative, utterly free from superstition, and certainly not wanting in courage; according to his own statement "the last person in the world who could expect to see a ghost." But, in reconstructing the experience, he recalled that there had been no sound of hoofbeats on the hard road as the rider had passed him, that his own horse had been badly frightened at the thing, whatever it was, that had rushed by to disappear in the distance.

Fearing ridicule, he had hesitated to tell of the experience; but he questioned several old settlers, friends of his father, and learned that others beside himself had seen the apparition, which was supposed to be that of a pioneer scout who had been killed by the Indians while carrying a message to tell of an uprising among the tribes. Unable to rest while his mission remained unfulfilled, he continued to make his hazardous ride, night after night, in the attempt to deliver his message to a little group of phantom men, waiting in vain to receive it.

"BISHOP" WEST AND THE TENDERFOOT[5]

Stage drivers, particularly those on dangerous Western routes, often had passenger trouble, as evidenced by the following excerpt from the history of the Rocky Mountain Front Range.

Hon. W. N. Byers, the Denver pioneer and noted journalist, in an interview recently said: "I remember 'Bishop' West, a noted driver on the Idaho Springs, Georgetown, and Central road. They used to call him Deacon, though how he got the nickname I am sure I can't tell. He was a small man, and crippled. The front part of his feet had been frozen off. But he was as brave as they make them: calm, cool, and a splendid driver. One day he had a party of Eastern men in on the road to Idaho Springs. One insisted on sitting with the driver, and made him-

---

[5] Root and Connelley, *Overland Stage*, 295–97.

self offensive to 'Bishop' all the way to the top of the mountain. He assumed to know all about staging, from his experience in New England, and talked a good deal about the magnificent specimens of manhood which were employed as drivers in that part of the country. 'Bishop' looked at his leaders and said nothing. Finally they got to Virginia Canyon, at the top of the ascent. 'Bishop' got out and put in the brake blocks. This amused the Eastern man very much, and he made various funny remarks about it. 'Bishop' said nothing, and they started down the steep descent. They flew along, a steep precipice on one side, and a high bank on the other. Then it would change and be vice versa. The tenderfoot grew more and more paralyzed. His extensive experience had not accustomed him to just that kind of a road. Finally, as the bank came around to his side of the stage again, he made one frantic leap and landed on the hillside. 'Bishop' never checked his horses. He drove into Idaho Springs and then drove on. Some hours later Mr. Tenderfoot followed on foot and had the pleasure of waiting for the next stage."

ON THE CENTRAL CITY LINE[6]

Many were the drivers, it seems, and many the tales told about them when the mountain road to Central was the terror of the West.

Among those who handled the reins in and out of Denver, the chief was Bill Opdyke, who drove the mountain line to Central City. That was a route requiring the maximum of skill and endurance, and Bill drove it for years. He was a man of powerful form, with an arm like a piece of steel, bluff, hearty, good-natured, daring, and unexcelled in the management of a coach-and-six. He could drive within one inch of a given line. Once while loading some express matter in the boot of the coach at the Denver office, the reins wrapped about the brake, his team took fright and started on a wild race down Fifteenth Street. Bill coolly seized the reins, but no human being could have stopped those six horses in their mad career. But Bill could guide

[6] William R. Thomas, "Lectures on History," edited by his son, Chauncey Thomas, *The Trail*, Vol. IX, No. 2 (July, 1916), 5–7.

them if he could not check their speed. Several blocks down the street was a corral, and seeing the gate open, he turned the running team into the entrance and brought them to a halt. Someone measured the gate and found that it was only six inches wider than the coach, but so closely had Bill calculated his distance that he passed into the corral without grazing either gate post. He drove triumphantly back to the office with his team under full control.

One of the long descents on the Central City route, where the road came down from the mountains to the level of Clear Creek, was known as Smith's Hill. Down this Bill was accustomed to drive at a furious gallop, and sometimes on a dead run, and the manner in which he once took a wheel off a Dutchman's milk wagon will interest you.

The Dutchman's ranch was a few miles this side of Blackhawk, to which camp he made a daily trip with milk. Returning home late in the afternoon, he would be ascending Smith's Hill with his old horse and cart just about the time the coach came along. The milk peddler frequently got in the way of the coach, and Bill used to curse him roundly—you know, stage drivers could swear those days—and threaten to take a wheel off his cart. The old Dutchman paid no attention to the warning, so one day Bill calculated his distance and took a wheel off the cart as neat and clean as if cut with an axe, without even checking the speed of the coach, and leaving the milk man a picture of consternation and despair.

For several days the Dutchman disappeared from the hill. He was having his cart repaired. The day he drove it home I was sitting on the box with Jake Hawk, whose run it was that day, and as we started down the Smith's Hill grade, Jake called my attention to the old fellow, near the foot of the hill, beating his horse in a frantic attempt to make a turnout ahead of the coach. He got there in safety, and as the coach swept by at its usual speed, the Dutchman looked up and, seeing Jake Hawk on the box, exclaimed with a tone of relief: "Mine Got! I dot it var de Opdyken!"

Bill Opdyke's favorite string was called the "Mountain Maid" team. They ran from Golden to Guy Hill. The team was composed of five mares and one gelding, and six more beautiful bays were never harnessed. They were great, rangy animals, powerful, speedy, spirited, and intelligent as the average man. They knew every inch of the Guy Hill road, and so well trained were they that I think Bill could have driven them over the route with a tow string for reins. "Joe" and "Mollie" were the leaders, and a handsome pair they were. It was with this "Mountain Maid" team that Bill Opdyke gave General Grant that famous ride in 1868.

In the summer of that year Generals Grant, Sheridan, and Dent visited Colorado and, of course, went to see the Gilpin County mines. I've forgotten who drove them up to Central City, but at any rate Bill Opdyke held the reins on the down trip, and proud man he was—with Grant seated alongside of him on the driver's box. From Central to the top of Guy Hill the road afforded no opportunity for rapid driving. At the foot of the hill the "Mountain Maids" were hooked to the coach, and drew it to the summit, from which point to Golden there was a steady downgrade of nine miles. As the coach crossed the crest of the hill Billy put a firm foot on the brake, tightened his grip on the reins, and with a crack of the whip told them to go. The "Maids" knew that Bill meant business, and away they flew at a wild gallop. They had a record to make that day. Never were reins more dexterously drawn—never was coach more skillfully handled—as down the precipitous road the "Mountain Maids" sped, with Bill grim, silent, and watchful on the box. As he checked their pace and drew up in front of the Golden station, Grant looked at his watch—"Nine miles in thirty-six minutes," he said, as he congratulated Billy on the splendid exhibition of stage driving which he had just employed. As the panting and smoking team was being led to the barn, the General eyed Mollie, the off leader, with admiration, and remarked to Bill—"If I had that mare in my stables in Washington, I would give $1,000."

SNOWBOUND IN A STAGECOACH[7]

Even today, winter travel in the Rocky Mountains is not a matter to be taken lightly, subject as it is to slides, washouts, and swirling storms. In frontier times the most optimistic travelers expected the worst.

Ab. Williamson, in the early days of Colorado staging, was quite a noted "knight of the lines." He drove north from Denver to Church's, Middle Boulder, and St. Vrain's, where Longmont is built. Ab. had a rough time on this route in January, 1865. He was caught in one of the worst storms ever encountered in the section. He pulled out from Middle Boulder at four o'clock, about the time a brisk storm had begun to fall. In a little while there was nothing of the trail visible, as could easily be observed by the jolting of the stage as the wheels passed over the rough surface of the ground. The place was about ten miles from Longmont. Years afterward Ab. delighted to tell of some of the experiences of that night and the following two days, before they found their bearings. In and on the coach were a lieutenant from Fort Laramie; a merchant, with his eighteen-year-old daughter, from Atchison; two miners; the express messenger; and an agent of the stage company, from Denver, on his way north to buy mules for the line. The team was stopped, and the genial driver got down off the box and, opening the coach door, proclaimed in cheerful tones that they were lost, and might as well know it.

It was Ab.'s custom to carry under the seat a good-sized bottle, and this he placed at the disposal of the male occupants of the stage, took off his horses, and, after making them as comfortable as he could under the circumstances, by invitation took up his quarters among the passengers on the inside. All night the snow continued to fall and the wind to blow. In the morning all that could be seen were the sides of a snowy embankment worn into hollows by the breath of the dejected-looking horses. The storm continued and there was no way out. For another night and day they stayed there. During all this time the young woman, under these terribly trying circumstances, proved the most

[7] Root and Connelley, *Overland Stage*, 553–55.

cheerful one of the party, entertaining everyone by a frequent repetition of all the songs she knew. All the hymns the party knew were sung and repeated, interspersed with a number of patriotic and lively comic songs. There was not much formality at eating, for the scanty contributions to the cupboard were Ab.'s lunch and a few sandwiches which the daughter had secured at the last station, fearing her father might be overcome by faintness. When the storm subsided, the two miners, in company with the lieutenant, started out in the snow, waist deep, to organize a relief expedition from the interior. They were out for hours, finally getting sight of St. Vrain's, where they repaired, and secured a posse to dig the stagecoach out; and some time after nightfall of the third day the little party had been rescued, and were calling for round after round of the battery steak served in the cozy interior of the St. Vrain's station.

THE RESCUE OF A HANDCART COMPANY[8]

Little more than a hundred miles north of the Colorado Front Range, where in the gold camp era every mountain traveler had his harrowing experiences, lies the old route of the Mormon and Oregon trails. There, too, in days even before co-ordinated Indian attack and the coldly planned ambuscades of white highwaymen, Mormons and the earliest of the "Overlanders"—Oregon and California pioneers—saw much, endured much, and left sharp but simply recorded impressions of the land through which they passed.

We [Mormons] traveled on in misery and sorrow day after day. Sometimes we made a pretty good distance, but at other times we were only able to make a few miles' progress. Finally we were overtaken by a snowstorm which the shrill wind blew furiously about us. The snow fell several inches deep as we traveled along, but we dared not stop, for we had a sixteen-mile journey to make, and short of it we could not get wood and water.

As we were resting for a short time at noon a light wagon

8 Edward W. Tullidge, *History of Salt Lake City* (Salt Lake City, 1886), 115–18.

was driven into our camp from the west. Its occupants were Joseph A. Yound and Stephen Taylor. They informed us that a train of supplies was on the way, and we might expect to meet it in a day or two. More welcome messengers never came from the Courts of Glory than these two young men were to us. They lost no time after encouraging us all they could to press forward, but sped on further east to convey their glad news to Edward Martin and the fifth handcart company who left Florence about two weeks after us, and who it was feared were even worse off than we were. As they went from our view, many a hearty "God bless you" followed them. . . .

The storm which we encountered, our Brethren from the Valley also met, and, not knowing that we were so utterly destitute, they encamped to wait fine weather. But when Captain Willie found them and explained our real condition, they at once hitched up their teams and made all speed to come to our rescue. On the evening of the third day after Captain Willie's departure, just as the sun was sinking beautifully behind the distant hills, on an eminence immediately west of our camp several covered wagons, each drawn by four horses, were seen coming toward us. The news ran through the camp like wildfire, and all who were able to leave their beds turned out en masse to see them. A few minutes brought them sufficiently near to reveal our faithful Captain slightly in advance of the train. Shouts of joy rent the air; strong men wept until tears ran freely down their furrowed and sunburnt cheeks, and little children partook of the joy which some of them hardly understood, and fairly danced around with gladness. Restraint was set aside in the general rejoicing, and as the brethren entered our camp the sisters fell upon them and deluged them with kisses. The brethren were so overcome that they could not for some time utter a word, but in choking silence repressed all demonstration of those emotions that evidently mastered them. Soon, however, feeling was somewhat abated, and such a shaking of hands, such words of welcome, and such invocation of God's blessing have seldom been witnessed.

I was installed as regular commissary to the camp. The brethren turned over to me flour, potatoes, onions, and a limited supply of warm clothing for both sexes, besides quilts, blankets, buffalo robes, woolen socks, etc. I first distributed the necessary provisions, and after supper divided the clothing, bedding, etc., where it was most needed. That evening, for the first time in quite a period, the songs of Zion were to be heard in the camp, and peals of laughter issued from the little knots of people as they chatted around the fires. The change seemed almost miraculous, so sudden was it from grave to gay, from sorrow to gladness, from mourning to rejoicing. With the cravings of hunger satisfied, with hearts filled with gratitude to God and our good brethren, we all united in prayer, and then retired to rest.

FIRE ON THE PLAINS[9]

Often, British sportsmen as well as other foreigners, inspired by stories of exploration and the massing of fortunes, found their way to the American Frontier. Nor did they fail, in their wanderings over mountains and prairie, to encounter certain phenomena there.

While traversing one of these dreary waterless stretches of "droughty" Plains, we got a severe but salutary lesson illustrating how easily devastating plain fires "let out." We had nooned at a wallow, and when we started again the small fire we had made to cook some beans had apparently long gone out. We had proceeded about two miles, and just were losing sight of the little "bottom" where we had camped, when, happening to look around, I perceived a huge volume of flame envelop the spot. Fires in the dry season are usually dangerous things, lasting frequently four or five months; and though timber, if there is any, is perfectly valueless, they are often very disastrous to straggling settlements, but especially to the cattle roaming over the country. Hence, the Territorial legislature has recently put a heavy fine and imprisonment on the offenses of "letting out" plain or forest fires.

Though we had already gone beyond the last white settlement, we were still in cattle land; and a timbered range of mountains eight or ten miles off would assuredly have been sacrificed,

9 William A. Baillie-Grohman, *Camps in the Rockies* (New York, 1882), 36–38.

had we not resolved, after a brief moment's consultation, to try our best to put it out.

Leaving Henry with the horses, the two men and I rode back as fast as our excited horses could carry us. A very gentle but steady breeze was blowing, and long before we got to the scene we heard the crackle and roar of the flames, spreading at a great rate among the sagebrush. Dry as tinder, and of good size, this shrub of the desert makes about the hottest and quickest fire possible. Our saddle blankets were the only available article with which to fight the flames. But alas! by the time all three were well soaked in the copper-coloured wallow water, there was not a drop left, and the next water was, as we knew, eighteen miles off. Taking the blankets, we rode bareback to the further extremity of the conflagration.

Running before the wind, the flames were leaping onwards very nearly as fast as a man can walk. So, to have any chance with what is here called counterburning, we had to begin several hundred yards or so ahead. One of us, taking a lighted sagebrush in hand, walked along setting fire to the dense growth, while the other two did their best to keep the new fire under control by confining it to a strip some twenty or thirty feet wide. This was hot work, and had to be done very quickly. Three times did we fail to complete the belt before the main fire was upon us, coming on with a rush and a subdued roar very grand to behold from a safe distance, but uncomfortably awkward at close quarters. Each time we had to retreat and begin again a considerable distance ahead. The fourth attempt at last succeeded, favored as we were by the lull in the breeze usual just before sundown.

It was the last effort, for we were thoroughly exhausted; and blinded and scorched, we staggered about like inebriates. It was a close shave, too, for the flames of the main fire were within a few yards of us when we completed the belt, and the last few seconds we were working right in the flames. Half blinded, our hands and faces, hair and beards singed, our boots burnt, nothing whatever left of our saddle blankets, two of us minus our shirts, which we had torn off to beat the flames of the counter belt, black as Negroes, we threw ourselves on the ground, too exhausted even to speak.

It was nearly dark by the time we extinguished the last sage-brush, and long after it when we regained our horses. It had taken us several hours to master the fire, and as the men expressed themselves, "nothing but a strip of sagebrush country, a mile long and a quarter of a mile in width, blackened and burnt, to show for it."

SLADE'S REVENGE[10]

In stagecoaching days of the sixties, Alfred Slade, division superintendent of mail lines operating between Old Julesburg and Salt Lake, provided background and facts for many a tale passed from driver to passenger. Even Mark Twain, chancing one day to meet Slade, was said to have trembled not at the man's gentle appearance but at the cold-blooded murders with which he was credited.

The Eastern stopping point of Slade's division was Julesburg. At this place there was a road station kept by a Frenchman named Jules, for whom the station was named. Slade and Jules had some difficulty regarding stock, but had arrived at an understanding which Slade supposed was settled amicably. The boys were then in the habit of playing cards for canned fruits, oysters, etc., it being the only way they had of getting them. The next time Slade came down he proposed a game for the oysters. Just as he stepped to the door, "Jule" leveled a double barrel shotgun at him and fired. Slade fell and "Jule," supposing he had killed him, said, "There are some blankets and a box, you can make him a coffin if you like." Strange to say, Slade was not dead, and after he revived a little was taken to Denver for medical treatment. Jules was so afraid of being shot or hung that he fled that night.

Jules had a man at Wagon Hound Creek trading with emigrants, and the next summer he went up to see him. Crossing to the north side of the Platte River, he came down the river until opposite Cold Springs Station, kept by a Frenchman named Shosaix. Crossing the river again, he stopped at the station, where

10 E. W. Whitcomb, "Alfred Slade at Close Range," *The Trail*, Vol. XIV, No. 6 (November, 1921), 11–15.

Slade had three men watching for Jules. They were mounted on mules, and Jules, being suspicious, mounted his horse and rode away. Overhearing the men ask Shosaix if he had seen any mules, he was thrown off his guard, returned, and dismounted. Instantly he was covered with shotguns and ordered to surrender. He started to run and was shot in the hip and relieved of his gun; he then crawled into a hole back of the house, was followed and compelled to surrender. He was bound hand and foot, and a courier was sent to get Slade. When Slade arrived he talked to him a while, stating that he could kill him if he chose, Jules all the time begging for his miserable life and a chance to see his wife. But Slade replied, "When you shot me you gave me no chance to see my wife, brutally trying to murder me without any chance to defend myself, so now, take your medicine." Jules was ordered to stand up against a post and Slade told him he was going to see how near he could shoot without hitting him. Slade fired several shots which grazed his hair and struck on either side of his head. Finally, he told him he would wound him, and shot him in the mouth. He fell, and Slade ordered him to get up, saying he was not dead and if he did not rise he would cut off his ears. Jules finally rose and Slade, after cruelly tantalizing him a little longer, remarked, "Now I am going to give you a center shot, so hold still," and shot him between the eyes. Jules fell dead and Slade cut off his ears, and at the same time said to the boys, "You needn't get any blankets or box for him, just dig a hole and chuck him in, as you would a dog." He carried the ears with him for several days, asking those he met if they would like some "souse."

IMPROMPTU JUSTICE[11]

Although more than one scandalized observer of life along the frontier trails may have been able to find little evidence of an advanced social system, that certain highly localized habits, customs, and "court" procedures did exist cannot be denied. The reminiscences of stalwart, sober-minded frontiersmen themselves constitute sufficient proof of the contention.

[11] Alvin E. Dyer, editor, *The Cattle Queen of Montana: Personal Experiences of Mrs. Nat Collins, familiarly known to Western People as "The Cattle Queen"* (Spokane, n. d.), 129–32.

The wagon master of a freighting train is considered the ruler of the company. He it is who directs the movements of the train, assigns to each person their particular duty, and lays down the rules and regulations to govern all.

While gambling and drinking is seldom approved of by the trainmaster, still in many instances it is tolerated by that official —for to strictly prohibit the indulgence of these vices would be to inaugurate a state of affairs which would render most difficult the procuring and keeping of teamsters and other laborers, as all at that time considered these as privileged practices.

Becoming excited and angered over the loss of money, frantic with disappointment upon seeing their last cent vanish from view, or, becoming engaged in a quarrel over some disputed point, these men would ofttimes engage in the most terrific hand-to-hand encounters, but were usually separated by their companions before they had done each other great bodily harm.

The initial tragedy of the train of which I was a member was brought about, however, in this manner on the second evening out from Omaha, on our second return trip. As usual, gathered about the campfire, seated upon blankets, in companies of four or five, with a small board laid on the ground in their midst upon which to lay the cards as they played, were the men busily engaged in gambling.

Suddenly among the members of one of these little groups a quarrel arose and, springing to their feet, they engaged in a fierce hand-to-hand encounter. Amid the curses and confusion there rang out the sharp report of a single shot, and, throwing his hands high in the air, one of the men fell, face downward, upon the ground. The man who had fired the shot stepped backward a pace or two, and there, with flashing eye and face distorted with anger, calmly gazed upon his fallen and dying foe.

The dying man was lifted and laid upon a blanket, his brow dampened and his lips moistened with brandy, while the man who had committed the terrible deed was taken in charge by the men and closely guarded. The wounded man rallied slightly, whispered the names and places of residence of his parents and sweetheart, and fell back dead.

Gathering about the body of the dead man the members of

the company—after selecting a jury to pass upon the evidence and render a verdict as to the guilt of the murderer—listened to the story of the accused man.

He admitted his guilt but offered as an excuse for his act the statement that he was intoxicated and so influenced by passion as to be unconscious of his acts. Without a word or question the men sat silently by and listened.

As the evidence was concluded the jury, in obedience to a sign from the wagon master, withdrew to the outer circle of the camp and within the period of a very few moments returned. Again seating themselves they awaited the signal for the presentation of their verdict.

This being given, the foreman of the jury—an old, white-headed man—arose and in a low voice said: "Boss, that 'er man is guilty. Bill warn't a fightin' cuss ef he war treated squar, and nobody had ter burn powder ter keep his claws offen ther carcass ez long as they wern't onery an' mean an' give him a far, squar deal. This er feller whats let daylight thro' th' boy oughter stretch."

The verdict was received with nods of assent by the other men and at once the work of preparation for the execution of the sentence pronounced by the jury was under way.

Two wagons were drawn to a spot just without the circle about the camp and placed with their forward ends quite close together, the tongues of the same being raised and joined at the top. The condemned man was bound hand and foot, a long rope was thrown over the top of the raised wagon tongues, and at the signal from the wagon master the victim was drawn from the ground to a height of some two or three feet and there left hanging until dead.

The following morning, before the start for the day's journey, the bodies of both men were prepared for burial and then placed in a rude grave, side by side—the murdered man and his slayer—and at the head of the mound was placed two rough boards bearing respectively the following epitaphs: "Shot. He was innocent." "Hung. He was guilty."

LEGEND OF THE LOST TRAIN[12]

*Western trails are old. Indians made them, and for **unnum-**
bered centuries followed them. Trappers and prospectors found
them; road makers widened them; stage drivers and express
messengers used them. Finally, railroaders—latecomers, but certainly lacking neither in color nor action—graded them, bridged
them, and added folk tale to folk tale about them.*

In common with other mountain railroads, "The Moffat
Road" has its almost endless series of wreck stories, most of them
apocryphal. In one of these tales, an entire train left the rails
and rolled down the mountainside into Yankee Doodle Lake.
Later investigation showed that the lead mail car was the cause
of the wreck, a "green" clerk having piled all the mail-order
catalogs on the same side of the car.

The Moffat also has its "lost train" story. During a very
severe winter blizzard, No. 3 westbound, seven hours late out
of Denver, crept out of the Fraser Canyon, whistled for the
Granby crossing, and picked up speed to cross the Granby
Flats. Running out of sand a half hour later, they tied down the
cab curtains and waited for daylight. In the morning, they found
the train parked "plumb center" in Granby's main street ("right
in front of Payne's Cafe," according to one version)! During the
night, No. 2 eastbound, two days late out of Craig, reached
Corona without passing No. 3. Subsequent investigation showed
that No. 3 left the rails just east of the Grandby crossing, and
traveled almost a mile over the frozen highway before running
out of sand. The engineer reported, during the hearing, that he
suspected something wrong, for "the going was too good west
of Fraser Canyon." The next day, a Chinook came up, melting
the frozen soil, and the train sank to its axles in mud. Building
of fifteen hundred feet of special track was necessary before No.
3 could be salvaged. This version, with its Granby locale, is current in Hot Sulphur Springs and Kremmling. Granby residents
have a substantially identical tale, the locale of the supposed occurrence being the Kremmling Flats.

[12] Roland L. Ives, "Folklore of Middle Park, Colorado," *Journal of
American Folklore*, Vol. XXXIV, Nos. 211 and 212 (Jan'y-June, 1941), 34.

Dating from the early construction days is the tale of the "Phantom Wrecker," which always showed up when needed, regardless of weather or track conditions. The locomotive of this train was supernatural in many respects, having a "carload of Hell" under the boiler, a balefire for a headlight, and a "Christopher as big as a gold pan" for a number plate. For a whistle, the engine was equipped with a live banshee, imported from Ireland in a silver cage. Pulling the whistle cord actuated a bell-crane, which lowered a bottle of Holy Water, "especially blessed by the Pope," into the cage. This made the banshee unhappy, producing a wail that could be heard "clear into Utah." Inquiries in the vicinity of Cheyenne, Wyoming, elicit a similar tale concerning Dan Casement's work train, used during the construction of the Union Pacific Railroad. In all probability, this tale was concocted about 1865 by "some horny-handed son of old Erin, whose family crest was a spike-maul rampant on a tie-pile."

IRON PINS AND A SILVER SPIKE[13]

Nowhere on earth have railroaders ridden as high, balanced as tipsily, or fallen as far as those of the Rocky Mountain West. That, old-timers say, may be folklore, but it is also the green, slab-sided truth.

One oft-repeated tale is that of the engineer on the Silverton branch who while descending the precipitous road discovered that two link and pin couplings had broken. The brakes on the locomotive failed to work and only on the last few cars had the trainman been able to set the manual brakes. The engineer took matters in his own hands. He gave the locomotive full throttle in order to outdistance the rapidly pursuing sections of his freight train. On reaching level territory he was able to apply the locomotive brakes and to enter a siding—just in time to gasp in relief as the engineless sections of the freight train flashed past him on the main line. Fortunately in those days there were few

[13] Henry Swan, *Early Beginnings of Transportation in Colorado* . . . (Princeton University Press, 1944), 21; S. T. Sopris, "Denver's First Railroad," *The Trail*, Vol. I, No. 2 (July, 1908), 5–11.

towns along the right of way and no damage was done. The runaway cars, reaching the end of the decline, soon slowed and stopped. Nonchalantly the train crew recoupled and continued their journey.—SWAN.

It was a great day for Denver, that 24th of June, 1870, when the last spike was driven that signalled the completion of the Denver Pacific. A train, drawn by a gaily decorated engine bearing the name, "Gen. D. H. Moffat," and having on board of its half dozen passenger coaches a delegation of Masons from Cheyenne, rolled into town early in the forenoon and a grand parade, the driving of the silver spike, the laying of the cornerstone of a passenger depot, a banquet out at the fairgrounds, etc., filled out the day. . . .

It was "St. John's Day," and the Masonic bodies of Denver, Cheyenne, and perhaps other towns, laid the cornerstone of the passenger depot that was to be used by both the Denver Pacific and the Kansas Pacific. After the laying of the cornerstone Governor Evans drove the silver spike, made up at Georgetown, then our greatest, as well as first, silver mining camp. At least the newspaper reporters said they saw the Governor drive the silver spike, wrapped in tin foil, which refused to be driven. The Governor had the silver spike all right, for he showed it to us, but it was no place to put so much silver, which was worth something in those days; and, being pure silver, it was probably too soft to drive into a hard log.

The Cheyenne Masons brought the military band from Fort Russell along, and that helped some.—SOPRIS.

A-WORKIN' ON THE RAILROAD[14]

In the days of free and unfettered American enterprise.

Hy Connor, northwestern old-timer, and his companions were sitting around the campfire one night. One of the men was telling of a hard-boiled foreman who docked his men if they were off the job. "If a man was offen his job only a minute, why

[14] Told by Lois Reat, of Twin Falls, Idaho, when a student at the University of Denver, to Levette J. Davidson.

that there foreman he went out with his watch and looked hard at it and docked the poor bugger for that much lost time."

Hy yawned and put a fresh quid of tobacco in his mouth. "Boys," he said, "you ain't heerd nothing, not a plumb thing. You should a-known the foreman I worked under when we was a-building the Oregon Short Line. That man wouldn't take no excuses. That man was tough. I remember one time I was runnin' in a cut with a single jack and drill and I drilled into a missed hole and the powder went off and blowed me high in the air. The boys, they looked up and watched me, and they said first I looked like a fly, then like a bird, and then down I come right where I was a-settin' before I left. I still had the hammer in one hand and the drill in the other, and I set right to work again. But say, you know what the foreman done? He docked me for the fifteen minutes I was gone!"

Rocky Mountain Gold

WEST of Denver, Colorado, the Rocky Mountains lift seemingly in one great barrier line, sweeping the traveler quickly up from prairie spaces, bringing him through a lovely region of creeks, rounded, grassy foothills and open pine timber, and losing him, almost at once, among the first true mountain ridges. Within fifty miles of the Colorado capital are peaks reaching fourteen thousand feet, passes rising above the eleven-thousand-foot point, forests of spruce, fir and lodgepole pine in which elk and deer and bear still roam, and gorges, many of them of surpassing beauty, which show the trends of mountain streams.

Within this Front Range region, so close to prairie cities and yet so remote, so utterly different in its wild and turbulent character, one may find today scarred waterwheels and placer diggings, caving prospect holes, shafts and tunnels, producing mines, abandoned mines, the sites of camps long dead, and those of other mountain towns which have lived and prospered through the years. Each hard-rock mine, each gravel bar retains its memories. All know old-timers still; and through each one flows that gold or silver thread, bright Rocky Mountain strand, on which the oldest residents have hung their tales of Rocky Mountain argonauts.

Rocky Mountain Gold

Robert McGonigle was one of those to whom the Rocky Mountains beckoned. His story was recorded, eventually, by a friend named Wilbur Stone.

Capt. Stone had been in the Cherry Creek diggings about five days when he met Robert McGonigle. His parents were Irish. He was a graduate of Oberlin, and had taught a country school in Tennessee.

Both were suffering from gold fever. "Mack," as McGonigle was commonly called, had it bad. He had spent his last cent in getting to Pikes Peak, but was not discouraged. The crowds at the diggings were boiling over with excitement. They were stirred by all sorts of reports, and the miners were scattering all over the territory.

A vague hint of discoveries of surpassing richness west of the headwaters of the Arkansas created a stampede. It was glowingly reported that a half dozen miners had discovered a valley sprinkled with free gold, and were keeping it all to themselves. Well, Mack ran against an Irishman named Brady, who was hot for the shadowy diggings. Stone told Mack that he would furnish him with an outfit and he could join Brady and he would go "snacks" in any discovery that was made.

Mack snapped at the offer, procured his outfit, and he and Brady were off without delay. They had no gun, no pistol, not even any matches, but carried a sunglass, with which they lighted their fires. They left Tarryall about the first of June, crossing the Snowy Range below Mt. Lincoln. They made for Grand River. Day after day they stumbled over rocky mountains and crept through gloomy canyons. They searched every gulch and bar, hoping to discover the miners who were taking out their thousands; but they never found them. Everywhere they sifted dirt, with the same unvarying result.

In time their provisions gave out and they headed for the plains. Through pathless valleys and over snow-capped mountains they struggled, subsisting on wild berries. They lost their

---

[1] Wilbur Stone, "Tales of Adventure, Experience of a Gold Seeker in 1860," *The Trail*, Vol. XIV, No. 3 (January, 1922), 3–5.

reckoning and had little idea of their position. Brady wanted to go one direction; McGonigle wanted to take another. Over a week they had lived upon berries, and stumbled toward the plains, when Mack became very sick. Eight days they had gone to bed supperless, and arisen without breakfast. Brady made up his mind that his comrade would die, and throwing his blanket over his shoulder, moved over the hill and deserted him. Mack recovered strength and struck for Ft. Garland. He was satisfied he knew the course. He found a few berries at intervals. Three days after he had been deserted he climbed to the peak of a high mountain and below him lay the San Luis Valley. So he went down into the valley. What happened after that, Mack himself couldn't remember. All that is certain is that eight days after he and Brady separated, Mack was picked up in the San Luis Valley, sixty miles from Fort Garland, in a dying condition. He was found by a party of United States officers on a hunt. It was several days before he recovered consciousness. His first inquiry was concerning the gold diggings. The fever was burning as fiercely in his veins as ever.

The officers of the fort had heard the report of rich discoveries, but had heard them located at the sources of the Rio Grande, instead of in the Grand River country. Then Mack, having entirely recovered, wanted to fly to the Rio Grande. The officers started him off with a new outfit. He left the fort the seventh of July. He sought for gold, but found none. He was chasing an *ignis fatuus*. He saw neither track nor trace of white man during the whole of his journey. Once in a while he ran against a grizzly or cinnamon bear, or saw a Rocky Mountain lion; but the beast was generally more astonished at Mack's appearance than Mack was at the beast's. He was sometimes alarmed by the howls of wild animals, and frequently climbed trees and tied himself to the branches, sleeping in that position until daylight. Again he ran out of provisions. Berries became as scarce as gold. He came across a swarm of grasshoppers. He roasted them with a shovel, and afterwards declared he had never tasted anything more palatable. He got into a snowstorm and nearly froze to death. It was certain that he had again lost his way and, while staggering aimlessly over the mountains, worn down by fatigue and faint from want of food, he heard a human voice. "Stop!" it said. Before him stood a Ute Indian with a drawn bow. "Stop!" the savage repeated. It was the only English word the Ute had learned, and it was used in a peremptory tone. The Ute took pity on him, gave him food, and lent him his pony to take him to Fort Garland, which post he reached thirty days after he had left it.

The second week in August he started to walk from Fort Garland to Tarryall. Near the present site of Canon City he struck a settlement of several huts. There he heard two hunters say that they had just brought in a man on the point of starvation. Mack hunted up the sufferer. It was Brady, but so changed that he was hardly recognizable. His elbows protruded from the skin, and his face was as thin as a hatchet. He was crazed for weeks, and incessantly raved about the gold diggings and raw bacon. The hunters had found him squatted on a sand bar in the Arkansas Canyon, almost naked. The glare of insanity was in his eyes, and his hair and beard were matted with mud. He plunged his hand into the water, and ran his arm into a hole up to his shoulder. He had apparently seen a muskrat enter the hole and was determined to catch it. His hardships had unsettled his reason, but he still clung to his prospecting pan, and seemed fearful that his rescuers intended to tear it from him. Brady recovered his health and reason, and is now a wholesale merchant in St. Louis.

Soon after, Mack joined Baker's party of prospectors, who in turn, joined other parties who had discovered some mines in the San Juan country. The mines were in the crater of a large, extinct volcano, probably twenty miles in diameter. There was great excitement. Over one hundred of the most lawless men had collected in that crater. The diggings were not rich enough to pay for digging, and the early snow scattered the adventurers, some drifting back to Cherry Creek and Gregory, others pouring into Utah, and a few stopping over into New Mexico and Arizona. . . . Mack received a letter from an old friend and schoolmate who had settled down in San Diego, California, and Mack resolved to go there. In the fall of 1861 he left Albuquerque, on foot and alone, intending to cross Arizona to California. . . . But no tidings were ever received from him. He never reached California. Whether he perished with thirst, or whether his scalp adorns the lodge of some Apache warrior, is purely a matter of conjecture.

REMINISCENCES OF THE FIRST MRS. TABOR[2]

Although much has been written concerning H. A. W. Tabor, Colorado's bonanza king, less well known is the part taken by his first wife, Augusta, in bridging difficult years before his rich strikes in the high country.

I came out here in 1859, from Kansas. Denver was the first place in Colorado that I came to. There were a few log houses here, but very few. I was the eleventh woman that arrived. Mrs. Byers was one of the women whose name I remember. Most of them were Mexicans or squaws. We only camped here about a week. Just long enough to get rest for our cattle. We came with ox teams across the Plains. We then went up to where Golden now stands and camped there three weeks, on Clear Creek, at the foot of the mountains. Mr. Tabor went up into the mountains to look after gold and I stayed in camp and took care of the cattle and the provisions. We had six months provisions with us. The cattle were footsore and could not go far, but I kept them from straying. I stayed there quite alone; there was no one there, no Indians, nothing there but just myself and our teams, silence reigned around, not a soul but me and my baby, and I was a weakly woman, not nearly so strong as I am now.

There was only one mine; that was up where Central now stands. It was called the Gregory Mine, where they found gold. There were two men who went with my husband to find gold. They did not find anything and returned to camp. They thought they had better move me farther up. We packed up and went beyond there up to Payne's Bar, now called Idaho Springs. We were three weeks going from there to where Central is now.

[2] Mrs. H. A. W. Tabor, "Cabin Life in Colorado," *The Colorado Magazine*, Vol. IV, No. 2 (March, 1927), 71–72. "This story was obtained from Mrs. Tabor by the historian, H. H. Bancroft, in 1884. The original manuscript is in the Bancroft Library, University of California."

Had to make our road as we went. We could only make about three miles a day; a wagon had never been there before. We would go a good many miles in order to get what now would be only a few miles.

The miners told Mr. Tabor he ought not to keep me at Idaho Springs during the winter, as there were often snowslides that would cover us all up. He became frightened and moved me back to Denver; when he returned to the camp, he found his claim had been jumped. Some of the miners had told him this to get him away so that they could jump his claim. There was no law in those days.

He returned to Denver and then went down to where Colorado Springs is now. He thought that Colorado Springs might be the center of the state, as near as he could locate it. He thought probably they would make the capital at the center of the state and wanted to be first in starting it. He always was very enterprising; so he went to Colorado Springs and erected the first house there. I stayed in Denver and took boarders through the winter while he went to the Springs and erected the first house which he intended to open for a sort of business house or place where people would meet; then he came to Denver and tried his best to get parties to go down and lay off a town. He did not succeed very well; so he thought it better to go into the mines and try our luck. We left Denver in February, 1860.

From there we went up to the headwaters of the Arkansas looking for gold. . . . I was the first woman in California Gulch. There was only one party ahead of us, one of seven men, and we were to join with them, but I was sick in Denver and they all went off a few days ahead of us. We were all this time trying to get track of them. We knew they had gone somewhere into the mountains prospecting about one hundred and fifty miles southwest of Denver. They were prospecting along as they went; tried several gulches before they found California Gulch. When we got to Cache Creek we stopped one month. My husband whipsawed some lumber to make sluice boxes and put them in. We found plenty of gold, but there was so much black sand and we did not know how to separate it. We had no quicksilver; so we had to abandon it. I would work all day long picking out with a little magnet, and when night came I would not have a pennyweight, it was so fine. Afterwards those mines turned out to be very rich; if we had stayed right there we would have had enough. . . .

Someone came down California Gulch and reported that they had found gold; they were looking us up and wanted to get in supplies. He came to our camp and told us to move up, telling us to go up until we came to the first large bald mountain on the road, then turn up that gulch around the bald mountain; it would take us all day to go with the ox team, we would probably see the smoke of their campfire. We went up there and found Slater and Abe Lee. Those were the first men that panned out in California Gulch. They got a dollar to the pan and that encouraged them right off. We killed our cattle that we drove in and divided the beef among them. We lived on that a few days until the man got back with some Mexicans coming in with flour. They turned to and built me a cabin of green logs, had it finished in two days. We lived there all summer. . . .

We arrived in California Gulch May 8th, 1860, and in 1861 we had acquired what we considered quite a little fortune, about seven thousand dollars. We came over into Park County, started a store and stayed there six years. We rode over the Mosquito Range. My husband was postmaster. It was called Buckskin Joe when we lived there. A man who wore buckskin clothes whose name was Joe discovered the first mine there. There was a little mining excitement; about two hundred people were there, so we went over with the rush and started a store there until the mines all played out. Then we went back and opened a place in California Gulch; still continued the mercantile business. My husband kept the post office and express office and I kept a boardinghouse in California Gulch. We were in better fix to keep those places, as most everyone who came in just had a pack on his back. We had a little house and things in shape to keep them.

A man named Wm. Van Brooklyn, who did not like mining as it was too hard work, said he had a pair of mules and he would start an express, would ride the mines alternately. He brought our letters in and we paid him seventy-five cents each for them and paid accordingly for any little express matter he could bring on a mule. He was a heavy man and could not bring much. I kept the express books, started the letters out and took the money. He said if I would board him while he was running the express he would give me his claim; but I would not board him for it, so he sold it to two men named Ferguson and Stevens; and that summer there was eighty thousand dollars taken out of that claim by those two men. I weighed all the gold that was taken out of the upper end of the gulch that summer. There was many a miner who did not know one thing about weighing gold. I never saw a country settled up with such greenhorns as Colorado. They were mostly from farms and some clerks. They were all young men from eighteen to thirty. I was there many years before we saw a man with gray hair.

A man named Green took the contract to get out the ties for the A.T.&S.F. The ties were got up where California Gulch is. They were owing Mr. Tabor a good deal of money for supplies and he found out the man was not going to make a success of it and became alarmed; so he took the contract off Green's hands to get his money out of it, and that is where he missed it. After he got through with the tie business we found that we had worked two years and not made a dollar. Had done all the hard work for nothing. He worked hard with the rest of the men. He was terribly pushed to get food enough for them. They would eat an ox at one meal, and more too. All that time I had the store for him to get money to run those ties through. . . .

The express man only kept that express one year; after that we got the U. S. Mail. It took a man generally four days to go to Denver after we got the roads through. It took him a week at first. It was generally a week and often ten days we would have to wait.

I have been taken along as a bodyguard a great many times when Mr. Tabor was going to Denver with treasure, because he thought he would not be so liable to be attacked. I have carried gold on my person many a time. He would buy all the gold that he could, and we would carry it down ourselves rather than trust the express, because our express was often robbed. I have gone across the Mosquito Range with him on horseback. Then we had no road at all. I had the gold in buckskins, then put in gunnybags, then laid on the horse, and then my saddle put on over the blanket, and bring it that way. Then there would be nothing visible but the saddle. If anyone came along they would rather search him than me. There were some miles that we could not ride our horses on account of the wind, it blew so fiercely. We had to have our clothes tied on firmly. In some places it was so steep we had to hang on to our horses' tails; it was all the horses could do to get up.

THE GOLD MINE ON THE ROOF[3]

Many miners followed their hunches, but few looked as high and as low as Colorado's famous Tom Walsh.

There's Tom Walsh—Thomas F. Walsh—for example, who discovered the Camp Bird [near Ouray, Colorado], one of the greatest gold mines known to the world. In the early days the rugged, indomitable, ever-hopeful American of Irish blood had been prospecting around Leadville, Colorado, and between times keeping a tavern. He cleaned up one or two little fortunes out of the placers, and lost them again hunting for more. His system consisted in having every curious or unfamiliar rock assayed. It was, of course, the best way to find out what was in the rock.

One would hardly look for a gold mine on the roof of a house, but Tom Walsh found one that way. In 1880, near Leadville, one day he was out hunting and prospecting both. He had his gun in case of game, and his prospecting pick in case of a mine. He was ready to bag one or the other. Trudging along he came on a cabin, built and abandoned by miners, and the shade there tempted him to sit down for a smoke. As he leaned his gun against the wall his eyes came on a level with the low, slanting roof. The roof was dirt-covered, and particles of quartz there caught his eye. Those particles of quartz made him all prospector. Fifty feet away he discovered a shaft. It had been sunk in barren granite. There had never been any chance to find values in that shaft.

Walsh quite understood then why shaft and cabin had been abandoned. Yet the miners had left quartz on the roof of their

---

[3] Eugene P. Lyle, Jr., "The Lure of Gold," *Hampton's Magazine*, Vol. XXIII, No. 6 (December, 1909), 764–68.

cabin. Walsh prospected assiduously. He entered the cabin and found that the earth floor was uneven because of partly exposed rock. He drove his pick into the rock and found that it was quartz. The former occupants in leveling the ground for their cabin floor had used the same dirt for covering the roof. The quartz found on the roof had come from the floor of the cabin.

While the miners had been sinking their shaft in barren ground, fifty feet away, they had been sleeping at night on the very apex of a silver mine. The roof over their heads was covered with rich ore. Walsh, better prospector than they, because of his system of interrogating every suspected piece of rock, picked samples from the roof, had them assayed, and they showed a value of one hundred ounces of silver to the ton. In two weeks he uncovered the vein, in two months he took out seventy-five thousand dollars net. That mine is still producing.

CRIPPLE CREEK[4]

At Cripple Creek, Colorado, in 1891, occurred one of the last great mining strikes in the Rocky Mountain West. Facts and tales about that strike, of course, are legion.

Until the discovery of Cripple Creek, in 1891, American prospectors were ignorant of ore that could not be distinguished by the eye from the mother rock. This accounts for the many years that Cripple Creek remained undiscovered, though the district lay only a short distance from Colorado Springs. And here we have the story of Old Bob Womack.

Bob Womack was an amiable, riotous, and irrepressible prospector. He was in the saddle most of the time, sometimes as a cowboy, as a prospector all the time. He had come to Colorado in the sixties from Kentucky, and acquired title to the property where the town of Cripple Creek now is. Later he sold his land, but stayed on in a log cabin in Poverty Gulch. In 1885 someone salted a mine on Mount Pisgah, and there was a stampede and disappointment. Nothing was left in the district except its bad name as a fake and Bob Womack.

Womack dug a little hole in what is now the El Paso lode of

4 *Ibid.*

the Gold King Mine. A dentist, J. P. Grannis, was grubstaking Womack to some extent, and Grannis helped Womack perfect his claim. Still his gold discoveries were discounted, and one happy-go-lucky night he gave, for a bottle of whisky, a deed to his half interest in the Gold King Mine, which with the El Paso became one of the big mines of the camp. A million a month is still the yield for the district.

When Bob Womack dug a hole in Poverty Gulch, he dug into a new gold ore that nobody could recognize. It was a tellurium combination, tellurium being a chemical element like sulphur that carries metal in composition with it. Calaverite and sylvanite, for instance, are tellurides of gold and silver, and these two are the best known in Cripple Creek. They have a silvery luster, but if a specimen is placed on a stove, the metal in it roasts and turns to the color of old gold. No one, though, thought to roast a specimen, and for six years old Bob Womack did little more than renew the monuments around his claim. He even neglected to do the annual assessment work required by law, and so failed to make good his right to the treasure lying beneath.

Then from Colorado Springs came two men, E. M. De la Vergue and F. F. Frisbee. In spite of the snow that covered the hills at that high altitude, they kicked loose several specimens that revealed traces of gold, and later on in the spring they returned and located a claim, which they called "El Dorado," next to Womack's hole. Hitherto the district had been known as Womack's District, but De la Vergue, when recording his claim and attempting to describe its location, used the name of a turbulent mountain stream, Cripple Creek, and by that name the entire district has been known ever since. . . .

A month or so after locating his first claim, De la Vergue met W. S. Stratton, a carpenter of Colorado Springs, who had prospected off and on for the past twenty years. On his trips he always carried a blowpipe and assay outfit. When he saw De la Vergue's samples he pulled stakes at once and went to Cripple Creek with De la Vergue. Poor old Bob Womack showed him some unlocated ground, and there Stratton, the future bonanza king, put up his first stakes.

Almost every daily act of this man Stratton, during his stay at Cripple Creek, seemed to reveal gold. One day he was attracted by a ledge of granite cropping out on the side of Battle Mountain, which is one of the hills in the district. Stratton looked at it closely, but could find no trace of mineral, not even of quartz, which until that time was regarded as the most likely gold-bearing material. So he passed it up, as had all before him. The problem continued to worry him, however, until the following Fourth of July when the wild theory struck him that the granite ledge might indicate the contact with the porphyry. He hurried to the spot, and staked out that granite ledge, and there he located the Independence Mine, the greatest gold mine ever owned by an individual. He broke off some pieces of granite and sent them by messenger to Colorado Springs, and the next day the messenger returned with an assay certificate showing that the despised granite rock had run three hundred and eighty dollars to the ton.

Stratton became one of the richest men Colorado has known, worth fifteen million dollars or more, all of which was taken from the earth. He was the first man to achieve great ventures in the district. In 1900 the Independence was sold to the Venture Corporation, Ltd., of London, for ten million dollars.

In the beginning of the rush, those who arrived first were often the luckiest. A dozen or more penniless men became owners of from ten to fifteen millions, and scores of others waxed rich. Among them were three whose story is pertinent here because it illustrated best how the men who found the mines were also those who developed them. One of these three, Jimmy Doyle, told me all about it. On Battle Mountain there was a small triangular patch of ground that had not yet been staked out. It covered no more than about one-sixth of an acre. The prospectors had taken up locations all around it, but this little patch they considered worthless. At the same time there was in Manitou Springs a carpenter out of a job who was driving a hack. This was Jimmy Doyle—James W. Doyle. Then there was Jimmy Burns, a plumber and a great wanderer. He and Doyle went in for politics, and had their headquarters mostly at the city hall of Colorado Springs. The third man was John Harmon, a street laborer in Colorado Springs. These three men left their jobs and tramped over the mountains to where the gold fever was raging, and Doyle staked out the little triangular one-sixth acre on Battle Mountain—the one that nobody else wanted. He had come west from Portland, Maine; so he named his claim "The Portland."

It is better than a matinee to hear Jimmy Doyle tell the story. He, Burns, and Harmon, partners three, lived together in a tent at the bottom of the hill and began digging on the top. They took picks, for they knew vaguely that mines had to be dug, but this was about all they did know about mining. They struck ore, but they did not shout. They were shrewd Irishmen. As there were claims located all around them on the hill, they feared that any news of a strike on the despised one-sixth acre would bring on them all the surrounding claim owners. There would be injunctions about the law of the apex, or assertions of former claims trumped up, or something or other to cheat them out of their bonanza.

They began digging the sinews of war. They wanted to get enough to buy off the threatened suits. So, though they knew that they were already rich men, they never said a word. And to keep off prying eyes, they built a slab-roof shanty over the hole; then at the dark of night, with their revolvers, candles, and picks, they would creep out of their tent and steal up the hill, and work till the approach of dawn drove them back again.

Through all that winter they worked, and kept their secret. They lugged their ore back in sacks to an abandoned shack where they buried it under the floor. Early in the game they contrived to get an assay of their ore, and found that it ran thirty-two ounces of gold to the ton, which meant six hundred and forty dollars. The three of them were getting out a ton every night, or a daily wage amounting to about two hundred and thirteen dollars apiece.

They soon had a great store of wealth around them, yet until they could realize on it—that is, get it to market—it was like so much plain, common dirt. Their strategy reached its height in getting that stuff hauled away. They smuggled a mule team to their shack in the middle of the night, and loaded the wagon with sacks of ore. And so they got their first consignment away safely. After that they smuggled their ore out along the route used by other teams. Toward the last, however, they left a track that looked as though a furrow had been plowed down the mountain through the snow. When the rest of the camp woke up and saw that furrow running around the mountainside, it rose in anger against the three Irishmen.

Then followed a cloudburst of injunctions, subpoenas, and all the other thunderbolts of the courts of law. The camp's wakefulness came too late. The three Irishmen had already netted ninety thousand dollars, and this they had to use as a first payment on two hundred and sixty thousand dollars to buy off the conflicts. They hired shrewd lawyers; Stratton himself helped them with some money. Other claims, which they could not buy, they fought in the courts. Then by buying and compromising they added to their acreage. This was the nucleus of the present Portland Consolidated Mines, which have produced eighteen million dollars, as against the sixteen million of the famous Stratton Independence Mine.

THE BURIED LOOT OF THE REYNOLDS GANG[5]

Within fifty miles of Denver, Colorado, according to old-timers, sixty-three thousand dollars in currency and gold dust lies buried, part of the wealth accumulated by an outlaw band which held up the Buckskin stage in 1864, and terrorized the mining communities south of Denver. Before he died in 1871, John Reynolds, leader of the band, too sketchily described the location of the treasure to a fellow desperado, Albert Brown; and since that time it has been searched for unsuccessfully.

When the coach drew up, Reynolds stepped out and commanded the driver, Abe Williamson, and Billy McClelland, the superintendent of the stage line, who occupied the seat with the driver, to throw up their hands, one of his men stepping in front of the horses at the same time. Their hands went up promptly, and after being disarmed by another of the gang, Reynolds or-

[5] John W. Cook, *Hands Up* (Denver, 1897), 14–34.

dered them to get down, at the same time demanding their money. Williamson resented the idea of his having any money, saying that it was the first time in all his travels that a stage driver had ever been accused of having any of the long and needful green about his person. But his talk didn't go with the bandits, and after searching him carefully they found fifteen cents, which they took. Williamson's eyes scowled hatred, and as will be learned later, he finally took an awful revenge for the outrage. They "shook down" McClelland with much better results, securing four hundred dollars in money and a valuable chronometer balance gold watch.

They then turned their attention to the express trunk, there being no passengers on this trip. Halliman secured an axe to break it open, when McClelland offered him the key. Reynolds refused the key, venturing the opinion that they could soon get into it without the key. Breaking it open they took out six thousand dollars' worth of gold dust and two thousand dollars' worth of gold amalgam that John W. Smith was sending to the East, it being the first taken from the Orphan Boy Mine, as well as the first run from the stamp mill erected in Mosquito Gulch. Capt. Reynolds then ordered Halliman to cut open the mail bags, passing him his dirk for the purpose. They tore open the letters, taking what money they contained, which was considerable, as nearly all the letters contained ten- and twenty-dollar bills, which the miners were sending back to their friends in the East. The haul amounted to ten thousand dollars in all, a much smaller sum than the coach usually carried out. . . .

Capt. Reynolds decided that it would be prudent to conceal the greater portion of their spoils until the excitement had died down somewhat. Calling his brother, John, they passed up the little creek that ran by their camp until they reached its head. Elk Creek also heads near there. They found a prospect hole which they thought would answer their purpose. Capt. Reynolds took from his saddlebags forty thousand dollars in currency and three cans full of gold dust and considerable currency to be divided among the band before separating. They wrapped the currency up in a piece of silk cloth and put it and the cans back in the hole about the length of a man's body. Returning to the camp, Capt. Reynolds told his men that there were no pursuers in sight, and announced his determination to disperse the band temporarily, as he believed there was no chance of escape if they remained together. He described the place of rendezvous mentioned, and told them that it would be safe to move on down to a grove of large trees on Geneva Gulch, a short distance below, and camp for dinner, as there was no one in sight. They went on down and camped, and turned their horses loose to graze while dinner was being gotten.

Two of the men were getting dinner, and the others were gathered around Capt. Reynolds, who was busily dividing the remaining money and gold dust among them, when suddenly a dozen guns cracked from behind some large rocks about two hundred and twenty yards from the outlaws' camp. Owen Singletary fell dead, and Capt. Reynolds, who was at that moment dipping gold dust from a can with a spoon, was wounded in the arm. The outlaws at once broke for the brush, a few even leaving their horses.

The attacking party, which consisted of twelve or fifteen men from Gold Run under the leadership of Jack Sparks, had crawled around the mountain unobserved until they reached the rocks, and then fired a volley into the robber band. When the robbers took to the brush, they [the pursuers] went down to their camp and secured several horses, the can of gold dust, the amalgam that was taken from the coach at McLaughlin's, Billy McClelland's watch, and a lot of arms, etc. It was coming on night, and after searching the gulches for a while in vain, they cut off Singletary's head, which they took to Fairplay as a trophy of the fight. This was July 31, 1864.

The next day Halliman was captured at the Nineteen-mile Ranch, and they kept picking up the guerillas one or two at a time until the Thirty-nine-mile Ranch was reached. John Reynolds and Jack Stowe, who were traveling together, were pursued clear across the Arkansas River, but they finally escaped, although Stowe was severely wounded. . . .

[Later on, most of the gang were taken prisoner and then shot by Sergeant Williamson, the former stage driver, who had been put in charge of them. John Reynolds, who escaped but

Jim Baker Tames a Drunkard

was prevented from returning to Colorado until 1871, had the misfortune to be killed while stealing horses, preparatory to retrieving the buried treasure. The map which he gave to Albert Brown was shown to J. N. Cochran in Denver, and the two men set out together to dig up the loot.]

They took the map drawn by Reynolds while dying, and followed the directions very carefully, going into the park by the stage road over Kenosha Hill [South Park], then following the road down the South Platte to Geneva Gulch, a small stream flowing into the Platte. Pursuing their way up the gulch, they were surprised at the absence of timber, except young groves of "quaking asp," which had apparently grown up within a few years. They soon found that a terrible forest fire had swept over the entire region only a short time after the outlaws were captured, destroying all landmarks so far as timber was concerned.

They searched for several days, finding an old white hat, supposed to be Singletary's, near where they supposed the battle to have taken place, and above there some distance a swamp, in which bones of a horse were found, but they could not find any signs of a cave. Running out of provisions they returned to Denver, and after outfitting once more returned to the search, this time going by way of Hepburn's ranch. They found the skeleton of a man, minus the head (which is preserved in a jar of alcohol at Fairplay), supposed to be the remains of Owen Singletary. They searched carefully over all the territory shown on the map, but failed to find the treasure cave. Cochran finally gave up the search, and he and Brown returned again to Denver.

There is no question but that the treasure is still hidden in the mountain, and although the topography of the country has been changed somewhat in the last thirty-three years by forest fires, floods, and snowslides, some one may yet be fortunate enough to find it.

THE LOST CABIN LODE[6]

Far afield from Colorado, in the early days, prospectors and drifters organized their treasure hunts. For even harder to bear, perhaps, than open failure to discover gold is that memory of the rich vein lost, the cache too well concealed, which still haunts the Rocky Mountain West.

Many years ago three white men went prospecting for gold up the Big Horn Valley. The country was alive with Indians, but the party made their way through the hostile country until the headwaters of some unknown stream was reached. Here the goldseekers ran across a body of ore so rich that they could scarcely believe the evidence of their senses. They built a boat with which to descend the river, and started back after supplies and enough help to stand off the attacks of the red men. On the way out, two of the miners were killed by the savages, and the third reached civilization more dead than alive. He related his experience, but could not give the exact location of the ledge. Through privations and constant ponderings over his immense wealth the survivor lost his reason and was never able to return to the lode. But the samples he had brought back with him from the first disastrous expedition proved the ore to be unusually rich, and demonstrated that the mine was not a myth.

The Lost Cabin Mine no doubt exists, and prospectors from Colorado, California, Nevada, and elsewhere have traveled north to the Big Horn Range in search of it year after year, but always without success. The story has been told time and again around the campfire by gray-haired veterans who have spent many months of their lives in search of the lode, until it has become a part of the unwritten history of the Northwest.

Bart Beckley and Jack McDonald spent a year hunting among the peaks of the Big Horn Mountains in search of this wonderful lode. Comstock's last prospecting tour was in search of the Lost Cabin. And many other old and experienced miners have hunted for it, but, like the "Pegleg," the "Nigger Diggings," the "Bell McKeever" and others, the whereabouts of the lost mine still remains a mystery.

[6] S. M. Frazier, *Secrets of the Rocks* (Denver, 1917), 185–88.

Rocky Mountain Gold

In the fall of 1877, a little more than a year after the Custer massacre in the valley of the Little Big Horn, a cavalry officer of the regular army was scouting after hostiles, who led him a wild goose chase among the peaks of the Big Horn Mountains. For days he followed them, but finally lost their trail and then became lost himself. One day about noon, after traveling since daylight, he called a halt, dismounted his men and ordered a rest of half an hour.

The soldiers threw themselves on the ground, holding to their steeds, while the captain tossed his bridle rein to an orderly and went off a little to one side and sat down on a mound of disintegrated rock.

The orderly lay on his back and rolled his eyes from mountain to mountain and from crag to crag, and then off into the clear blue above the clouds. After a while he brought them back to earth again and looked at his captain; from there he turned them to the officer's temporary seat—the mound of decayed rock and earth—and immediately his optics began to bulge out like saucers. The soldier was momentarily paralyzed in all his faculties at what he saw. At last he could control himself no longer, and letting the horses go, he jumped to his feet, rushed over to the officer and shouted in his face: "Captain, you are sitting on a gold mine!"

Had the captain been sitting on a powder mine he could not have sprung to his feet more quickly. The orderly acted like an insane man, for, while the officer was looking at him in astonishment, the former was down on his knees and breaking off great lumps of the mound with his bare hands.

Reaching under a projection of the quartz—for the auriferous rock was in truth decomposed quartz—the excited soldier broke off a little yellow pendant, icicle shaped, which proved to be virgin gold. Both officer and subaltern crushed the rotten rock in their hands and were delighted to see their palms and fingers sparkling in the sunlight with the dazzling yellow particles about the nature of which there could be no question.

The remainder of the command had neither seen nor heard the little drama enacted so near them by the two lucky men, and the latter, by a mutual understanding, agreed to keep their discovery a secret. A sample of the rotten mound was carried away, and an assay of the same made afterwards yielded a remarkably rich percentage of gold.

For a number of days the command wandered about among the gulches, ravines and badlands, and finally struck a trail which carried them out of the mountains. With horses played out and rations gone, they at last reached camp more dead than alive, having wandered for nearly a month over the roughest country on the North American continent.

The orderly was killed shortly afterwards in a skirmish with hostile Indians and at this late date every member of that scouting party has been killed or discharged, so that even their names are forgotten. But the officer still lives, and up until recently was doing duty with his regiment at one of our frontier posts. He has tried more than once to find the lost mine, but has always been unsuccessful. To use his own words: "It is utterly impossible to tell the precise locality of this lead now, as the country was terribly rough, the surroundings new and strange, and hostiles swarmed through all the region in great numbers. I had my hands full at the time, and every subsequent attempt to find the rotten gold quartz outcrop has been balked in one way or another."

GOLD DIGGERS IN UNIFORM[7]

Buffalo Bill, whose chief preoccupation in the West was that of hunting and scouting, seems to have had time nevertheless to collect a story or two about Uncle Sam's prospectors in blue.

One day, when we were on the Great Divide of the Big Horn Mountains, the command had stopped to let the pack train close up. While we were resting there, quite a number of officers and myself were talking to Colonel Mills, when we noticed, coming from the direction in which we were going, a solitary horseman about three miles distant. He was coming from the ridge of the mountains. The Colonel asked me if I had any scouts out in that direction, and I told him I had not. We naturally supposed that

[7] Henry Inman and William F. Cody, *The Great Salt Lake Trail* (Topeka, 1914), 472–76.

it was an Indian. He kept drawing nearer and nearer to us, until we made out it was a white man, and as he came on I recognized him to be California Joe.

When he got within hailing distance, I sang out, "Hello, Joe," and he answered, "Hello, Bill." I said, "Where in the world are you going to, out in this country?" (We were then about five hundred miles from any part of civilization.) He said he was just out for a morning ride. I introduced him to the Colonel and officers, who had all heard and read of him, for he had been made famous in Custer's *Life on the Plains*. He was a tall man, about six feet three inches in his moccasins, with reddish gray hair and whiskers, very thin, nothing but bone, sinew and muscle. He was riding an old cayuse pony, with an old saddle, and a very old bridle, and a pair of elkskin hobbles attached to his saddle, to which also hung a piece of elk meat. He carried an old Hawkins rifle. He had an old shabby hat on, and a ragged blue army overcoat, a buckskin short, and a pair of dilapidated greasy buckskin pants that reached only a little below the knees, having shrunk in the wet; he also wore a pair of old army government boots with the soles worn off. That was his make-up.

I remember the Colonel asking him if he had been very successful in life. He pointed to the old cayuse pony, his gun, and his clothes, and replied, "This is seventy years' gathering." Colonel Mills then asked him if he would have anything to eat; he said he had plenty to eat, all he wanted was tobacco. Tobacco was very scarce in the command, but they rounded up sufficient to do him that day. When invited to go with us, he said he was not particular where he went, he would just as soon go one way as the other; he remained with us several days, in fact, he stayed the entire trip.

He was of great assistance to me, as he knew the country thoroughly. He was a fine mountain guide, but I could seldom find him when I most needed him, as he was generally back with the column, telling frontier stories and yarns to the soldiers for a chew of tobacco.

One day I rode back from the advance guard to ask the Colonel how far he wanted to go before camping, and while I was riding along talking to him we noticed that the advance guard had stopped and were standing in a circle, evidently looking at something very intently. They were so interested that they did not come to their senses until the Colonel and myself rode in among them. Then they immediately moved forward, leaving the Colonel and myself to see what they had been investigating. It was a lone grave in the desolate mountains, and whoever had been buried there evidently had friends, because the spot was nicely covered with stone to prevent the wolves from digging up the corpse.

We were looking at this grave when old Joe rode up and as he stopped he threw down his hat on the pile of rocks and said, "At last."

The Colonel said, "Joe, do you know anything about the history of this grave?"

Joe replied, "Well, I should think I did." The Colonel then asked him to tell us about it.

Joe said: "In 1816"—we didn't stop to think how far back 1816 was—"I had been to Astoria at the mouth of the Columbia River with a company of fur traders, and had been trapping in that country two or three years, and by that time the party had made up their minds they would start back to the States, across the mountains. They were headed for the Missouri River, and when they got there, they intended to build a boat and float down to St. Louis. As they were coming across the Continental Divide of the Rocky Mountains, had reached the eastern slope, and were coming down one of the tributaries of the Stinking Water, some one of the party discovered what he thought to be gold nuggets in the bed of the stream. The water was clear. Every man went down to the water prospecting. The stream was so full of gold nuggets that they all jumped off their horses, leaving them packed as they were, and commenced throwing gold nuggets out on the banks.

"They abandoned everything they had with them, provisions and all, excepting their rifles, and prepared to load the gold.

"Then they started for the Missouri River again, and when they reached the spot where this grave was, a man was taken suddenly ill, died in a very few minutes, and they buried him there."

Old Joe gave a sly wink, as much as to say, "We buried the money with the man."

At this time quite a number of officers gathered around where the advance of the command had halted, and there may have been thirty or forty soldiers listening to this story; some took it to be one of Joe's lies that he usually told for tobacco.

The Colonel ordered the bugler to sound "forward." The command moved on and within five or six miles went into camp. But every man who had listened to Joe's story of this grave, feeling that there was some hundred thousand dollars buried in it, gave it a look as they passed by.

We moved on and went into camp. Joe was messing with me, and after we had supper he said, "Bill, would you like to see a little fun tonight?" I said, "Yes, I am in for fun or anything else." He said, "As soon as it gets dark you follow me." I said, "You bet I will follow you," thinking all the time that he was going back to dig this fellow up.

As soon as it was dark he started and motioned me to follow him, but instead of going back on the trail, he went in the direction that we intended to go in the morning. Thinks I to myself, "That is good medicine, we won't go directly back on the trail but follow another."

I asked him if we did not want to take a pick and shovel with us, and he said, "What for?" I said, "We will need it." He said, "No, we won't need it; you come on."

When we got outside the camp he commenced to turn around to the left, getting back on our trail. I said, "This is all right." He was now going back toward the grave. We went about a mile on the trail and he said, "Sit down here." I said, "Don't we want to go on?" He said, "What for?" I said, "To dig that fellow up and get the money." He said, "The money be damned; I never saw the bloomin' grave before," or something like that. I was disappointed. He said, "Wait a few minutes until after 'taps' and you will see that camp empty itself."

Presently here they came, scouts, soldiers, and packers by the dozen, sneaking through the brush and hurrying back on the trail. Old Joe laid down behind the boulder and just rolled with laughter to see them going to dig up the grave.

The next morning the boys told us that they dug up the grave and found some bones; they dug up a quarter of an acre of ground and never got the color of a piece of gold; then they "tumbled."

A LUCKY STRIKE IN MONTANA[8]

Ed Swan, gulch miner, freighter, rancher, and finally real-estate man, tells his own story of the ups and downs of prospecting in Montana, winter of 1864–1865.

We followed up some streams crossing over the divide to the west side. We went down a gulch and camped overnight, about twenty-five of us. Then we returned by Ophir Gulch, where I never worked but which was familiar to me. Now we had not done any prospecting and one of the Californians said there were no signs. They were all afraid of the Indians. When they decided to go back to Ophir Gulch, Cain and Fargo and I talked it over. . . . Fargo and Cain decided to go, and so we divided right there. They went on in route to Ophir Gulch, while I went to work at once and worked hard. That day I sunk a hole as deep as my waist and came to water. I washed out some of this hard gravel and got about nine dollars in gold in the first pan, finding good-sized nuggets. I had no rubber boots or rubber gloves and the water was very cold, and so the next day I traveled across country and by many cutoffs got into Ophir Gulch by night.

I went into Peg Leg Smith's store and bought my supplies. Here came Bob Cain. He said, "My God, where'd you come from, Swan?" I bought him to secrecy and told him what a fine thing I had; asked him if he wanted to be my partner. He said, "My God, if you will let me in." I asked where Fargo was and he said, "A couple of miles farther down in a bush wickiup, trying to dicker up for some claims." He said he would go to him and talk it over in secret. I told him they must be back to start out by three o'clock if they were going with me. They were there at the appointed time. . . .

[8] From a typescript, "Autobiography of Ed Swan," in the files of The Range Cattle Industry Study, H. O. Brayer, director, Denver.

We went on up to the claim and there Bob jumped down into the hole and scrabbled out a pan of gravel from the side and found large nuggets and free gold. Louie Fargo looked with his eyes bugging out of his head and almost went entirely crazy in the excitement of so great a find. "We got it," he said over and over. "We got it. We've got the world by the tail with a downhill pull." Then he jumped in the air and danced around and when we tried to quiet him he would say, "We got it, we got it."

Then we told him his noise would attract someone else or maybe the Indians. His only reply was, "We got it," getting louder and louder all the time. Then we decided to tie him, which seemed to bring him to his senses. We worked all day, finding more and more gold.

Then men came riding along the top of the ridge. They were shooting and hollo-ing, evidently hunting our camp. We fired in answer and built campfires. The men came to us, for they had tracked us. The news of a new find went out from Peg Leg Smith's as I had paid for my supplies in this new gold and it was a different color. Now there was nothing to do but take our claims according to the law at that time. This allowed me four hundred feet, the rest only one hundred feet. Then it was up to me to choose where to stake off my claim. My ground ran to the top of the dalles or low waterfall. Bob and Louie took above me. Among the men who staked claims were the Dalton brothers, their two cousins, Wyman by name, and a Mr. Ireland, who was not a relative. I found I had about one hundred feet of good ground. All above was worthless. We found the vein ran diagonally across the stream. The Dalton bunch, who staked below my claim, took out $500,000. They bought fast horses and built race tracks, ran a fast house and drank and generally went to ruin. . . .

While we were mining on this claim, they hired a man to take my place and wanted me to prospect the bar which lay about two hundred feet from where we were working. I had worked there for two or three days and started a drift. The second day of my work there, was mostly in sand and gravel. Several small rocks fell down on me, but not to hurt me. I stepped back about two steps to the front and just as I stepped back there was a cave-in came down on me from the front, covering me clear up. I was so close to the mine one of the men saw the cave-in; so he and my two partners came and dug me out. I did not know anything, but they soon caught my hair in a shovel of dirt and then by hand cleared the dirt away from my face. I didn't know anything about it until they were pulling me out, hurting my shoulders and foot badly. I was ill and in the cabin for two or three days.

We worked on about two weeks after I got well. This was in July. Then I proposed to the two boys to sell out to them or buy them out. They wanted to know my price of my third. I told them I would take $700 for my share, or I would join with either one of them to buy either one out, or I would buy both of them out. They said if we would make the arrangements they would give me one-third of all the gold, which was about $2,100 and as much more for my share. I agreed to take it. It was $1480.80.

BONANZA HUMOR[9]

Many were the yarns told for the benefit of tourist and green-horn who wandered into the Rocky Mountain boom camps. To these tales the only limit, apparently, was the willingness of the listener to be browbeaten and generally imposed upon.

When the tenderfoot strikes the Cripple Creek district he usually puts himself on exhibition, and if the whole town does not know he has arrived it is not because he hasn't tried to let the people know all about it. He is surprised that he does not see men leisurely chipping gold out of the rocks when they need a little spare cash. Generally he is burdened with a curiosity that nearly causes his head to split. He must see the camp—he must know all about it. He hires a rig and a driver, and starts out after the manner of a man thirsting for knowledge—burning up

[9] Newspaper clipping in the Western History Collection, Denver Public Library (advertisements on reverse side indicate Denver, 1896) *Rocky Mountain Herald* (Denver), February 26, 1876; *Creede* (Colorado *Candle*, February 18, 1892; various clippings.

with a desire to acquire information and add to his stock of gray matter. Usually he runs against someone who seems to have been looking for him, and bites. But this particular tenderfoot did not have time to bite—he swallowed everything in sight.

Coming round the road into Mound City the creek takes on a decidedly yellow appearance, after its waters have passed through the chlorination mill there, and of course he tries to keep silent. But he can't. His head would burst if he didn't speak.

"Curious color—the water, I mean."

"Yaas. Assays $40 a ton in gold."

"Aw—all staked off, I presume."

"Sure thing—clean down to Galveston."

"An' another thing. Pardon the suggestion, stranger, but if you is a drinking man, wot can't dam hisself up agin the likker habit, all yer has ter do is ter drink outern this yer stream an' it's all same gold cure."

"You don't say so," he gasps.

"Who don't say so? I tell—"

"Beg your pardon. Aw—so ones have been affected?"

"Hundreds on 'em, stranger."

"I would like to meet some of the men who have been cured. Where are they?"

"Dead."

"You don't—I mean—what was the cause, effect of the cure?"

"Now you're shoutin'. They come up here an' swill down this here water, an' while it stops the likker habit, it are certain death—no mistake about it."

"How?"

"Well, I tell yer, seein' as how you is a stranger in these 'er parts. They drinks this stuff an' it settles in their systems, an' they becums regular topers of the stuff, and they keeps on, an' by-an'-by they gets so full of the blamed stuff that the temptation is too great fer mortal man—or enny other man, to stand it, an'—"

"Why, I declare. You mean—"

"That's it. Yes, siree. They is jest waylaid an' shot down, filled full of lead by men wot is poor an' can't help it. Then they is all ready fer the smelter, has the proper amount o' lead in 'em fer flux, an' they goes th' way of all ore. Many a otherwise decent and desarving man in this here destreect got their start in that way."—DENVER PUBLIC LIBRARY.

An old "fifty-niner" was recently bragging that in the early days he once packed two sixteen-foot sluice boxes, weighing over two tons, a distance of two miles. A bystander hinted that the load was rather heavy, when a second fifty-niner came to the rescue of the first by saying that he knew his story to be true, as he was on the same bar at the time and "tracked his friend half a mile across a piece of bare bedrock, into which he sank over five inches at every step he took."—*Rocky Mountain Herald*.

A story illustrative of the richness of Cripple Creek is going the rounds of the camp and has reached this city. It is, in effect, that last Monday night a burglar entered a tent where a miner was asleep. This thief took the miner's limited amount of cash, $6.25, and was just departing when the sleeper awoke.

He started after the burglar, chased him several blocks and being unable to catch him returned to his tent. The miner was barefoot and on his return his feet hurt him badly. Sitting down on his cot he took his candle and with his penknife picked out $6.80 worth of gold out of the soles of his feet.—*Creedle Candle*.

A prospector who had stopped out on the plains overnight, before going up to the diggings, was overtaken by a windstorm. While attempting to cook his breakfast, he found his campfire swept away. But he chased his vagrant fire, holding a skillet over it all of the time; and when the bacon was done, he found himself fifteen miles from his camp.

Two miners in Gregory Gulch ran out of provisions after having been snowed in for two weeks. Weak from lack of food, they finally decided to eat their dog—but neither one could bear to kill the pet. So they just chopped off his tail and made soup out of it, giving the dog the bone. Their renewed strength enabled them to go out and kill some game, which lasted them and the dog until they could break a way out to the settlements.

Rocky Mountain Gold

In the clear atmosphere of Colorado, distances are quite deceptive. Two prospectors once started out before breakfast to walk from Denver to the mountains. Finding their destination seemingly just as far away as ever, after they had walked for more than an hour, one of the men went back for a carriage. Upon his return with the horses and buckboard, he found his companion taking his clothes off on the bank of a creek with only a trickle of water in it, preparatory to swimming across. He wasn't going to be fooled a second time.—CLIPPINGS.

CEMETERY PROSPECTS[10]

The following tale is representative of those concerned with well-meaning but inexperienced morticians who became preoccupied.

It was winter; Scotty had died, and the boys, wanting to give him a right smart burial, hired a man for twenty dollars to dig a grave through ten feet of snow and six feet of hard ground. Meanwhile Scotty was stuffed into a snow bank. Nothing was heard of the gravedigger for three days, and the boys going out to see what had happened to him, found him in a hole, which, begun as a grave, proved to be a sixty-ounce silver-ore mine. The quasi-sexton refused to yield, and was not hard pushed. Scotty was forgotten, and stayed in the snowbank till the April sun searched him out, the boys meanwhile making prospect holes in his intended cemetery.

INTRIGUING CLAIM CONTESTS[11]

One fact these stories reveal: the clash of individualists, in times of laissez faire, was never sharper than in the rugged Rocky Mountain West.

Just now one of many contested claims causes a good deal of excitement. Fritz John Porter, of Army memory, represents

[10] Baillie-Grohman, *Camps in the Rockies*, 21.

[11] Newspaper clipping in the Historical File of the State Historical Society of Colorado; Jesse L. Pritchard, "To Pikes Peak in Search of Gold in 1859," *The Trail*, Vol. IV, No. 6 (November, 1911), 6–9.

one of the rival companies, and Smith and Mather the other. While the suit was pending, Chief Justice Harding granted an injunction restraining Smith and Mather from any further work upon their shaft, but permitted Porter to go on with his. This was denounced as an unjust discrimination; but the opposing party placed a rural injunction upon Porter, quite as effective as Judge Harding's, and a good deal more offensive.

There is a draught from one excavation into the other, and Porter found a column of smoke, from burning sulphur, rising through his shaft, rendering it impossible to work or even to enter it. Smith and Mather have been attacked for this curious contempt of court; but the smoke still continues. Both sides are bitter, threatening, and fully armed for a possible collision; and the whole community is arrayed into two parties on the subject. It even involves much political feeling, though it is difficult to comprehend the exact logical relation between Loyalty or Copperheadism and the rights of property.—Colorado Historical Society.

Up in Nevada Gulch, about a mile above Central City [no city then], I found a man at work with a sluice, washing out gold. I asked him if he knew where I could get a job. He said he was working for another man, but had given notice he would quit soon and perhaps I could get his. I hunted up the owner, whose name was Pat Casey, and found him to be, apparently, about as green a specimen of an Irishman as I had ever seen. My nerve came back to me and I determined to appear brave and independent at least. The dialogue that took place between us was something like this:

Argonaut: I am in search of work and would like a job.

Casey: Are yez a miner or a tenderfoot?

Argonaut: I am a miner.

Casey: Where did yez mine?

Argonaut: In California, Australia, South Africa—and had he not stopped me would have added Nova Scotia, New Zealand, and Alaska. I was in for it and thought I might as well make it good and strong.

Casey: How much does yez want a day?

Argonaut: Ten dollars (emphatically).

Casey: Holy smoke! Yez have yer gall wid yez. Yez had better take the mine and I'll work for yez. I'll give yer three dollars a day and yer board, and not a cint more.

The Argonaut tried to compromise on seven dollars a day, but Pat would not raise it; so I agreed with him and was to go to work the next day.

I can freely admit at this late date, without blushing, that all I knew about mining I had picked up in the camp—and as yet I had not been the possessor of a paying mine—it was not much. What I lacked in knowledge, however, I fully determined to make up in hard work. In mining one cannot tell until the day's work is done and the "clean-up" made, whether one has saved any gold or not. My anxiety to show good results and thus hold my job kept me on the rack all day. The memory of that day's work abides with me even until now. Never in my life, either before or since, have I worked so hard. It seems to me now that I must have handled several hundred tons of mud and gravel. It makes me sweat now to think of it.

Anyone can throw mud and gravel into a sluice, but "cleaning up"—that is the separating of the gold from the black sand, a mineral almost as heavy as gold—is another matter, and here is where a knowledge of the mysteries of "panning" is required. It was very late in the evening when I got through and was gratified to know that I had saved about ten dollars more than the man who preceded me and thus made myself solid with my new employer.

About this time Casey got into trouble about the title of his mine. Some other miner set up a claim to it. There were no courts in Colorado at that time other than those established by the miners themselves. The judge of the court was the president of the mining district, and the jury were the miners, assembled in mass meeting, one day in each week to adjudicate differences between persons. This was a supreme court and from it there was no appeal. Casey told me his trouble and I assured him that I was as good a lawyer as I was a miner—and that was no story. He said if I would win his suit for him he would pay me about fifty dollars. Needless to say I took the case.

Several days before it came up for hearing I instructed him to ride through this and adjoining camps and inform every Irishman he saw that his presence was requested at the miners' meeting to be held on the following afternoon. After the testimony was all in the opposing counsel made an eloquent plea for his client. I followed as best I could, and in the division, as I had planned, we had a large majority—of Irishmen—on our side and won the suit. In 1862 this man Casey sold this same claim on which I worked for $100,000 and became a very noted character, both in Colorado and New York.—Pritchard.

THE LOST MINE OF THE CACHE LA POUDRE[12]

Cache la Poudre Canyon is a winding cut, braced with vertical red-stone walls and swept by a rushing stream, in the Front Range of the Colorado Rockies. In such places lost-mine tales, and dread whisperings of murder, find their surest breeding grounds.

In the early days, Fort Collins [Colorado] was a real fort. There was little surrounding the fort but wilderness. Out of this wilderness there appeared one day a Dutchman and an Irishman laden with gold. They cashed their gold with the sutler and went on a protracted spree. After spending most of their money they sobered up and one day they were gone. This was in Civil War times.

Whence they came and whither they went was an absolute mystery. This episode was repeated several times till the soldiers became inquisitive as to where this great mine was which yielded gold so readily. So they hired a celebrated Indian scout to follow the Dutchman and the Irishman and discover the mine.

The Indian assumed that the mine was close by and took but little food. He followed the miners for three days. They went straight up the Cache la Poudre. The third night it snowed and the Indian was hungry. The next morning he followed a deer

---

[12] Caroline Bancroft, "Lost-Mine Legends of Colorado," *California Folklore Quarterly*, Vol. II, No. 4 (October, 1943), 257–59. This is the version given by George Jarvis Bancroft, *Rocky Mountain News*, January 11, 1914.

trail to get meat and about the time he got his deer, it began snowing again and the miners' trail was lost.

As time went on, the Dutchman and the Irishman kept bringing in larger burdens of gold and returning with heavier loads of supplies; so they bought a donkey, which they used for a time, but the loads becoming too heavy for the donkey, they traded it off and got an ox. They said a bear had killed the ox right at the cabin door, and they were obliged to carry their gold on their backs. This time they had an unusually long spree and in a quarrel between the two, the Irishman killed the Dutchman.

There was not much law in the land in those days and besides the commanding officer was away, so a party of soldiers seized the Irishman and told him that he would be hanged unless he would show them his mine.

The Irishman stoutly refused, whereupon the soldiers put a rope around his neck and led him out to a cottonwood tree, the plan being to choke him a little and then let him down for a final chance to save his life by revealing the mine. They threw the rope over a limb and pulled the Irishman up in the air for thirty seconds. When they let him down he was dead. The protracted spree had weakened his heart and a little strangulation finished him.

So both the Dutchman and the Irishman were dead and the location of the mine was as much a mystery as ever.

VIOLENT DEATHS OF DISCOVERERS[13]

As with the obscure miners of the Cache la Poudre, strange and terrible destinies, it seems, pursued more famous followers of America's golden trails.

There is a well-grounded superstition that ill luck or violent death is the legacy of all discoverers of hidden treasures. And the facts in the case seem to justify the belief. The original locators of between thirty-five and forty of the richest gold and silver mines in this country are known to have come to evil ends.

Out of the number twelve met violent deaths in saloons and

[13] Frazier, *Secrets*, 185–88.

other brawls; six suicided; three were buried alive under snow-slides; five turned highwaymen and were caught and executed; one perished in a boiling spring; and the others have dropped out of sight.

To particularize, Fryer, once millionaire owner of the Fryer Hill Mine, suicided in Denver after squandering his last nickel. ... The discoverer of the Great Standard Mine in Mono County, California, slept his life away in a snowstorm while making his way to the mines. Colonel Story, who gave his name to the county in Nevada where the Comstock is situated, was killed in battle by the Pyramid Lake Indians. Thomas Page Comstock died a beggar in a strange land, committing suicide at Bozeman, Montana, in 1870 by shooting himself. He was the leader of the famous Big Horn expedition that was sent out by Nevada capitalists in search of the Lost Cabin Mine, supposed to be somewhere among the Big Horn Mountains. The expedition was a failure, and Comstock, whether from disappointment or some other cause, while encamped near Bozeman, sent a pistol ball through his head and died instantly. He was buried near the spot, and to this day his grave remains unmarked and unknown.

Near the wild spot where twelve years before the hidden treasure of Alder Gulch was first revealed to him, William Fairweather was laid to rest. The date is forgotten now, but like Comstock he stranded on the shoals of dissipation. Each of these erratic men in his day had turned a key—the one silver, the other gold—which unlocked millions for others, but nothing for himself. William Farrell, who "struck" Meadow Lake, died a victim of remorse in a San Francisco hospital, "haunted by the spirits of other deluded prospectors passing and repassing his dying couch."

The locator of the famous Homestake in the Black Hills of Dakota is said to have afterward turned road agent. Times going hard with him he attempted to hold up a stage loaded and primed for just such emergencies, and he was planted alongside the road by the tender-hearted express agent whom he had tried to rob.

Home, of the Home district, California, followed in the suicidal tracks of Comstock. After squandering a fortune he shot his brains out on the streets of San Francisco.

"Old Virginia" after whom the Consolidated Virginia was named, and who sold his claim for $25, a pony, and a bottle of whisky, came to his death by an overdose from the heels of a bucking mule near Dayton, Nevada.

"Doughnut Bill" was planted in the Lone Mountain cemetery in Utah, in 1868. A single grave under a pine tree in a California frontier mining town tells where poor old Eureka sleeps his last. Kelse Austin was killed in Elks County, Nevada, many years ago. Lloyd Magruder, while conducting a number of wagons loaded with treasure from Virginia City to the nearest railroad, was murdered and robbed by his teamsters, who were Plummer's outlaws in disguise. George Rankinson and Henry Plummer were captured and strung up without the delay and formality of a trial. Plummer was an arch rascal. In the early days of the mining camps of Montana he was elected sheriff of the camps about Virginia City, and used his position to further his own ends of robbery and murder. Plummer was the original locator of the rich ground around Virginia City, but thought he could make more money and quicker by taking what was already mined than by laboring in the gulch day after day, and getting it by hard, honest toil. But he was unveiled at last, and died an ignominious death at the end of a lariat.

The fate of our own Creede is of recent occurrence and had too much of the element of tragedy to have been forgotten by the readers. And H. A. W. Tabor, erstwhile millionaire ten times over, died the incumbent of a salaried position, conferred upon him in his last days, it is alleged, because he needed substantial pecuniary support.

Frontier Towns

WESTERN towns today are bright towns. Their streets are broad and well paved, guiding the traveler easily on his way. In keeping with American tradition —that tradition arising out of the restlessness and questing spirit of a nation—service is quick, accommodations colorful and of the most modern kind. For those who wish to visit them, libraries and museums stand with doors wide throughout the year, repositories of Western lore and records of action. As in older cities, parks have been set aside and carefully nurtured, their landscapes blended with the larger spaces which surround them. Everywhere business enterprise flourishes. Everywhere plans are projected and carried through, and in the smallest, most remote settlement there is life, movement, hope, a sense of expansion familiar to every man in the West.

Certainly, then, it is clear that these Western towns are not mere barracks towns, born overnight and doomed to disappear, as temporary camps have disappeared, when the need for them has vanished. Though short, their history lies deep within them. In Plains towns the main-street cafes, garages, and stores of the present were perhaps, in other days, the saloons, stage stations, and trading posts of the Frontier. In mountain camps massive mahogany bars, ornate mirrors, and fragile, shining glassware are still to be seen; hotels, firehouses and county headquarters remain much as they were; and the solid opera houses, pride of every citizen, display old frontier billings along with their notices of modern festival revivals. Western history—the clipped official statements, old-timers' memories, the folklore tales, and sly, humorous yarns of a people—stands back of all of these. For it, too, is everywhere, keeping pace with the new life, lending balance and perspective, adding to the brightness of land and towns its own continuity, its own richness of story background and incident.

Frontier Towns

Somewhere along the dusty cattle trails from Texas to Montana, Granada had its day. As with many another trail town, that day was short, but, according to the men who knew Granada, well worth while.

It was an unusually warm day on the 17th of May, 1886. All eastern Colorado lay bathed in bright sunshine, but above all rested a light haze, peculiar at times to the Great Plains. The heat arising from the ground, which had yet hardly commenced to turn green with its carpet of buffalo grass, formed here and there mirages, looking all the world like lakes of purest water, in which the surrounding objects appeared distorted and upside down. Along the south, cutting the plain in two, arose the range of low sand hills, bedecked in sagebush and bunch-grass. To the north the Arkansas glistened and glittered as it wound its sluggish way over the quicksands of its bed, in and out through the sparse timber that lined its banks.

All over this great region, that extended from the eastern boundary of the state to the foothills of the Rockies, and from Canada to the Rio Grande, a silence somber and almost appalling brooded and oppressed. No sign of civilization, except at long distance some ranch house and low corrals lay indistinct on the horizon, or perhaps a cloud of dust arose and floated away, betokening the presence of cowboys working their herds. Crisscrossed in all directions were the old buffalo trails leading to and from the river or some old buffalo wallow. To the east the tender green of the XY meadows formed a soft and cooling shade; to the north another ranch house appeared in a small grove of cottonwoods, all else was deserted and silent.

But into this picture came several men, and with chain and compass commenced to plot the town of Granada. It seemed a hopeless task in this great wilderness, just as Nature had left it ages before, but starting from a stone, or the little mounds and holes that government surveyors had left to mark township and range, the task was accomplished and the new town had its be-

[1] Hamer Norris, "Along the Cattle Trail," *Lamar* (Colorado) *Register*, March 7 to May 2, 1928.

ginning. A small herd of timid wild-eyed antelope stood and watched the men in silent protest, or a lone coyote raised a louder one from the fringe of sand hills, for was this not an invasion of their hitherto undisrupted domain, the advance guard of the immigrants that were to sweep across the Plains, founding towns, opening farms, that were to drive them from their hunting and grazing grounds?

On the morrow a load of rough lumber, more men, and in a few hours a rough shack, with battened cracks and a stovepipe extending through the roof, and at noon the first meat served on the townsite to the surveyors and saw-and-hammer carpenters. The guests were welcomed at the door with a kindly smile by a man whose shoulders already sagged beneath the years, and whose locks were already whitening in the passing of time: in one corner a woman bent over pots and pans, and the pleasant aroma of food, clean and tasty, filled the room.

The next day a saloon reared its unwelcomed head, then a general store, and so on, day by day, a new store, another saloon, a bank building, lumber yard, the inevitable livery stable, hotel and real-estate office, and finally the newspaper whose mission it was to lie and boast and solemnly affirm that Granada, "The Child of Destiny" and the "Gateway to Colorado," was to become the metropolis, the teeming city of the new land.

So Granada made rapid strides; all the characteristics of the boom town were present, the sound of saw and hammer from early morning to evening shadows, streets filled with eager-eyed men, all possessing the gambling spirit, speculating in town lots, locating on timber claims and homesteads, eagerly pushing their various businesses as merchants, real-estate men, or hotel rustlers. . . .

It was determined that something must be done to induce the Santa Fe railroad to recognize the coming metropolis and stop its trains. Hitherto the nearest station was Old Granada, three miles away, now a place in name only, possessing a great and exciting past, it was true, as one of the important towns on the Old Santa Fe Trail, but now having only a drab and dreary future. There was no need for trains to stop there, but every reason why they should stop at the new town. The proposition was put to the railroad officials and after a little time came the ultimatum. "As the Santa Fe practically owned all the towns along its lines in Kansas it would have to have fifty-one per cent of all unsold lots in Granada and fifty-one per cent of all the money heretofore realized from lot sales before it would give Granada a depot." This was a solar plexus blow. Indignation meetings were held. It would never do to surrender its birthright to the soulless corporation, and answer was made "that the town company would build at least one town without railroad interference."

This answer hurt the pride of the Santa Fe officials and filled their hearts with anger, to even dare to intimate that anything could be put over on the Great Plains without the sanction of the railroad. For the next month the silence was ominous, and the next move of the railroad came when surveyors appeared on the spot where Lamar now stands and laid out the new townsite. The new town was sponsored by the Arkansas Valley Town Company, which was part of the Santa Fe land department, and was taken up and boomed by a lot of Kansas town boomers who knew how to make things hum. In a few days a depot was moved to the townsite, a lot auction was arranged, excursions were run, the U. S. Land Office was promised and buildings sprang up everywhere.

Meanwhile Granada assumed a pose of watchful waiting, and this attitude was maintained for a year when the town surrendered unconditionally to the railroad. But it was too late, all the settlers insisting upon going further west. Lamar continued to grow and Granada wallowed around in a slough of despond. But one hope remained, Granada proposed to be made the county seat of the proposed new county of Prowers. Arrangements were made for an honest election, it was not proposed to have any disgraceful Kansas county-seat war, so Bat Masterson was employed to look after the interests of Lamar and Ben Daniels was similarly employed by Granada. Lamar won, and Granada's hopes, like the deceptive mirage, flickered and faded, and the sun of "The Child of Destiny" hid its face behind the dark and somber clouds of a pleasant vision, and Granada became a deserted village of the plain.

THE LOST FORTUNE IN MOLASSES[2]

Some miles to the west and north of Granada, another Colorado frontier town was having better luck. Though fire, flood, and Indian war swept upon it, Denver, one day to become the capital of America's Centennial State, endured all in its first years and witnessed every conceivable kind of transaction.

Anthony Arnett remained on his farm until the spring of 1859, when the news came of the rich gold strikes in the Pikes Peak country. This excitement was a welcome relief to the reckless spirits of the country, who were beginning to chafe at the quietude. The land seethed with the news of this new discovery, following as it did so closely upon the heels of the forty-niner strike. It was "Pikes Peak or Bust."

Arnett outfitted three wagons with enough supplies to start a store. This time he took his wife and son, Willamette. A young man, John Topping, accompanied the party. They reached Denver without any trouble, stopped one night, and proceeded to Golden City, ten miles west, which was at that time more important than Denver.

It was in Denver that an event occurred which the family had reason to remember in after years. Arnett camped near a small log grocery store and saloon. The storekeeper came out to talk with him about his trip. Finding that he had a supply of provisions, the business man was ready to drive a bargain.

"What's that in the barrel?" he asked, pointing to a barrel in one of the wagons. "Ain't whisky, is it?"

"No," was the answer. "That's molasses."

"Molasses!" exclaimed the other. "You don't mean it. Why these Missourians have been runnin' me fair crazy askin' for molasses. What'll ye take for it?"

Arnett was informed as to prices in the new country. "She's worth $300 just as she sits."

The storekeeper looked thoughtful. "Would ye trade it?" he finally asked.

"Don't know. What for?"

2 Forest Crossen, *Anthony Arnett, Empire Builder* (Pamphlet, 1933, n. p.).

"See that land right over there?" queried the merchant, pointing to a strip of prairie land on their left. "I'll trade you the whole hundred and sixty for the barrel."

Arnett looked the land over—it was raw prairie—and then at the little cluster of cabins. No, he decided, she was no good. He could take that molasses and peddle it out for five hundred dollars.

"Nothing doing," he told the storekeeper, and that closed the deal.

That hundred and sixty acres of land is the heart of the downtown district of Denver.

Going on to Golden City, Arnett established a store in a tent. The precious molasses barrel was rolled in. The young man, John Topping, slept in the tent. During the first night he kicked open the spigot on the barrel and let all the molasses flow out on the ground. The queer part about it was that he did not awaken until the next morning, but spent the night in a welter of stickiness.

PERSONAL JOURNALISM[3]

Editor William N. Byers and associates, of Denver's Rocky Mountain News, *were humorous men. Unfortunately for them, however, subscribers at times found themselves too close to the point.*

Mr. Byers was often in "hot water" because of his nerve in showing up certain of the residents, principally of the sporting element, and had some narrow escapes. I have been in the office with him when men ready and seemingly quite willing to kill him entered and endeavored to provoke a quarrel, but he managed to avoid a shooting affray by keeping his head and standing for all the indignant visitor had said. Having relieved themselves of a lot of mean words, his callers usually retired and left him with a whole skin.

I had one experience with an indignant citizen that cured me of any further desire to provoke hostilities. Across the street

[3] S. T. Sopris, "Early Day Reminiscences," *The Trail*, Vol. VII, No. 7 (December, 1914), 20–21.

from the *News* office on Larimer Street, was some vacant ground, part of which was used as a wood yard. The wood was delivered to purchasers in a wagon drawn by one horse, and that horse was the thinnest animal I had ever seen. Standing in the sun he wouldn't throw a shadow, and no X ray was needed to show what was inside his hide. That horse got on my nerves. Sitting at the "local" desk, facing the front of the office, every time I looked up and out I could see that poor beast, and the sight unfitted me for the work I had to do, which was inventing items for the local column.

Finally one day I perpetrated the following brief reference to the unfortunate horse: "There is a man in this town who drives a horse that is so poor the owner has to tie a knot in his, the horse's, tail to keep the animal from slipping through the collar." That was all, but it proved amply sufficient. Any elaboration would have been a waste of printer's ink. The item appeared in the morning issue the following day. In the afternoon of that day, while at my desk, I happened to look out on the street and noticed the owner of the aforesaid horse coming toward the office. In his right hand was a gun, one that seemed to me to be unnecessarily large, and the manner in which he swung the gun, and the more or less uncertainty of his steps, indicated that he had taken aboard a full cargo of "pizen," which happened to be the case. Mr. Dailey was in the front of the office working on the books, and it suddenly occurred to me that two of us were not needed in the office just then; so, grabbing my hat, I slipped quietly out the back door. Returning an hour or so later, I learned from my friend Dailey that he had had a lot of trouble quieting the excited visitor, who had been induced to depart after promising to shoot me full of holes the first time he caught me on the street. And I was admonished to let up on such "personal" items, or else stick around and fight my own battles.

VOLUNTEER FIRE FIGHTERS[4]

In frontier cities like Denver, filled as they were with miners, cowpunchers, greenhorns, tin-horns, and Indians, members of the volunteer fire departments were outstandingly colorful figures. Annual balls, contests, fire, death and destruction—all added to the picturesqueness of these intrepid and impetuous gentlemen.

Two of the most important fires in Denver's history occurred less than twenty-four hours apart. At 12:30 A. M. on March 19, 1877, fire broke out in the Denver Theater, at Sixteenth and Lawrence streets. The playhouse was completely destroyed. The fire trucks were still at the ruins, hose was stretched on the streets, still wet, and firemen were overworked when a stove in James Rockford's hotel caused a fire that swept one square block of Denver's business district. All buildings on Wazee and Blake streets, between Twenty-first and Twenty-third streets, were destroyed. A high wind fanned the flames for twelve hours, and the work of the companies could do little against such a conflagration. It was here that the second volunteer fireman gave his life to the city. Albert Gardiner, of Hook and Ladder Company No. 2 and Hose Company No. 4, was caught under a falling brick wall and was so badly crushed that death came in a few hours.

On the evening of July 18, 1878, the Archer Hose Company gave their monthly "hop" in the ballroom over their station. All firemen wore full dress suits; the hall was decorated for the occasion, and an unusually large number were present. Just at midnight, when the music was at its highest pitch, in the middle of a Virginia reel, the fire bell clanged. Instantly the volunteers in their dress suits left their fair ladies on the ballroom floor and answered their call to duty.

There was no more dancing that night and never another appearance was made in those dress suits. The fire, which was at the Jackson Foundry, on Ninth between Lawrence and Larimer

[4] E. R. Battles, "Denver Volunteer Fire Department," *The Trail*, Vol. IX, No. 9 (February, 1917), 11–14.

streets, caused little damage, but the Archer boys, by some un-accountable fact, were mistaken for the burning foundry and all streams turned on them. When the mistake was discovered the fire was extinguished.

William Sanderlin, a volunteer of Woodie Fisher Hose Company, tells the following story of his company:

In 1877 the company made a run during the night to fight a small blaze in the rear of a saloon. The fire was quenched with little difficulty to the delight of the saloonkeeper, and to reward the firemen for their quick work he offered them a half-keg of whisky. As Chief Clayton had returned to headquarters, the gift was eagerly accepted. But here an obstacle confronted the company. How could they get the liquor to the station unknown to the Chief? Then someone thought of a bright idea, and every bucket on the truck was filled to its capacity with whisky. Never before in the history of the fire companies was a truck moved so cautiously. All rough places in the street were avoided and every stone kicked into the gutter.

When the company returned, Chief Clayton, who was a temperance man, entered the station.

"Could have been worse, boys," he said. "It was a wonder some of that liquor didn't explode. Funny why you fellows didn't hurry a bit returning; must have been awful tired."

Then he took a long whiff in the direction of the truck.

"Phew! You can smell that awful stuff yet."

He bumped against one of the buckets while hanging up his trumpet. And then—well, to be brief, not a volunteer knew how the liquor splashed into the buckets. It was a mystery to them. Each bore a solemn, innocent expression, even when they were emptying the whisky into the hose rack in the rear of the station.

The fire companies had another experience with liquor at the burning of Zang's Brewery some years later. The building, on the site of the present brewery, was completely destroyed. Hydrants had not yet been installed near the brewery, and it was necessary to stretch hose from Eleventh and Larimer streets. Owing to the scarcity of water all buckets were filled with beer to extinguish the flames. Some of the beverage, it is said, was put on the fire.

JOHN MORRISSEY'S WONDERFUL WATCH[5]

Good fortune in prospecting descends indiscriminately, like rain itself, upon the good and the bad. So, at any rate, the story of John Morrissey—as told by a famous Denver raconteur— would lead one to believe.

When you have lived a long, long time in a city you love, there come days when you walk with ghosts. You are passing a building that, on a street where the years have brought many changes, looms unchanged and as it was in your youth, and suddenly in the entrance a form that long has been dust appears and a voice long silent greets you and you walk along with the friend, you two lost in the crowd, oblivious to everything, living again in a buried day.

And so it is as I pass the Boston Building and see, leaning against the pink stone wall, Colonel John Morrissey and hear him say, "Hey, Smithy, me lad! Come on, now, an' tell me if I'm right in the bet I've made with meself on the time o' day." And just as in the days of nearly half a century ago, I go to the shabby big Irishman with the kindly blue eyes, and at his bidding, as he turns his head and the veined lids curtain his eyes, I take from his threadbare vest pocket the finest watch in all the West!

"I bet with meself it's three-thirty-five. If I'm right, we'll go into the Boston bar an' have whatever ye fancy in a drink or smoke," he continues, with averted eyes as I open the three gold covers, the first thick for protection, the second half as thick, and the third very thin, these two, it is evident, to keep out the most minute particle of dust.

That big "turnip" must have weighed between two and three pounds, and the chain, formed of gold nuggets, fully as much again, but the chain many months since had changed ownership when pride of possession gave way to the pangs of hunger. The watch, which had been specially made to his specifications in Geneva, Switzerland, cost $1,500. Under the glass was not only

[5] Joseph Emerson Smith, "Personal Recollections of Early Denver," *The Colorado Magazine*, Vol. XX, No. 1 (January, 1943), 64–65.

the big round porcelain face bearing the hour numerals and hands, hour, minute, and second, in gold, but a miniature barometer foretelling changes in weather, a thermometer, and a calendar in colors, set in the face, showing the month and day. A little lever gadget on the side, near the winding stem, when pressed produced plainly heard silvery chimes telling the hour and quarter hour: for example, three-thirty would be denoted by three strokes of the concealed gong, then a brief interval and three strokes, followed by another interval and three strokes. However, there was no way of ascertaining by the chimes the exact time, to the minute, between the quarter hours.

Morrissey had no "learning"; he could neither read nor write and, after long practice, could barely sign his name. Never able to master figures, the Roman numerals on his watch face remained a mystery to him. But this he never admitted. Desiring the time, he would call a friend and go through the subterfuge of a "bet with meself." As he never guessed correctly, he was safe, with penniless pockets, in promising refreshments or a cigar if he won his "bet" by naming the hour and minute. Every newspaper man knew him and gravely obliged in the pathetic little game. We handled the enormous timepiece with respect if not with awe, knowing that in another sense it was one of the most, if not the most, expensive watches in the country, for it had cost the Colonel his fortune.

In the center of the stem was a piston, its head distinguished by a chip diamond. A pressure upon the diamond and lo, you held a stop-watch to time the horses to a fraction of a second! Morrissey shied away from women, but gave free rein to gambling, horse racing and champagne. Offsetting this was his open-handed generosity. In tailored black and white check sport suits, wide-brim tan sombrero, binoculars in black case hanging by a strap over a shoulder, magnificent watch in his hand, he was a familiar figure at famous tracks the country over. His betting losses were tremendous.

Mines, as they used to say, "peter out," and Morrissey's million or so in time disappeared, leaving no trace except his watch. Too late, but equipped as no other prospector in the long history of mining, he started looking for new wealth. In the back of that astonishing watch, between the outer and inner covers, were a detachable compass and a superfine magnifying glass for use in examining ore rock. But it was of no avail. His nugget chain finally went and then—one day his watch went; report had it, to the pawnbroker. The Colonel was no longer a familiar figure downtown. In obscurity he died not long afterward.

PAUL REVERE RIDES IN THE WEST[6]

History, it is said, repeats itself. Although British redcoats failed to penetrate to Colorado Springs and the Pikes Peak region, other marauders, bedecked in red war paint, managed to keep Western reincarnations of the famed horseman almost constantly on the dead run.

My second sharply etched recollection has as its background Birks Cornforth's remarkable grocery store. Birks was an Englishman and his store was filled with the best potted foods his native land could send him for the delectation of palates of the many English here in the days when they were "rawnching" in the Platte Valley and helping to make General Palmer's newly laid-out Colorado Springs, known over the country as "Little Lunnon." Mother was there shopping when in walked two figures so strange and ill-assorted that even my child brain registered curiosity. The man was a little over medium height, graying hair fell in straggly curls to his shoulders, his eyes were steady and commanding—that is the word to use—and his face was thin and deeply lined. A blue wool shirt was tucked into the band of buckskin-fringed trousers, old and dirty, and he wore beaded moccasins. The woman was an Indian, more than stout, but clean and fresh looking in her bright-colored gingham wrapper. Her hair in long plaits also was graying. She kept close behind the man who was shaking hands with Birks Cornforth. I heard the storekeeper say, "You needn't think about it, Mr. Gerry, not for a minute. Good Lord, man, your credit is good here as at everywhere else! I'm not worrying, so don't you."

"Mamma," I piped, "who is that man, and why has he the Injun with him?"

"Hush," she said, "hush!" as the squaw slowly let her eyes

[6] Smith, "Recollections," 8–10.

run over mother and me. Then she smiled. I knew, without looking up, that mother had smiled at her. As the man turned to leave, mother did what I thought was a startling thing. She dragged me by the hand to him and said, "Mr. Gerry, I want my little boy to shake hands with you so that he will always remember meeting the Paul Revere of the West."

"You do me too much honor, madam," he said; and then, with a laugh that blew out of me the fright at the nearness of the Indian woman, "but, I'm free to say, I like it. What is your name, little man? Well, well, I am glad to see you're a true Westerner, and wear your hair in curls, like I do."

There were interested glances as customers saw mother shaking hands with the woman whom she called Mrs. Gerry. A long time later, when I heard more of the story mother told me that day, the full realization of a dramatic highlight of my life came to me. Elbridge Gerry, grandson of the signer of the Declaration of Independence and delegate from Massachusetts of the same name, came west when a youth, married an Indian maiden—a ceremony afterwards legalized by him—and finally took up a ranch in the Platte Valley.

One moonlit night in the summer of 1864 the two brothers of Gerry's wife came to the adobe ranch house and wakened her so quietly her husband was not disturbed. Outside, they gave her warning of an uprising wherein the Plains Indians had vowed not a white should be left alive three days hence. They told her when and where the tribes would strike. They had come to whisper what they had sworn would not pass their lips, for they knew that "Little Gerry" was kind to their sister and that she loved the white man. "Go away with him and your children," they said. "Hide him well or nothing can save him." Their ponies bore them swiftly into the night as she stood battling within herself, her blood and its loyalty to her people pointing one way—to keep her peace while finding an excuse to flee—her love urging the breaking of her promise not to divulge what she had been told.

Love for the white man who was good to her and proud and loving to the children she had borne him won, and she entered the room, woke Gerry, and told him everything.

"Where are you going?" she asked in alarm.

"To save the ranchers. I will not betray your brothers, and with me gone you will be safe here. I will come back."

He saddled his best mare and as the dawn came, was pounding on the door of the nearest ranch. For two days he sped to the right and the left of the lazy Platte, warning the isolated families so they could gather for protection at hamlets and Fort Lupton, Fort Collins, and Boulder. And from his fourth horse, lathered and sagging as he threw the reins over its neck, he staggered down and into the governor's office in Denver. The telegraph lines to Julesburg and to Colorado City were working. Messengers were dispatched to ranches east and south of Denver in time. Instead of a wholesale slaughter by surprise, but few whites were murdered, thanks to Elbridge Gerry, hailed now as the Paul Revere of the West.

He was a true gentleman, was Gerry. Friends occasionally would say, "Why don't you take your rightful place in society, assume the station your breeding and birth entitle you to? Leave your wife like so many whites have done—"

Always came the stern "Stop! You forget she is my wife and I respect and honor her as the mother of my children. Nothing can part us. I owe her much happiness."

THE RESURRECTION OF DICK TURPIN[7]

One of the best-known raconteurs of Pueblo, Colorado, in the early days, was the journalist, R. M. Stevenson. Yarns of all varieties, from Dick Turpin escapades to the most insignificant local affairs, flowed from his pen.

The boom of 1872 had reached Pueblo. The Denver and Rio Grande Railroad was completed to the metropolis of the Arkansas, and the citizens of the town were awakened from a sleep of several years by an influx of gamblers, dance hall denizens, thieves, railroad laborers, and all varieties of the odds and ends of the human family that usually follow the progress of a railway through the new West. Tents were usually pitched in the

[7] Alice Polk Hill, *Tales of the Colorado Pioneers* (Denver, 1884), 286–90.

outskirts of the town, and gambling houses and dance halls invaded localities unaccustomed to such visitors.

Among the houses occupied by dance halls was a plank building located on Second Street, on the borders of the mill ditch, formerly occupied as a boardinghouse by the employees of a brickyard. About noon, on a lovely spring day, the crack of a forty-five calibre revolver sounded within the building; a man lay on the floor shot through the abdomen and fatally wounded. The poor fellow was a blacksmith, known as "Dick Turpin," a good enough fellow in his way, but badly demoralized by whisky; he had followed the railroad to Pueblo.

He had been an habitue of the dance hall, and that morning quarreled with the bartender, and during the quarrel received the fatal wound. When a physician arrived he found the poor fellow lying upon a bunk with a pair of blankets under him, groaning in agony. The ghastly wreck of what had once been a woman, was giving such attention as was possible under the circumstances, while a crowd of bloated and degraded bummers stood around, some of them in a maudlin way expressing sympathy, and some jeering at the dying man.

A brief examination demonstrated the fact that the victim was fatally wounded. So, giving the poor fellow a heavy dose of morphine to ease his pain, the doctor departed, after informing the bystanders that his patient could not last more than twenty-four hours.

The prediction proved true, and within the time mentioned the man was dead, and in two or three hours after his spirit had taken flight, he was buried at the expense of the county in the old cemetery on the brow of the bluffs overlooking Pueblo and immediately in the rear of its principal street.

And so Dick Turpin was dead. In the vigorous, though somewhat coarse vernacular of the natives of southern Colorado, "he was too dead to skin," and was apparently planted with his toes to the daisies, there to rest for many years, until the storied horn of the Angel Gabriel should finally awake the sleepers in their graves, rouse them from their beds, and create a scramble for bones in the old cemeteries of the world.

One evening, shortly after the event above mentioned had

transpired, two individuals might have been seen (so to speak) sitting on a stoop of a business house on Santa Fe Avenue, enjoying the moonlight and their cigars, and engaged in a conversation which ran somewhat as follows:

"Professor Nathan R. Smith, I would like very much to know where that ball went that disturbed poor Dick Turpin's digestion, and caused him to be planted in the wareroom up there," pointing with his thumb over his shoulder towards the cemetery.

The other man took a contemplative puff or two at his cigar and replied, "Well, Dr. Samuel S. Gross, if you are very enthusiastic in the pursuit of science, I have an idea that a small resurrection might be organized for the occasion and the body of Mr. Turpin removed to a locality where the desired examination could be made."

Another friend of medical science about this time put in an appearance, and taking part in the conversation, remarked, "How long has Turpin been buried?"

"Well, about two weeks."

"Don't you think he would be a little rancid by this time?"

"Oh, no, not more than some I have handled before," remarked the gentleman addressed as Dr. Samuel S. Gross. "Now, Smith," said the same party, "you see the boys and get a few of them to join us tomorrow night, and we'll raise the defunct Richard and examine his damaged anatomy."

"All right," was the reply, "tomorrow night at twelve we will be on hand."

The appointed time came. The party assembled, some of them just a little stimulated with old bourbon. Prominent among the party was George Rawle, a man who generally had a hand in everything that was going forward in the town, and was in his normal condition—about two-thirds full of whisky. Picks and shovels were soon procured, and the amateur resurrectionists were quickly on their way to the cemetery.

The grave was found, situated on the extreme edge of the bluff, within a foot or two of a steep declivity stretching down almost into Santa Fe Avenue. Picks and shovels were vigorously plied by willing hands, and the tools soon sounded upon the coffin lid.

The lid was raised at one end; the officious Rawle dropped into the grave, and placing a foot upon each side of the coffin, caught the late-lamented Turpin under the arms, and drew him from his pine overcoat. The grave was shallow, and Rawle, having partially drawn the body out, clambered to the surface of the ground at the head of the grave, embraced the corpse around his chest, and standing with his back to the edge of the bluff, pulled with all his might. Probably owing to the rum he had consumed, Rawle exerted more strength than was necessary, and losing his balance, fell over the cliff and rolled down the declivity with the corpse clasped in his arms. Away they went, first Rawle on top, and then Turpin, halfway down the hill, almost into Santa Fe Avenue, amid a cloud of dust and a storm of flying gravel. Rawle held gallantly onto his unconscious companion, until the strange pair were brought to a halt in a shallow arroyo.

It is a wonder that the shrieks of laughter which came from the party in the cemetery did not arouse the whole town, but, somehow, nobody but the resurrectionists heard the noise, and Rawle and his bosom friend were soon rescued. The examination was made and the demand of science was satisfied. The disemboweled corpse was afterward stolen from the improvised dissecting room, and one of the body-snatchers, who slept on the ground floor, was surprised one morning to see Dick Turpin calmly regarding him through the glass of his curtainless window, the corpse having been placed there during the night by some of his impish companions.

A WASHTUB OF EGGNOG[8]

Again Pueblo, widely known trail town and miners' outfitting point, figures in the high jinks of the Frontier.

The "Greasers," half-breeds, and adventurers from every point of the compass who largely made up the floating population of Pueblo in those early days, if we may accept the local

[8] Frank Hall, *History of Colorado*, III, 452. Retold from the earlier version in *History of the Arkansas Valley, Colorado* (Chicago, 1881), 770.

color sketches by "Tite Barnacle" (General Stevenson) of the *Chieftain*, would have made delightful studies for a Shakespeare delineating his Sir Andrew Ague-cheek and Toby Belch. According to this veteran journalist, doctor, soldier, and raconteur, who indeed, is today chronicler par excellence of Pueblo's "Auld Lang Syne," at this early age the convivial propensities of the people of Pueblo began to crop out in an unmistakable manner.

One day a returning tenderfoot, who had been in the mining regions with a load of "groceries," stopped in the settlement on his way home to Missouri. He had a portion of a barrel of whisky left and offered to sell it to a party of Puebloans. They purchased the liquor, and soon manufactured a washtub full of eggnog. The scene of the revel was in Pat Maywood's blacksmith shop, down by the river bank. The male inhabitants of the town all gathered there and after several fights, many of the revelers were overcome by the bilious compound. An eyewitness gives the closing scene as follows: "One man hung doubled up over the bellows; another sat sound asleep in the tub of water in which the smith cooled his hot irons; a third reposed with his face in the ashes of the forge; a dozen more slept in various positions in the dust of the earthern floor of the shop. But two showed signs of life. In one corner lay the proprietor of the shop and astride his breast sat an individual, afterward a well-known citizen of Pueblo, armed with a funnel and a tin cup and engaged in pouring eggnog down the prostrate man's throat, the victim protesting that he could not drink another drop."

Tradition has it that Jack Allen's whisky was considered by the rougher pioneers of southern Colorado as most excellent, because when drunk it made them feel as if a torchlight procession was galloping down their throats. The nonarrival of freight wagons drawn by patient oxen, in those days, never induced a whisky famine at Jack Allen's, and it was thought his distillery was wherever he happened to be. His fine old handmade, copper-distilled "blue grass dew" was probably manufactured, according to Stevenson, from alcohol, chili-colorow [chilacayote], Arkansas River water, old boots, rusty bayonets, yucca and cactus thorns. It always had the same flavor and startling effect.

OLD JIM BARKER'S FIRST COURT[9]

Legal interpretations west of the Pecos River, as presented by Judge Roy Bean, have become justly famous. No less unique, however, were the methods and premises at law of Justice Jim Barker of Colorado, in the seventies.

Jim Barker, a well-known character of the mountains, whose latchstring hangs out at the head of Blue Lizzard Gulch, was duly elected a justice of the peace for that section of El Paso County, at the September election, and Mike Irving, a companion of Jim's, was empowered to officiate as the executive officer of his court. Last week Jim convened his first court, to hear the complaint of Elder Slater, a traveling missionary, who had caused the arrest of Zimri Bowles, a resident of the foothills, upon the charge of stealing the Elder's one-eyed mule. Zimri had been arrested by Irving, the constable, while in the act of easing the descent of the mule down Mad Gun Mountain, with his lariat fastened to the tail of the animal. The proof against Zimri was conclusive. Accordingly, the Justice, after much legal perplexity of mind, proceeded to sentence Zimri to one year's confinement in the Territorial penitentiary, which sentence he concluded as follows: "An' now, Zim, seeing as I'm about out of things to eat, an' as you will have the cost to pay, I reckon you'd better take a turn among the Foot Hills with your rifle, an' see if you can't pick up some meat before night, as you can't start for the Big Canyon before morning." Which marketing duty was performed by Zim, bringing in one blacktail fawn and a rabbit within the time prescribed as a postscript to the sentence.

On the following morning, the Constable, mounted on his broncho, accompanied by the prisoner astride of the mule which the Elder kindly loaned him, started through the mountains for the penitentiary, where they arrived the second day out, their animals loaded with a deer, two antelopes and a small cinnamon bear, which they sold to the warden of the prison. After dividing the money the Constable proceeded to hand over Zimri on

[9] Reprinted from the *Greeley* (Colorado) *Tribune*, December 1, 1875 in *The Colorado Magazine*, Vol. XIV, No. 6 (November, 1937), 232–34.

the following *mitimus,* which is carefully preserved and may be seen in the possession of the warden:

"To the hed man of the Colorado prison, down at the foot of the Big Canyon on the Arkansas.—Take Notice:—Zimri Bouls, who comes with this here, stole Elder Slater's one-eyed mule, and it was all the mule the Elder had, and I sentenced Zim officially to one year in the Colorado prison, and hated to do it, seein as Zim once stood by me like a man when Injuns had me in a tight place an arter I sentenced Zim to one year for stealing the Elder's mule, my wife, Lizzy, who is a kind o' tender hearted critter, come and leaned her arm on my shoulder, and says she, Father, don't forget the time when Zim, with his rifle, covered our cabin from Granite Mountain, and saved us from the Arapahoes, and Father, I have heard you tell that arter you was wounded at Sand Creek, an helpless, it was Zimri's rifle that halted the Indian that was creeping in the grass to scalp you.' And then there was a tear fell splash upon the sentence I was writing and I changed my mind sudently as follows: seeing the mule had but one eye, an warnt mor'n half a mule at that, you can let Zim go at about six months, an sooner if the Injuns should get ugly, an, furthermore, if the Elder shud quiet down and give in any time, I will pardon him out instanter.

Witness my official hand an seal,

JAMES BARKER, J. P."

The warden, after informing the Constable that he could not receive the prisoner upon the committant offered, proceeded to explain that he should have given a bond in the sum of about three hundred dollars to appear at the district court. Accordingly the Constable withdrew with his prisoner, when it was agreed between them that Zimri should give the Constable his bond for the amount mentioned by the warden. This was accomplished by Zimri subscribing his name to an old replevin bond calling for three hundred dollars, found among the papers transmitted to the Constable by his predecessor. Then, as the Constable intended returning by the way of Piñon Mountain, to examine a bear den where he had seen a couple of cubs playing last spring, he gave the bond to Zimri, to take back to the

Justice. But Zimri, while on his return, traded the three hundred dollar bond to a mountain squatter, just in from Missouri, for a horse, saddle, and bridle, and the prisoner is believed to be, at this time, a dashing hunter on the Plains.

A VISION OF WEALTH[10]

Many an old-time prospector, rebuffed in his search for hidden lodes, sought solace on the land, only to be struck down again by swift and implacable bolts from the blue.

I was mining up Central City way one day, and there come along an old chap with onions to sell. You bet we was glad to get vegetables about then. They were as small and mean onions as you ever saw, but I was bound to have a dozen. He charged me a dollar and a half. Well, sir, I didn't say nothing, but I just allowed that farming must be an everlasting sight better business than mining, and I'd better go into it myself.

So I quit my claim and struck a likely kind of a ranch, hired a Dutchman at one hundred dollars a month to take charge, and I skipped out East for seed. It took a long time then to go and come, and when I come back, first thing I saw was an old fellow ploughing in my field. Then, when I come to the house, I saw someone had jumped that. There was a widow woman from Georgia had moved in and was living there. I sung out that that was all right, and I hoped she'd take her time and make herself quite at home, but that I had sort of an idea that that was my house.

Well, I got things all straightened out, and my vegetables began to come up. And one day Jim Ewell, a sort of marketman, come along and stopped to dinner, and had a cigar on the piazza, and I knew that he was counting the cabbages in one of my fields; and then says he, "Joe, I must have them cabbages," and he offered me $1800 for the lot, and I took him up, and he pulled out a bag of gold dust; but I didn't want it in the house, and I told him to put it in the bank, and give me a check when he liked, and to send for those cabbages any time.

[10] A. A. Hayes, Jr., *New Colorado and the Santa Fe Trail* (New York, 1880), 117–18.

And when he'd gone I sat smoking, and with the fumes of the tobacco came visions of wealth. Why, at that rate, there was $30,000 good in that crop, and I began to feel *tony, tony,* sir, I tell you. And as I kept on smoking, the sun was kind of obscured, and I looked up over Table Mountain, and saw a queer kind of a cloud; and while I was looking, out come the sun, and the air was full of millions of diamond points, just *skintillating, skintillating,* sir, I tell you. And what *was* it? Grasshoppers' wings! And they settled down, some inches deep, on my ranch, and the next day, out of my $30,000 worth, I hadn't one hatful of lettuce that was under glass!

And when I went down to Denver some time afterward, the boys asked me to supper; and they'd put up a job on me, and got a jeweller to help them, and the chairman made a speech, and give me a coat-of-arms, and it wasn't nothing but a *grasshopper rampant.*

"GASSY" THOMPSON UNLOADS SOME WOOD[11]

"Gassy" Thompson was one of those people. While a great many of his mining-camp neighbors might have said that his presence led, in general, to calamity, Colorado mountain life certainly would have been less lively without him.

Empire, March 4, 1886

Editor *Colorado Miner:*

I see the *Tribune-Republican* and Georgetown *Courier* have each had their say about "Gassy" Thompson. I think it about time the big *Miner* should speak its piece. We knew him well here in Empire in pioneer days, and at one time he worked for us on the Tenth Legion lode. He is really the eccentric wag he is represented to be. As proof of it I will give you a sketch of our first introduction to "Gassy."

It was in the fall of 1862, when John H. Adams, my partner, and I were working the Tenth Legion Mine at North, or Empire on the Hill. It was a live little gold camp (as it will be a live big one the coming season). It had two stores, two boarding-

11 "Oddities," *Dawson Scrapbooks,* Vol. II, 59. Clipped from the *Colorado Miner* (Georgetown).

"Gassy" Thompson Unloads on the Roof

houses, and a quartz mill, Isaac W. Vores'. My partner and I batched, as he preferred it, being a good cook. Our men, O. H. Harker, William Cheetly, Park Disbro, and Dick Spring, boarded at the Jones House. Our cabin was in the gulch, partly dug in the ground on the sidehill below the mine, and the road up the mountain ran above and close to our cabin.

About this time "Gassy" appeared unto us with a wagon and yoke of oxen, engaged to haul wood for the mill. One evening we hoisted out the water for the night shift. It ran down into the road and froze just above our cabin. Adams went down to supper, I to sharpen the tools. When I went down John had a fine supper—mountain sheep stew, fried venison, etc. Our cabin was covered with poles, brush and dirt. Just as we sat down to supper, crash came something on top of our cabin, we knew not what, and a wheelbarrow of dirt on our table, spoiling everything. Adams, being rather quick-tempered, ran out around the cabin and saw a man standing in the road and a wagonload of wood on our cabin, wagon on top. John angrily asked the man, who stood in the road with folded arms:

"What in h——l are you doing here?"

The man in the road says: "Keep cool, my friend. In the millionth part of one second we will have this thing all righted. What will you give me for that load of wood on top of your cabin?"

He was so cool about it that it took all the mad out of John, and we helped put the wagon back on the road. When done, "Gassy" says to John: "I will give you that load of wood on your house to pay for spoiling your supper. It will cook many more for you."

That was my first introduction to "Gassy" (George) Thompson. After that he worked for us in the mine; and Harker and Cheetly, both good miners, considered Gassy the best drill striker or hammerman in the territory. We prospected many days together.

The last I heard of "Gassy" was one year ago. He was then in Eagle City, or Murrayville, in the Coeur d'Alene country.

"T. B."

SILVERHEELS[12]

Fairplay, Colorado, today is a mining camp set in the high and surpassingly lovely South Park country of the Rocky Mountains. Still to be heard there is the story of Silverheels, dance-hall girl of the Frontier.

In the early twilight of a winter evening, Senator Charles S. Thomas and I [Edward Ring] took the train to Georgetown for home. As we came down the Clear Creek Valley in a swirling snowstorm, the Senator told me this story.

Silverheels is the name of a mountain near Fairplay. Not so high as the surrounding peaks, but its crest is always covered with snow. Against the sapphire sky of summer it is a picture.

The belle of Bill Buck's dance hall wore silver slippers. She bound a fillet of silver around her dark hair. Then men called her Silverheels.

She was Bill's girl. One New Year's Eve he developed pneumonia—almost certain death in the mountains. After a few hours of pain and delirium he died in the girl's arms.

Then followed the worst winter Fairplay ever knew. The pneumonia spread—a frightful epidemic. The dance halls were closed and the saloons all but deserted. Many mines shut down. The doctors worked without rest and sent to Denver for nurses who were badly needed. Only one or two came. The danger was too great.

Silverheels was not a good girl but she was a brave one. Through the long, dark weeks she went from cabin to cabin and ministered to the suffering. She held the hand of more than one stalwart miner as he crossed the range. Her bosom was the dying pillow of more than one little child.

In April, when the sun fought its rays through the gray clouds, the scourge passed. Fairplay, in its brief career, had known its millionaires, its badmen, wild women, great figures of tragedy and romance. Now it had its heroine.

The town felt that something should be done for Silverheels. It made up a purse—four thousand dollars. When Senator Wol-

[12] Edward Ring, "Silverheels," *The Colorado Magazine*, Vol. XVII, No. 1 (January, 1940), 27.

cott came up from Denver and heard the story, he raised it to five.

The presentation was entrusted to a committee. Then the unexpected happened. They could not find Silverheels. She had gone, nobody knew where. At the post office she left no forwarding address. Some thought she was in San Francisco, or Australia, or the Orient. She never came back.

The fund was returned to its donors and Fairplay did the next best thing. It named its beautiful mountain "Silverheels." At dawn and at sunset the glorious white summit soars to the Colorado sky and commemorates the heroism of the wanderer who knows not that it bears her name.

REAL ESTATE AND POLITICS[13]

Far to the east of the mountain camps, in the general territory of Old Granada, politicians and real-estate agents often were to be seen cruising the land in their buckboards. These gentlemen, it is said, eventually issued bonds against—or sold at considerable profit—every buffalo wallow and cactus patch on the Plains.

Colorado has a wise law in regard to voting bonds for public improvements, but like all laws there is a way of getting around them. There was the chance that old Bent County would be divided into several new counties by the coming legislature, and Las Animas, the county seat, suddenly awoke to the realization that a new courthouse would be most desirable, so if they wanted all Bent County to share the expense it was time to act, and a bond proposition was proposed.

Under the law at that time only those who paid taxes the preceding year could vote. There were not a dozen legal taxpayers in the eastern part of the county, and very few elsewhere. That could be easily overcome by paying taxes on a saddle or broncho and dating the receipt back to the preceding year. In the eyes of the promoters that did not constitute an illegal act, or even involve moral turpitude, considering the end to be

[13] From a typescript belonging to the State Historical Society of Colorado of an interview with an old resident of Prowers County, Colorado. WPA Document 355, 192–94, 200.

achieved, for the owner of the saddle or broncho had always intended paying his taxes, he had felt it a duty he owed the community, but in the stress of other things he had not gotten around to it, but now that Las Animas philanthropists offered to pay the tax it would be nothing more than courtesy to vote for the bonds.

Of course under these circumstances a limited amount in bonds was voted. It was such a modest sum that the people congratulated themselves in getting a brand new courthouse on such reasonable terms, until it was discovered that when a public improvement was begun under a bond issue, which was afterward found to be too small to complete the job, the county commissioners could appropriate enough money to complete the work and levy a tax to meet it. This lack of money occurred so often, so many unlooked for expenses arising, that finally the appropriations amounted to three or four times the amount of the original bond issue.

These things perhaps worried the commissioners, especially as the building did not seem to be worth half of what it was costing. Oh well, they were doing their best; some of the boys had to be taken care of, even if it was at the expense of the taxpayer. One of the large items of expense was the cornerstone, upon which was to be engraved the names of the county commissioners and the date. The artist who carved that stone happened to spell the word "commissioners" with but one "m." Basing an estimate upon the number of letters on the stone, this gave an editor the opportunity of telling how much the taxpayers had saved because of bad spelling.

Connected with all real-estate firms was the land locator, whose duty it was to take the prospective homesteader to a piece of government land that was still open to settlement. His task seemed an impossible one to the settler; here was a county without landmarks of any kind, a great level plain, where at the rim sky and land seemed to meet and blend. But the locator never made a mistake; starting from a government range and township marker, he would tie a rag to his buggy wheel, and every revolution of the wheel meant so many feet to the mile.

While keeping account he was expected to carry on a conversation with the settler, telling him of soil, climate, and picturing to him the wealth that would flow into his pockets once he possessed the land. Generally they were honest and pointed out the exact land; however, there was one locator who got into the habit of showing one particular quarter of land which he claimed was open to tree claim entry, and then make out the papers on land miles and miles away, the deception only being discovered when the entryman appeared to do the necessary tree planting.

TRAIL TOWN[14]

East of Old Granada, on the Arkansas River, lay Dodge City —onetime "Cowboy Capital of the West." In the seventies Dodge was riding high, playing host to boomers, cattlemen, and gun fighters from the Rio Grande to the Musselshell.

As we approached Dodge City there were buffalo bones piled up along the track for miles; the heads all in one pile and the bones in another. About noon we arrived at Dodge City and I got my first sight of a wild Western town. The town was built like most Western towns on one street facing the railroad on the north side.

Our first work was to unload the outfit which had been shipped by freight. It consisted of about eight wagons and necessary supplies for the trip, five two-wheeled carts and about forty work oxen. After unloading the outfit the camp was made on the south side of the Arkansas River, just south of town.

After we got camp established we started out to see the town. First on the east side of the block was the Dodge House, run by Cox and Boyd. Then came a saloon or two, and then the mercantile establishment of Charles Wrath, who sold the buffalo hunters their supplies and bought the buffalo hides. The vacant lots adjoining were covered with buffalo hides piled up six or eight feet high and tied down to keep the winds from blowing them away. Next to Wrath's store came more saloons and dance halls.

[14] John P. Dickinson, "On a Government Survey in the Early '70s," *The Trail*, Vol. X, No. 7 (December, 1917), 14–16.

The first place I stepped into I met an old friend, Jake Schaefer, who afterwards became the great billiard player. He was from Leavenworth, and, along with another Leavenworth boy, Charlie Rownon, had started a saloon in Dodge. I walked up and ordered a glass of beer which he set out. It had been on tap some days. I laid down ten cents on the bar just as if I was used to paying ten cents for beer. He pushed the dime back to me saying, "This is on me. All drinks are twenty-five cents here." Then I knew I was in the West.

I walked down the street and went into another place larger and finer than Schaefer's. This place was run by the mayor of the town, named Kelley, who was commonly called "Dog" Kelley, as he kept a pack of greyhounds and at that time had twenty-eight of them. He was a tall, slender man, wore a pair of high-top boots, good trousers, a blue shirt, a large white hat, a red sash tied around his waist, and a silk handkerchief around his neck. This was the "full dress suit" for men of standing in Dodge....

It was pretty quiet in the daytime but as soon as night came on the music commenced. Chalk Beeson, who afterwards helped to organize the original famous Cowboy Band, was playing the violin in one of the dance halls. As soon as the music commenced the buffalo hunters and ladies would show up and the dance would be on. There were no waltzes, turkey trots, two steps or anything of that nature in those days; just plain old-fashioned square dances—"right and left through" and "swing your partner and balance up to the bar." Treat your partner, and as that took fifty cents each time our boys, who were nearly all broke, did not do much dancing. I was looking on, my eyes wide open taking in everything. Here was surely the wild West. I noticed one man in particular; he was over six feet tall and would weigh over two hundred pounds, well built and well dressed. He seemed to be a favorite with the ladies. I asked an old buffalo hunter who he was. He told me they called him "Hurricane Bill." Here was what I had been looking for—a genuine "badman," one of the kind I had read about; one who would "eat 'em alive." The old buffalo hunter said "He is all right; he won't hurt anyone but it ain't safe to pick a row with him."

184

I soon had all the prominent men of the town tabulated in my mind. I was surprised not to see any shooting or anyone killed. I had supposed that I would see a killing the first day; so I asked the old buffalo hunter if these men never killed anybody. He replied "No, not often, if they attend to their own business." Then he added "You need not be afraid of that kind of a man, but look out for a kid or a fool with a gun." In my life in the West of over forty years, I have never heard a truer saying.

One evening one of our men, named Ferrill, got pretty well enthused and noisy and wanted to whip one of the notables. He thought he would commence on one of the most prominent men; then if he came out first best he would establish a reputation as being the worst man in Dodge. But he did not get very far; the so-called badman simply put his arm around him, took his gun and called some of his friends. They put two ropes around Ferrill—not around his neck, but around his body, and pulled them both ways, led him down to the Santa Fe water tank and let about two tons of water down on him. This took all the fight out of Ferrill. He never went back to the dance hall.

Another night I saw a man come in, a stranger he seemed to be, long-haired and wild-eyed. He carried a Springfield rifle in his hand and commenced to keep time with the music pounding the butt of the rifle on the floor. One of the leaders walked up to him, when he started to raise the gun, but he did not get very far, and before he knew it he was on his back with his gun gone. Not being hurt he wanted to fight. He jumped up and wanted to whip the whole crowd; said he was a half-breed Cheyenne Indian and would bring his band in and burn the town. One fellow walked up and gave him a shove, and then another, and by the time the boys got through with him all the fight was taken out of him.

Chapter

Open Range

BEYOND the rolling country of middle America the land rises in an undulating line, like a wave-formed shelf, to the long escarpment of the Rocky Mountains. With a gradualness which takes the traveler often by surprise, changes occur, the earth broadening, skies widening and becoming bluer, clouds, borne on by steady currents, showing a new kind of bigness and whiteness. Old villages, with their courthouse squares and elm-lined streets, are left behind and Plains towns come to view, clinging stubbornly to their places on the land. Hardwood plots and well-plowed fields, so numerous in the eastern valleys, give way to prairie short-grass. Sand hills drift out from sprawling, shallow rivers. Timber all but disappears; sentinel buttes, mesas, and vermilion cliffs lift unexpectedly from cap-rock breaks; and cactus, Spanish bayonet, and sage spread far beneath the blue.

In emigrant days this vast, flat space was looked upon in dread, as the great interior desert of America, lonely, desolate, incapable of sustaining decent human existence. Today, though seemingly as wide and empty as before, it teems with secret life. This is cow country, home of windmill and water tank, of ranch house, cedar corral, and bawling white-faced cattle. Long before its trails became the transcontinental highways of the present, stockmen noted its succulent grasses, on which massed herds of buffalo had grazed for untold lengths of time, and found its hidden dripping springs and canyon shade. Here, in pockets offering privacy as well as shelter from the coursing prairie storms, these stockmen settled. Here for eighty years they have lived hardily, riding long hours, expanding their holdings, and improving equipment, always essaying the new but preserving too, in a day of fences, power machinery, and crisscrossing county roads, old cow-country customs and the lore and tales of the American range.

186

Open Range

Thompson H. Richardson knew the cattle country. His reminiscences picture not only rangeland comedy and tragedy, but the monotony and sharp periods of hardship which every cowpuncher endured.

This was a wonderful stock country then [Wyoming in the late eighties]. It was all one big, open pasture, with a luxuriant growth of grass, and water in nearly every draw. There were droves of cattle everywhere, it seemed, in the little valleys and scattered all over the hills. Many big outfits ran cattle over the far-flung range, that as yet knew very few fences. One of the largest outfits was the Union Cattle Company, that was formed by the merger of three big ranches, the S&G, the Bridle Bit, and the 7 OS.

On the fourth day of May [1887], I went to work for the Union Company. My first job with the outfit was far from the exciting life that I had pictured. Some of us younger men were detailed to roll wire in the mud. If there is one thing a cowhand hates, it is riding or making any kind of fence. We loafed on the job until the boss came and gave us "thunder." He sent us to the bunkhouse and we thought sure we were going to get our time, but instead he just gave us another good "bawling out" and said, "Now go on back and do as d—— little as possible." Well, we finally managed to get the fence fixed, and on the tenth day of May the big roundup started.

Every year, about eight outfits met on Hat Creek at the Bar T Ranch [The American Cattle Company]. The LAK, the AU 7, the YT, the Z Bell, and Union all met there and "reps" from the Bar ES and 101 also arrived. Each outfit had two wagons and about sixteen men apiece, and each man had a string of about eight horses. Altogether there were between eighty-five and one hundred and ten men employed. We worked up the Cheyenne River to the AU 7 and cut across to where Newcastle now stands; crossed over Mush Creek and Alkali Creek and back down the east side of the old S&G Ranch. There we

[1] From an interview with Thomas H. Richardson, of Custer, South Dakota, by a Wyoming worker in the WPA Writers' Project.

split up and each company went separately to work out the smaller territories.

The old hands were detailed to take groups of four to eight men and ride circle, combing the country thoroughly for cattle. Every bunch of cattle that was brought in was held separately on the roundup ground near the camp. On an average, one circle would bring in about a thousand head a day. All cattle found off their range belonging to any of those companies had to be held in a day herd, and there were eight separate day herds. The reps cut out and held in separate herds all cattle belonging to their outfits, and the calves had to be branded the same as their mothers. These herds had to be night guarded, of course, and this meant work and plenty of it.

We ate breakfast at daylight, which in May and June is about three o'clock. Then we had to saddle up and work all day long, branding and separating cattle. We all had to take turns standing night guard of two-hour periods each. Many a time we got to sleep only four hours unless we stole a little nap on guard, and we didn't dare let the boss catch us snoozing on duty. And talk about rodeos! We had one every morning while on the general roundup. It took a good hour to saddle up and prepare for the day's ride. When about eighty men are busy saddling up half-broken horses there is bound to be some excitement. Many of the boys were thrown from their bronchs and other hands had to run down the horses that got away and rope and bring them back. Some had to stop and fix their saddles, others had to go to their "war sacks" [bags in which they carried clothes and all kinds of paraphernalia] to get saddle strings, flank cinches, etc.

One morning my horse threw me and took off across the prairie, bucking for all he was worth. My stirrups were flying in the air, and some cowboy threw his lariat and caught my stirrup, right up close to the saddle, ripping the strap loose. Such instances were common, and very often a bunch of us had to get together and do some repair work, while the rest would be halfway to the head of the creek on circle.

Sometimes we ate dinner at ten o'clock, sometimes at two. Supper was generally at four and right after supper we went to bed, if we didn't have to stand first watch on night guard. The only recreation the men got, while on the roundup, was card playing, and they didn't get much time for that. Some of them snatched a few games between circles.

"Old Ginger," so called because he was redheaded and bad tempered, was the cook of the Bar ES. The boys loved to pester him because he flew into such terrible rages. They would make some remark about his cooking, and then Ginger would take after them with a butcher knife and run them around the mess wagon. He had a deck of cards and was continually persuading the boys to play monte with him, and of course he always fleeced them good and proper. He kept his winnings on the top shelf of the mess box and anybody that came near the box was in danger of getting carved; so the money was about as safe as in the bank, or so Ginger thought.

One time a big, tough fellow by the name of Mizzou joined the outfit. Every time he got a chance, he played monte with Ginger, and of course the old cook won every time. It looked as though Ginger had taken in all of Mizzou's money, for there was a big pile of bills on his side of the blanket, when suddenly the cowboy jumped up and pulled his six-shooter. He shot into that pile of money and blew it all to pieces. Ginger was pretty much surprised and scared at that, and he made a run for the wagon with Mizzou right after him. Mizzou said, "You get up there and hand me out the dough from that mess box. Be dam quick about it too." To hurry things along he began prodding Ginger in the ribs with his six-shooter. Ginger was trying to climb the wagon wheel, but he was so scared that he kept slipping off. "Well, dam it!" he shouted, as Mizzou kept poking him with the gun, "Can't you see I'm hurrying?" He took a bag full of money out of the mess box and handed it to Mizzou, who promptly pocketed it and proceeded to shake the dust of the camp from his heels.

Of course there was always plenty of excitement right in the line of duty, and the boys didn't have to go to town looking for any while the roundup was on.

After the general roundup that summer of '87, our horses being all ridden down, a new string was brought in for us. These new horses had been brought from the Goshen Hole near Cheyenne, and were supposed to be broken, but they had only been ridden a little the year before. We drove them within seven miles of Dewey, in sight of Elk Mountain on ground now owned by myself. Here we selected our bronchs and prepared to break them. The boss asked us to choose our own horses, so he would not be responsible for broken bones and necks. We went into the "cavvy" and picked out our horses until each man had six mounts.

The next morning an old cowhand by the name of Soaper was up before anyone else. He had selected a nice brown horse with a white blaze in its face, and he woke the rest of us talking to the cook about the horse. He says to the cook, "Don't you think he has a good sensible head on him?" We got up laughing, ate breakfast and prepared to saddle our new mounts. Of course we all had some trouble, but Soaper had the most of all with that horse that "had such a good, sensible head." Every time he went to set foot in the stirrup, the horse reared and fell over backwards and every time he fell over Soaper got a little paler. I was having a good deal of trouble with my horse, too. It took two men to help me bridle him and we tied his front feet together, and yet he lunged around over the prairie dragging us with him. Finally I managed to get mounted and still Soaper was on the ground. Then we all went to roasting Soaper, telling him that only about twenty men were waiting on him and his sensible horse. The horse fell over about five times, and Soaper was getting more and more scared, but he decided that he had to ride that horse or lose face in front of the whole outfit. When he did mount, of course the horse keeled over on him and then got up and ran while Soaper just lay there, "plumb knocked out." One hand that was an exceptionally good man with horses caught the bronch and gave him a workout, that took some of the "orneriness" out of him. Then Soaper came to and got on the horse and rode him all afternoon.

He didn't ride him again for quite a while until the boss asked him what he had done with his horse that was so sensible looking. Soaper said, "I'm jest a-goin' to ride him today." He caught and saddled the horse and tied him to the wheel of a big bed wagon, and then went to breakfast. The boss had ordered some young tenderfoot to grease the wagons the afternoon before, and the tenderfoot had forgotten to put the bur of that particular wheel back on. While breakfast was going on, something "goosed" Soaper's horse. He reared back, jerking the wheel off the wagon and went down through the sagebrush with the wheel hitting the high spots behind him. Well, of course that caused a lot of fun and we razzed Soaper again about his sensible horse. Something like that was always going on.

When the roundup camps moved, it was a wonderful sight. The great herds of cattle and cavvys of horses spread out over the prairie for miles. The roundup cooks jumped in their wagons and raced each other for the best camping grounds. They wanted to get under trees, near to the water as possible.

For one thing we always had plenty of good, wholesome food and hot coffee. All cooking was done over the coals in big dutch ovens, and no better method of cooking has ever yet been devised. Huge coffeepots stood full of hot coffee nearly all the time. Our meat was the best to be had. Every day a fat yearling heifer was selected from the herd and brought up near the cook wagon. She was killed and skinned right there and only the hind quarters were used. When the boys got hungry between meals, they would take the ribs and roast them over campfires, then stand around gnawing on those bones.

The old-time cowhand had to be alert every minute, for emergencies were continually arising, and those who weren't equal to the situation or who hung back either lost their lives or were looked upon as "tenderfeet." We worked and the rain never poured down too hard, the gumbo never got too slippery, or the blizzard too fierce to stop our work. The floods never raised the waters too high, but that we were supposed to cross in the line of duty.

It really rained in those days. We wore our slickers and rode in a downpour most of the time. The ground was sodden with moisture and ever so often floods came down the creeks and turned them into raging rivers. I recollect when a flood came down Beaver Creek, when we were working near where Dewey is now. Our herd of cattle was on the other side of the stream and we had to cross to get to them. We were swimming our horses across and one big, young puncher failed to make it. As his horse made a desperate leap to climb the bank, its legs sank so deep in the soft sand and mud that it fell over backwards. The saddle horn struck the boy in the stomach, knocking him breathless. The horse drifted down the stream without a rider. We saw the cowboy's hat come up above the water several times, but we could not see him. His hat was tied on with a small gee string, but no one seemed to know that; and in spite of all the cowboys gathered there as eyewitnesses to the scene, that boy lost his life. On account of the water being so swift and muddy, we never saw his body until it drifted out to where the current was more shallow.

COWPOKE[2]

Like Thomas H. Richardson, Adelbert H. Whaite was an old-timer to whom the passage of years, in itself, meant little. He retained to the last his impressions of the Western range country and his enthusiasm for the life which, as a young man, he had led there.

When I first started out to ride the range I was only a kid, in fact I was known everywhere as "The Kid." It was a free life to me and I wanted free air. My mother could not see it in that light. In her point of view the rough cowpunchers were not good for my morals nor the Indians good for my health, but my father thought that I had better go and get the idea out of my system; so with his help, I won the day. Gee! but I was glad to be able to go! It was a great day when we set off.

"Stay with her! Johnny! Stay with her! Darn her wild soul!" sang out a dozen fellows, gathered to see us depart for the roundup on a beautiful spring morning. The old mare went pitching off down Tejon Street, in Colorado Springs, scattering the blankets all along the way. She didn't seem to take kindly to the pack and before we could make fast the diamond hitch she made a break to get away. "Johnny" held on to the rope for dear life while Frank jumped on his "Barney" horse and gave

[2] Adelbert H. Whaite, "Rambling Reminiscences of an Old Cowboy," *The Trail*, Vol. IV, No. 8 (January, 1912), 9–14.

chase. He let down his rope as he ran and when he began to swing it around his head, in full sight of the old mare, she stopped her flight at once, for she had been brought up short many times before by a rope around her neck and she was not taking any chances.

We started off across the country for Las Animas, where the big spring roundup began. We struck the Arkansas River at Rocky Ford, which town, a number of years later, became famous all over the United States for the fine cantaloupes raised there. We arrived at Las Animas and after several days of preparation loading up the chuck wagon with grub and reserves and grain for the horses, the cowmen all came together on horseback and elected an *"El Capitán."* As the great outfit got under way and moved off to cover the first day's roundup it made a sight never to be forgotten.

I was detailed with the bunch that worked up the Apishapa and down the Purgatoire. I had fine *caballos* [horses] to ride now, and just as many were assigned to me as to the older punchers, so I was feeling very "chesty." My brand-new outfit was a sad giveaway, however, and the boys all guyed me for a tenderfoot. The second night out we camped in an arroyo and I foolishly made my bed in the bottoms. A great rush of water came tearing down about midnight and we had a job saving my outfit. I lost my fine new bearskin chaps and got soaked through as well. The boys all allowed the Kid would hunt the high places after that, and you can bet I did. Anyway, I ceased to be the punt for their jests, which was a great consolation for the loss of my chaps.

Cowpunching was glorious work for me; all day long in the saddle, with some night herding along with it, in all sorts of weather. All days were the same to us—we forgot their names and the calendar was no part of our lives. The work was hard but more or less exciting and the hours were long. We turned in with the chickens and got up with the cows.

My favorite "bronch" was a small bay horse, with a blazed face and side stockings, which the punchers had dubbed "Potatoes." This was on account of the many sacks of potatoes I had won with him in horse races with emigrants passing through the country, who were well supplied with that article. He was the fastest quarter-horse I ever saw and the best cow dodger in the camp. I always discarded the heavy saddle before a race, and have often ridden him with nothing but a hobble rope. He was never beaten in a quarter-mile run while I owned him.

We were camped two nights near the little Mexican settlement of Tuien Mesa, where we attended a Mexican fandango. All the cowpunchers came arrayed in their best outfits, from six-shooters to spurs. The dance was given in a large adobe building, built to store wool; long wooden benches extended along each of the two sides of the wall and a Mexican orchestra with guitars, mandolins and shells, was stationed at the end opposite the entrance. There were no introductions made—you simply made a beeline for the senorita you might pick out, beating the other fellow to it. A side door opened into a saloon and the trail thereto was kept hot by the cowboys "lickering up" on Mexican gin, which was displayed in a row of flat bottles with the picture of a large red rooster on the labels. It had the desired effect, too, as they were soon crowing and singing with the music.

When they danced the quadrille the cowboys stayed out, as Old Tex had cautioned—"you boys jest anti and stay out!" The Mexicans were a motley looking bunch, in their different costumes; some wore shoes much too large for them, but they were all graceful in limb and in pose of body. Nowhere on earth do they dance the quadrille with more grace than among the Mexicans. In the first rush for partners I beat out a Mexican boy to the best looking senorita in the bunch and I repeated this several times. After the first waltz she helped me cut the "Mex" out, saying *amigo* [friend], to which I would answer *bueno* [good]. She could not talk American nor I Mexican, but we had a jolly good time, nevertheless, which, however, came near being my undoing. While I was leaving, her lover made a wicked lunge at me with a knife and but for the quickness of Frank, who rode the "Johnny" horse, old Tex "allowed the Kid was d——n near cut out hisself."

We moved camp the next day near to a big sheep ranch, close to the canyon of the Purgatoire, where the country is very broken, with a large growth of piñon trees and the finest of feed—buffalo grass. We were very much surprised to find snow on the ground next morning. There was snow and sleet for the next two days, the second and third days of June. The old Scotch-American sheepman had just finished his shearing and he lost eight hundred head of sheep in the storm, mostly jammed to death while crowding together in the corral. All this naturally put the sheepman in a bad temper and, on learning that one of his Mexican herders was engaged in "rushing" sheep over the canyon to a brother, he became furious and started out to look for that herder. A few of us, with the day herd, saw him come up with his herder, who was in the act of lowering a sheep down with a rope. The sheepman lifted the startled Mexican high in the air and threw him down the chasm on the rocks, over two hundred feet below, breaking every bone in his body. The public sentiment was with the sheepman, he had acted according to the law of the land, and the Mexicans said among themselves "*el se ha matado*" [he killed himself]. On the day following, with the sun shining brightly and all the earth seemingly glad, we soon forgot the tragedy of the sheepherder and the snowstorm as well.

The next day while running a steer out of the piñons, my pony making every turn with me lying flat on his back to avoid the low limbs, my red bandana, which was tied loosely around my neck, caught in a branch and jerked me to the ground. Old Tex swung from his horse and somehow got the breath of life back into me, then stood, shaking his grizzled head. After several efforts Old Tex got me on his horse and led him back to camp, as he would not stand for a double load. Tex was sure I would never go home in the saddle.

A few nights ago at the theater I overheard a lady ask why the cowboys always wore those red bandanas around their necks, hanging down their shirt fronts, and the man with her replied that it was done for show. A great many people, I presume, think we wore them for ornaments, as an Indian would a string of beads. The truth is that we wore them to protect our lips and noses from the alkali dust, which was something fierce when driving cattle. Hanging loosely about our necks they were always available and were easily thrown up over our mouth and nose.

Old Tex was a great entertainer with his stories around the campfire. His flights of imagination were something wonderful to hear. The length of his years of experience on the range marvelous, indeed! We boys kept tab on him until we had him, one night before our campfire of cowboys, making statements which, if true, would make him to be at the ripe age of ninety-eight years. Then we lit into him and howled ourselves hoarse. But it never fazed Tex; he just took his old pipe out of his mouth slowly and remarked, "Well, I never exactly knowed, for sure, what year I was born, and that's God-Almighty's truth."

A gun with a belt full of cartridges was considered too cumbersome to tote and was strapped to the pommel of the saddle, with the rope or lariat on the opposite side. When camped near a town we always went into the place with guns carried at the hip (not half way down the leg) and looking very important. It used to remind me of the poor old stage horses plodding along the trail and at the outskirts of the town the driver gathered up his reins and his "six" swings up to the hotel at a canter. Sometimes those guns of ours and forty-rod whisky would mix badly.

A bunch of us rode into a small town one night and stopped at a saloon. The building was a typical Western one, made of logs with a very imposing front—glass windows and doors. On a large piece of canvas tacked on the front was painted "The Alhambra." Inside, over the bar, a sign read "*Cervesa, uno peso*" (beer, one dollar a bottle), and "*aguardiente*" (two-bits a drink).

The man who ran the place was called "Cackling Hank," on account of his squeaky voice. A few rounds of his "tanglefoot" put us all in a hilarious mood. We discovered a man sleeping off a drunk. One of our crowd, "Big Tex," said no man could sleep in the presence of such congenial company. "Who is your amigo," asked Tex of Hank. "I allow he be a sheepherder," said Hank. We were about to throw him out bodily, for a sheepherder was the "red flag" that roused the fighting blood of cowpunchers. "Vamose," shouted Tex to the bunch. "I got my rope on him; no gun play in this biz."

We were certainly surprised, as Tex had no love for a sheep-herder. But Tex got busy, and cutting several notches in a cork which he procured from Hank, he stuck in several sulphur matches and placed them under the herder's nose. Then he lit the matches and we all yelled, "Fire!" "Fire!"

The way that herder got out of there was surprising, and no record made as to the order of his going. Some "fool killer" emphasized his enthusiasm by taking a shot at the disappearing herder, which started the "gun talk." The bar looked like a Carrie Nation raid when the smoke cleared away, with Cackling Hank peeping out of his ice box and yelling, "For God's sake, don't shoot; you'll kill all my family." (They were living over the saloon). The shooting was over, however, for no one had a cartridge left. So we mounted our cayuses and rode away like a bunch of Comanche Indians.

Next day "Blue Nose" Sawyer, who hailed from Boston, took up a collection among the two hundred cowpunchers to compensate Cackling Hank for the raid of the dozen miscreants. The collection was in I.O.U.'s, which was the cowpuncher's medium of exchange. A hundred and fifty dollars was turned over to Cackling Hank, who took it to the general store and got his money or its equivalent. The store charged the I.O.U.'s to each cattle company the puncher was working for and the company held it out of the puncher's pay in the fall, after the roundup season was over.

STAMPEDE[3]

"The boys all got to talking about stampedes one night while we were waiting on a sidetrack, and I related to them an experience of my own." So Frank Benton, Wyoming cowpoke who one day stumbled onto a pen and some ink, introduces his version of a night run with the longhorns.

A number of years ago, I bought some 15,000 steers in southern Arizona, and shipping them to Denver, Colorado, divided them up into herds of about 3,500 head in each herd and started to trail these herds north to Wyoming. About 4,000 head of

[3] Frank Benton, *Cowboy Life on the Sidetrack* (Denver, 1903), 99–108.

these steers were from four to ten years old and were known as outlaws in the country where they were raised. These steers were almost as wild as elk; very tall, thin, rawboned, high-headed, with enormous horns and long tails, and as there was great danger of their stampeding at any time, I put all of them in a herd by themselves and went with that herd myself. I worried about these steers night and day, and talked to my men incessantly about how to handle them and what to do if the cattle stampeded. There is only one thing to do in case of a stampede of a herd of wild range steers, and that is for every cowboy to get in the lead of them with a good horse and keep in the lead without trying to stop them, but gradually turn them and get them to running in a circle, or "milling" as it is commonly known among cowboys. Cattle on the trail never stampede but one way, and that is back the way they come from. If you can succeed in turning them in some other direction, you can gradually bring them to a stop. These long-legged range steers can run almost as fast as the swiftest horse.

So we kept our best and swiftest horses saddled all night, ready to spring onto in case the herd ever got started. We were driving in a northerly direction all the time, and every night took the herd fully a mile north of the mess wagon camp before we bedded them down. I had fourteen men in the outfit, half of them old-time cowboys and the other half would-be-cowboys; several of them what we used to call tenderfeet.

Amongst the green lads at trailing cattle was the nephew of my eastern partner, a college-bred boy, with blonde, curly hair and a face as merry as a girl's at a May Day picnic. The boys all called him Curley. He was as lovable a lad as I ever met, but positively refused to take this enormous herd of old, outlaw, long-horned steers as a serious proposition.

We had always four men on night herd at a time, each gang standing night guard three hours, when they were relieved by another four men. The first gang was eight to eleven o'clock in the evening, the next eleven till two, and the last guard stood from two till daylight and then started the herd traveling north again. I kept two old cowhands and two green ones on each guard, and had been nine days on the trail; had traveled about a hundred miles without any mishap. We had bright moonlight nights. The grass was fine, being about the first of June, and I was beginning to feel a little easier, when one night we were camped on a high rolling prairie near the Wyoming line.

Curley and three other men had just gone on guard at two o'clock in the morning. The moon was shining bright as day. Everything was as still as could be, the old long-horned outlaws all lying down sleeping, probably dreaming of the cactus-covered hillsides in their old home in Arizona. Curley was on the north side of the herd and rolling a cigarette. He forgot my oft-repeated injunction not to light a parlor match around the herd in the night, but scratched one on his saddle horn. When the match popped, there was a roar like an earthquake and the herd was gone in the wink of an eyelid; just two minutes from the time that Curley scratched his match, that wild, crazy avalanche of cattle was running over that camp outfit, two and three deep. But at that first roar, I was out of my blankets, running for my hoss and hollering, "Come on, boys!" with a rising inflection on "boys." The old hands knew what was coming and were on their horses soon as I was, but the tenderfeet stampeded their own horses trying to get onto them, and their hosses all got away except two, and when their riders finally got on them, they took across the hills as fast as they could go out of the way of that horde of oncoming wild-eyed demons. The men who lost their hosses crawled under the front end of the big heavy roundup wagon, and for a wonder the herd didn't overturn the wagon, although lots of them broke their horns on it and some broke their legs. When I lit in the saddle, and looked around, five of my cowboys were lined up side of me, their hosses jumping and snorting, for them old cow hosses scented the danger and I only had time to say, "Keep cool; hold your hosses' heads high, boys, and keep two hundred yards ahead of the cattle for at least five miles. If your hoss gives out try to get off to one side," and then that earthquake (as one of the tenderfeet called it when he first woke up) was at our heels, and we were riding for our own lives as well as to stop the cattle, because if a hoss stumbled or stepped in a badger hole there wouldn't be even a semblance of his rider left after those thousands of hoofs had got through pounding him. I was riding a Blackhawk Morgan hoss with wonderful speed and endurance and very sure-footed, which was the main thing, and I allowed the herd to get up in a hundred yards of me, and seeing the country was comparatively smooth ahead of me, I turned in my saddle and looked back at the cattle.

I had been in stampedes before, but nothing like this. The cattle were running their best, all the cripples and drags in the lead, their sore feet forgotten. Every steer had his long tail in the air, and those four thousand waving tails made me think of a sudden whirlwind in a forest of young timber. Once in a while I could see a little ripple in the sea of shining backs, and I knew a steer had stumbled and gone down and his fellows had tramped him into mincemeat as they went over him. They were constantly breaking one another's big horns as they clashed and crowded together, and I could hear their horns striking and breaking above the roar of the thousands of hoofs on the hard ground.

As my eyes moved over the herd and to one side, I caught sight of a rider on a grey hoss, using whip and spur, trying to get ahead of the cattle, and I knew at a glance it was Curley, as none of the other boys had a grey hoss that night. I could see he was slowly forging ahead and getting nearer the lead of the cattle all the time.

We had gone about ten or twelve miles and had left the smooth, rolling prairie behind us and were thundering down the divide on to the broken country along Crow Creek. Now, cattle on a stampede all follow the leaders, and after I and my half dozen cowboys had ridden in the lead of that herd for twelve or fifteen miles, gradually letting the cattle get close to us but none by us, why we were the leaders, and when we began to strike that rough ground, my cowboys gradually veered to the left, so as to lead the herd away from the creek and onto the divide again. But Curley was on the left side of the herd. None of the other boys had noticed him, and when the herd began to swerve to the left, it put him on the inside of a quarter moon of rushing, roaring cattle. I hollered and screamed to my men, but in that awful roar could hardly hear my own voice, let alone make my men hear me, and just then we went down into a steep gulch and up the other side. I saw the hind end of the herd sweep across from their course of the quarter circle towards the leaders, saw the grey hoss and Curley go over the bank of the gulch out of sight amidst hordes of struggling animals. But as I looked back at the cattle swarming up the other bank I looked in vain for that grey hoss and his curly-haired rider. Sick at heart, I thought of what was lying in the bottom of that gulch in place of the sunny-haired boy my partner had sent out to me, and I wished that eighty thousand dollars worth of hides, horns, and hoofs that was still thundering on behind was back in the cactus forests of Arizona.

As the herd swung out on the divide they split in two, part of them turning to the left, making a circle of about two miles, myself and two cowboys heading this part of the herd and keeping them running in a smaller circle all the time till they stopped. The other part of the herd kept on for about five miles further, then they split in two, and the cowboys divided and finally got both bunches stopped; not, however, till one bunch had gone about ten miles beyond where I had got the first herd quieted.

It was now broad daylight, and I started back to the gulch where poor Curley had disappeared. When I came in sight of the gulch, I saw his dead hoss, trampled into an unrecognizable mass, lying in the bottom of the gulch, but could see nothing of Curley. While gazing up and down the gulch which was overhung with rocks in places, I heard someone whistling a tune, and looking in that direction, saw Curley with his back to me, perched on a rock whistling as merry as a bird.

He told me that as his hoss tumbled over the rock bank, he fell into a crevice, and crawling back under the rocks, he watched the procession go over him.

We were three days getting the cattle back to where they had started and two hundred of them were dead or had to be shot, and hundreds of their horns broken off and hanging by slivers. It had cost in dead cattle and damage to the living at least $10,000. But I was so glad to get that curley-headed scamp back alive and unhurt I never said a word to him.

TRAIL CAMP[4]

Although Hamer Norris, Lamar, Colorado, storekeeper in 1893, disliked fireworks and other kinds of public disturbances, he managed nevertheless to maintain a tolerant attitude toward cowpunchers celebrating at the end of long drives. Of the many tales spun in his store, he wrote one time—in the quiet of old age —to the local newspaper editor: "All this talk was very interesting to me, coming as it did at firsthand; and I feel sure most of your readers are going to be interested in this recount and what your imagination can picture for you."

To avoid friction and tragedy as far as possible between the new settlers and the cattlemen, the government set aside a range of townships in Kansas and another in Colorado, over which all herds being driven from Texas to Montana were compelled to go, and Trail City, a few miles from Coolidge, suddenly came into existence. It was the first place on the trail where the cowboys accompanying the immense herds would receive any pay. So twenty-five or thirty saloons and gambling houses and nearly as many brothels to house the camp followers came into working order, before the first big herd and army of cowboys came up the trail.

Immediately on their arrival, and as soon as they received their pay, they proceeded to paint the town red. The saloons and gambling houses were filled to overflowing with drunken, boisterous men; Americans, half-breeds and Mexicans filled the streets; pistol shots and lurid oaths mingled in wild confusion; painted and half-tipsy women hung about the men beguiling them with their arts and helping themselves from their wallets. Nearly all the women developed into Lady Godivas, and, mounted behind the cowboys, would ride naked up and down the streets and even to the corporation line of Coolidge, where officers with Winchesters would warn them off. The scenes daily enacted were unbelievable, reaching the utmost depths of degradation and debauchery.

[4] Hamer Norris, "Along the Cattle Trail," *Lamar* (Colorado) *Register*, March 7 to May 2, 1928.

Open Range

One day three cowboys rode up from the south at a furious gallop and, jumping from their horses to the porch in front of a saloon, immediately opened fire on someone within. Apparently satisfied with their work they remounted their horses and disappeared in a cloud of dust to the north. On the floor lay a dead man, blood gushing from a dozen wounds, and still clasping a half-empty whisky glass in his stiffening fingers. The dead man was Print Olive, a well-known cattleman, who was bringing a herd up the trail. It was said that he had once caught some cattle rustlers, and instead of employing the civilized method of hanging, had lapsed into savagery and burned them at the stake, and that a brother of one of the men had become the avenger, following him like Nemesis up and down the trail until the last chapter of the tragedy was written in this hellhole on the Arkansas. With the passing of the trail the town faded as rapidly as it arose and a dark blot was removed from eastern Colorado.

Amusement, aside from shooting up saloons, or the too frequent killings, was mostly found in the dance. Any vacant room would do for a dance hall, but preferably it would be a saloon, where the participants could belly up to the bar at the end of each dance and imbibe freely in that which would tend to the exuberance of spirits, even if it did interfere with the rhythmic measures of the dance. To these amusements came the cowboy, arrayed with spurs and chaps, generally two forty-fours dangling from his belt, and the girls from the ranch, bedecked in gaudy costumes, and any other girls from the town, who had the nerve to participate. To the tunes of a squeaky violin the dance waxed warm and hilarious; the waltz or the stately minuet had no place in the scheme, it was the polka or any square dance that would give the chance for the display of exuberant spirits that appealed, and as the evening merged into early morning hours, even the movements of the dances became peculiar and irregular, and would finally develop into high jumping contests. Amid shout and ribald songs, the occasional bark of a revolver as some hilarious soul would put a bullet into the ceiling or a hanging lamp, the jingling of spurs, and the constant tinkling of glasses on the bar, the dance would come to an end with the feeling among the participants that it was the end of a perfect day....

After a crossing was made the herd was allowed to rest and given a chance to graze, return to the water for a drink or otherwise to be at ease until they had a chance to dry off. This gave the chance to all but a couple of the boys whose duty it was to be on guard to come back to town [Lamar] for a few hours' recreation. These boys together with the boys from the last two herds to have crossed and those from the next two herds approaching would sometimes make quite a large crowd of visitors in town, and it was an everyday occurrence to see Main Street from the Huddleston corner to the bank corner completely filled with these cow ponies saddled and bridled, with reins hanging to the ground, milling around switching their tails and throwing the reins in the effort to fight the flies.

The boys would leave for the herd when their time for duty came, only to release others who would find their way into town, and so it went on until late into the night.

WILD HORSE DRIVE[5]

When Charlie Baldwin, of Boulder County, Colorado, came back one day from "rounding up" wild horses, he told a lurid tale to J. S. Floy.

Some ten miles beyond the Bijou, and between what was known as Walker's Station and the Republican River, was a numerous band of wild horses. The attempts to capture them had proved futile for many a year. They had been pursued by daring riders, mounted upon the fleetest horses in the country, but to no avail. Among these horses was a milk white stallion, with flowing mane and tail, who knew no gait but "pace," so said the trappers and hunters, yet the fleetest runner with rider upon his back could not overtake him. He was the Godolphin of the prairie—"King of the Winds." An English sportsman had once seen him, and offered a thousand dollars in gold for him if he be captured without injury. There was also a white mare—

---

[5] J. S. Floy, *Thrilling Echoes From the Wild Frontier* (Chicago, 1893), 223–26. For a realistic picture of the methods commonly used in catching wild horses, see Homer Hoyt's reminiscences "Catching Wild Horses," *The Colorado Magazine*, Vol. XI, No. 2 (March, 1934), 41–45.

a beauty, apparently the leader of the band—that stood sentinel with her head always high in the air when humans were in sight and with one blast from her bugle-nose two hundred fleet racers would make the earth tremble beneath their tread.

In the fall of 1869 Mr. Baldwin attempted to execute a plan to capture the entire herd. This he would do by turning a number of his trusty and well-broken horses and mares loose among these wild animals, and after leaving them a sufficient time to make their acquaintance and affiiliate with them, then he would commence to approach day by day until he and his riders would fail to terrify them. This done, he would commence to drive a little each day until he would have them, unawares, off their range or feeding ground; then his own mares would strike for civilization, and the younger members of this wild horse family, if not the older ones, would surely follow, when he would land them safely in some enclosure or corral.

His arrangements being made to start, Mr. Baldwin took with him four men and a month's supply of provisions. His party consisted of Mr. Loren Clark, a gentleman well known in these parts in an early day, Mr. Moss, as guide, Mr. John Grief, and a Mr. Cutter. Mr. Moss' and Mr. Cutter's given names are now forgotten. They left Denver on the first day of September, and after three days' travel, arrived upon the ground where these wild animals fed, and turned loose their decoy horses.

For several days they had circled about in sight of the band of horses, and at night returned to their camp at Walker's Station. One morning, when about five miles from camp, they discovered of a sudden that they were surrounded by at least two hundred Indians. They were all in war paint, armed with guns and spears, and were yelling like demons. Mr. Baldwin ordered his men to dismount, use their horses for breastworks and fight. Clark obeyed the command; the others were panic-stricken, and made a dash to escape. Baldwin called loudly to them to halt, but they were too badly scared to hear his command.

As they stampeded Moss dropped his gun, and Cutter's horse became unmanageable and ran among the Indians. Grief was so frightened he stood still while the Indians rode up, put their guns against his head and shot him down. In twenty minutes from

An Indian Attack on the Horse Hunters

the first attack the three named men with their horses lay dead upon the plain. After scalping them and swinging their bloody scalps in the air, the infuriated devils turned their whole force upon Baldwin and Clark. The two had mounted, thinking there was an opportunity for an escape; but the Indians came upon them so rapidly Baldwin cried to Clark to dismount again and fight. Before he could do so, his horse fell under him, and he himself received three wounds almost instantaneously.

The dead body of the animal served for a breastwork, and for a time the wounded man fought with desperation, until from the loss of blood he had become too weak to longer hold out, when he advised Baldwin to leave him to his fate and take care of himself as best he could. Baldwin replied, "Never! You stood by me, and I will die with you!" Fortunately, the Indians fell back a pace for a moment, when Baldwin helped his wounded comrade upon the only horse they had left, and commenced a retreat toward the station, which was now three miles away. The Indians rallied and pursued, but at every advance he would drop upon his knees, take a steady aim, and an Indian or his horse would surely bite the dust. At last they arrived in camp, and the enemy retreated and left the field.

After much suffering Clark partially recovered from his wounds, and is now a resident of California, while Cutter, Moss and Grief lay buried on a little hillock by the roadside on the old Smoky Hill route.

A HORSE SELLING EXPEDITION[6]

Fred Bath's parents came to the new town of Laramie, Wyoming, in 1868. In 1876, when he was eight years old, he and his elder brother were called upon to retrieve, if possible, a band of horses stolen by the Indians. Later, on a somewhat similar occasion, life must have seemed to this Wyoming boy even less pretty and easy.

It was in 1894 that we had a hard year financially as far as livestock was concerned. Horses were almost worthless, al-

[6] Published from a manuscript in the Wyoming State Historical Department by *The Daily Bulletin* (Laramie, Colorado), 1936.

though there was a slight demand for cattle. We had plenty of feed and range but our stock netted us nothing.

A party including my father, Henry Bath, my brother, Herman, a friend, Tom Carroll, and myself, decided to try to dispose of our horses in some manner. We looked up all market reports and conditions of the country, finally concluding that the most feasible thing we could do was to trail our herd of horses down into Arkansas and trade them off for cattle. Arkansas was in a pioneer process too, and we thought they would need horses for settling the country.

We rigged up a camp wagon, employed a cook and rounded up three hundred head of horses. After leaving Fort Collins, Colorado, the country was more settled and we began to run out of feed. The saddle stock began to run down. In passing through so many small towns between Fort Collins and Denver, our animals would walk up and feed under the washings on the line, right up to the porches of the houses. We traveled right down the main streets of Denver, but in those days it was sparsely settled and our unusual cavalcade created no stir.

It was hot and dry that summer with the grass on the plains parched and dead. We traveled in hot desert winds that took out all the pleasure from our journey. No one had yet offered to buy any of the horses, and we were reaching the financial state of being more than temporarily embarrassed. We had no money and each morning our grub box looked thinner and thinner.

Although we were naturally discouraged with our prospects, we kept plodding on. We passed through villages that were dismally deserted because of the drouth and hard times. We approached Pueblo and our hearts sank again. Two horsemen came by and looked our herd of horses over. They offered us twenty dollars for the prize horse of the bunch. We moved forward with the hot sun and the wind. We arrived at Pueblo, a burned up, hot and sandy town, about sunset. Cactus was everywhere—as high as a horse's back, but otherwise not a green thing flourished. People warned us to return to our home, to shoot the stock if necessary, but not to go any further into the desert heat. That night while trying to rest on the ground, we decided to spare our horses and ourselves any further torture from the hot sun and wind and return to the Laramie plains. . . .

We decided to stay one more day—our grub box was now empty and so were all our pockets. I was the only one of wealth. I had fifty cents to feed us all. We decided to do something about our desperate financial situation. It was not long before the curiosity of the townspeople led their feet to our "open air horse show." They expressed admiration of the animals and mentioned how they would like to have this or that horse.

On the spur of the moment we decided to give a little wild West show in an attempt to swell our empty grub box. We began to advertise that we would put on a performance at sundown. The news traveled quickly and when I went down to do some advertising myself, I accidentally bumped into the man who had offered me twenty dollars previously for our best horse. My pride was in my empty pocket now and twenty dollars seemed a great fortune to me then. There were few people carrying that much cash in those days.

"Boys, here is where we fill up our nose bag for the home trip," I told other members of the party excitedly. The horse that was sold was about the wildest of the herd and the purchaser said that he would like to see it ridden. That evening my brother, Herman, made one of the prettiest rides I have ever seen. We all rode and sang our cowboy ballads for the audience and took in six dollars—mostly in pennies.

The next morning at dawn we were on our way home. Our hearts were light and our grub box was full. Everything went along fine on our return trip until the hot afternoon we reached Fort Collins. We were all singing and telling jokes, when suddenly the sun disappeared behind a black cloud and it began to sprinkle. My brother, Herman, put on his raincoat and started for the herd of horses. Then, thinking of me, he hastened back to the wagon and got my raincoat, then started to ride towards me, singing merrily.

When he was within twelve feet of me a sudden, blinding bolt of lightning flashed and knocked him from his horse. At the same moment fifteen of our horses went down to the ground in a heap of cringing, burning animal flesh. Hailstones as large as eggs beat down upon us, but we were too paralyzed from the shock to notice anything other than the silent form of Herman stretched beside his horse—now also dead.

Stricken with grief, we drove about a mile to the first ranch house, while I held my dead brother in my arms. A kind woman met us at the door and told us to bring the body in and lay it on her bed. The trip which began so gaily turned out to be a heartbreaking journey, the hardest road that I had ever ridden. My mother never recovered from the shock.

THE SWIMMING OX[7]

Andy Adams, author of the classic Log of a Cowboy, *was a man who knew the West. His story of cattle at a river crossing was but one of many he preserved.*

The use of an ox, as a saddle animal, recalls an incident which came under my observation. On the trail, one spring we lay for nearly a week water-bound with a freshet in Red River. During the delay of high water, herd after herd had arrived, until there was within striking distance of the old ford fully fifty thousand cattle and over two hundred men. Every day, not less than one hundred well-mounted horsemen gathered at the crossing, noting the condition of the river and to exchange the chronicles of the day. Everyone was impatient to cross, as the cattle were congesting on the Texas side, the close proximity of the herds making the risk dangerous in case of a stampede by night. Instead of the freshet falling, it gradually rose, overflowing the banks and lower bottoms, while driftwood and other debris was borne downstream with the onrushing flood, the waters being fully three hundred yards wide. Frequently, large trees floated by, swirling and turning as the angry currents toyed with the flotsam of the flood, while the muddy river itself rolled on, disputing our advance.

Across the stream stood a general store, and, like forbidden

---

[7] Andy Adams, "The Cattle on a Thousand Hills," *The Colorado Magazine*, Vol. XV, No. 5 (September, 1938), 169. From "the manuscripts from his estate that were presented to the State Historical Society of Colorado by the writer's nephew, Andy T. Adams, of Denver."

fruit to children, every man amongst us wanted to cross and price its wares. Scarcely a day passed but some daring lad would attempt to swim the river on his horse, and in every case was forced to return to the Texas side. Frequently, half a dozen would make the effort together, first awaiting an opportunity until the channel was fairly free of driftwood; but the eddying currents caught men and horses and ducked them like toys, both swimming for their lives to regain the nearest friendly shore, and often landing fully a mile below the entrance of the ford.

Matters ran along this way for five or six days, none of which were allowed to pass without some daring spirit making the attempt to reach that store, so near and yet so far, when one evening a freighter drove up. His team consisted of ten yoke of oxen, drawing a lead and two trail wagons, behind the rear one of which was led a good saddle horse. On the arrival of this wayfarer of the Plains, there were an unusual number of men present from the different herds, and speculation ran high as to what this freighter would do. He camped within sight of the crossing, quietly unyoking his team, belling several of them, and finally tied a large black wheel ox to the wagon. After picketing his horse and making things snug for the night, he led his big wheeler down to the ford, hastily made a halter out of the rope and, without inquiry of the hundred or more men present, mounted his ox bareback and put into the river. We admired his nerve, though we doubted his discretion, and I feel positive that every rascal amongst us, who had met defeat in those waters, secretly wished them to rebuff the freighter. But, guided by the word of his master, that big black ox swam like a swan, picked his way through the driftwood, breasted and quartered the swift currents, and finally, to our unanimous disgust, landed safe and sound on the farther bank.

The teamster lazily dismounted, turned the ox loose to graze, went up to the store and almost immediately returned, leading his mount well upstream before re-entering the river. On the return trip they encountered some dangerous driftwood, but the voice of the master reached us, cautiously talking to his ox and, when the crisis was safely passed, shamed by our envy, we shouted encouragement. The teamster waved his hand in reply, landing shortly afterward, squarely in the entrance to the ford, and we greeted him as a victor. Curiosity, however, ran high as to his errand across the river at such risk and, as there was no visible reason, our inquisitiveness was aroused. Men whispered to one another and, as the freighter led his ox up the bank and turned him loose, a foreman of one of the herds detained him long enough to ask, "Say, pardner, what in the name of common sense did you swim that river for, anyhow?"

"Why, I was out of tobacco," innocently replied the teamster; "Any of you boys care to smoke?"

The point I wish to make from this incident is this: In physical courage that freighter had no advantage over those trail men, as the latter were known for their daring, and all credit must be given the ox. With the seventeen herds that lay waterbound on this occasion, there were fully two thousand picked horses, and no lack of riders to dare the flood, but it remained for an ox to force the passage, and doing it as easily as one might walk from church to home. The ox, and not the rider, deserved the credit of the feat.

THE LOST STEER[8]

Practical jokes were a cowpuncher's birthright by unwritten law—especially where a titled "furriner" was concerned.

Along in the early eighties the Bar Triangle was the largest cow outfit in the Adobe Walls section of the Texas Panhandle. One of the boys employed there was Robert Thompson, whom his *compadres* nicknamed "Cyclone". While in Denver recently, Thompson told the following story:

"An English dood, Earl of some place, had bought two thousand head of two-year-old steers from us and we was takin' 'em up to tally 'em over to him. We was gettin' along all peaceable and quiet when here come a big, rollickin' yeller steer from around a little raise, headed right into our bunch. Bill Miller went to head him off but ye might as well try to head an engine, so on he come. Well, we rapped along easy, tryin' to cut him out but he was too foxy.

[8] "Frontier Sketches," *Dawson Scrapbooks*, Vol. VI, 113. A clipping probably from a Denver newspaper.

"He was too good a steer for the Englishman, so when we camped for noon the next day on a little crick we made up to get shut of him. We found a old camp right along the crick with some old pants an' clothes scattered around an' a bucket with a long piece of balin' wire to it. Well, this yere changed our proceedings some. Old Boner dropped his twine on Mr. old steer an' Miller headed him, an' me an' some of the boys dressed him up. We put them pants on his front legs and wired 'em on solid with balin' wire. Then we spit his eyes full of tobacco juice an' turned him loose. The old boy stood there a minute an' then he seen there was somethin' wrong and he lit out.

"Well, sir, of all the bucking and bellering ever ye heard he does it. He seen d'rectly he couldn't buck them pants off, so he lit in a runnin' an' we seen the last of him for some time in a moving cloud of dust. The next time we seen that 'ar steer he had shed his pants all right but I reckon the episode had kinder affected his mental equilibrium. He had a kind o' wistful look like he was huntin' somethin' an' he wouldn't stand much in one place. His flesh kind o' dropped off, with all his mental trouble, an' he looked bad, sure. We all called him "the Lost Steer." He died in about a year or two, or mebbe three. Say, if any man ever tells ye he's an old-timer from that country an' he don't know this yere tale about the Lost Steer ye can bank he's a liar."

A BRUSH WITH CATTLE RUSTLERS[9]

Where cattle grazed, rustlers were never far away. The country of the Wyoming and Colorado border, far out toward the Uintas, was big enough and wild enough to hold them all.

Bob Meldrum, a typical gun fighter of frontier days, has been given the job of cleaning out the cattle rustlers who have been making life miserable for the cattlemen in one of their last Western strongholds—the Little Snake River country, on the Colorado-Wyoming line, near Utah. . . .

For years the country adjoining the Little Snake River has been the haunt of characters more or less undesirable. It is a

[9] "Cowboys and Cattle," *Dawson Scrapbooks*, Vol. I, 297. An unidentified newspaper article dated January 24, 1909.

wild and unfrequented country, remote from railroads. On the vast ranges are run countless thousands of cattle and sheep. There have been bloody conflicts between the cattle and sheep men, but finally their differences were adjusted through the recognition of a "dead line." The sheep are kept north of the Colorado-Wyoming line and the cattle range south of that line, except when being driven to the railroad for shipping purposes.

Before this dead line was established clashes were frequent between herders and cowboys, and many partisans of the sheep and cattle barons lost their lives in duels with rifles. Cattle rustling used to be a flourishing industry in this locality also, and some of the old log cabins along the Little Snake River have been the gathering places of bands of desperate outlaws, ready for any mischief, from cattle rustling to robbing trains.

When "Butch" Cassidy, premier of all train robbers, stuck up the crew of the Overland Limited at Tipton, Wyoming, and made his getaway with thousands of dollars from the express messenger's strong box, it was through the Little Snake River country that he eluded pursuit. There were plenty of confederates all along the route to give the train robber a helping hand, and he was never in danger of capture. The outlaws and cattle rustlers generally operated in bands, and were so bold that they had the whole country terrorized. They used to clatter into the little town of Baggs, on the Colorado-Wyoming line, whooping and yelling and shooting out all the panes of window glass they had missed on previous occasions. Finally the cattlemen resolved to fight fire with fire. They were losing thousands of dollars annually through the depredations of these men, so eventually there appeared in the country one Tom Horn, scout, guide and hero of many pistol duels. Horn was hired by the cattlemen as a stock detective, and his orders were to rid the country of rustlers at any cost.

Soon a series of mysterious assassinations spread terror among the rustlers. One man after another, who had been suspected of cattle rustling, was shot dead in his cabin or out on the open range. Always there was the deepest mystery surrounding the assassinations. No tracks were left by which the slayer could be traced. The rustlers swore vengeance, but their oath was futile

The assassin kept up his work until five of the suspected leaders of the rustling trade had been slain. Always a stone under the head of the victim, as a sort of pillow, showed that one hand had done all the work.

The cattle rustlers began to move out of the country, particularly after one man, who had refused to obey a warning, was found with his ears pinned to his cabin door and his head pillowed on a stone. It was not until Tom Horn overplayed his hand and assassinated the young son of a ranchman near Cheyenne that the mystery of the murders in Rustler Land was cleared. Horn confessed that he had plied the trade of murderer, and that he always went in his stocking feet when trailing a victim, and that he left a stone under his victim's head as proof to his employers that he had done the work.

After Horn was hanged at Cheyenne cattle rustling was begun again, but on a smaller scale, in the Little Snake country. But Bob Meldrum was then a deputy at Baggs, and he intimidated the remnants of the rustler army and drove the last one out of the country.

Meldrum's fame as a gun fighter had spread, and he was in active demand wherever there was trouble. He was for some time employed by the mine owners of Cripple Creek and Telluride, during Colorado's bloody war of mining interests. Later he appeared at Boise during the Haywood-Moyer trial. Always his appearance on the scene resulted in a sudden quieting of boisterous spirits. Men who had announced that they "were hunting trouble" vanished when the trouble appeared in the form of this quiet, determined gun fighter, whose revolver handle is so notched with death scars that it looks as if a bear had been chewing it.

During Meldrum's absence from the Little Snake River country, the industry of cattle rustling showed a decided revival, until now it is said to be almost as flourishing as it was before the day of Tom Horn. The cattle owners claim that there is a regular system of "railroading" stock out of the country. They say that most of the homesteaders who have taken out small ranches along the Little Snake Valley and its vicinity are not legitimate ranchmen, but are cattle rustlers, who pass on the stolen stock into Wyoming and Utah. In this way it is claimed thousands of head of cattle are being rustled every year.

It is to break up this system that Bob Meldrum has been called upon. The nervy gun fighter knows his men, and he knows just the capacity for resistance in each. As a general rule, Meldrum never has recourse to his weapon, with which he had established such a record in the West. He fixes his hard blue eyes on his victim, and the individual generally vamooses or goes quietly to durance. . . .

There are few places left in the West where such a stirring drama can be enacted. Even the Little Snake River country will not be held by the stockmen for long, as the railroads are headed that way now, and the cattle ranges will be invaded by homesteaders. But long before the pumpkin huskers arrive the cattle rustlers will be cleaned out, or Bob Meldrum will have died with his boots on.

THREE HORSE THIEVES MEET THEIR FATE[10]

Of all men on the dodge in the West, horse thieves were the most despised. Shooting, or hanging from the nearest and tallest cottonwood tree, was considered to be the only permanent cure.

I [Josh Deane] had not been back on the [Big Horn Basin] route more than three months when two strangers rode into mail camp, where I was spending the night. I invited them to stop, as was the custom in that day, when human companionship was among the rarer blessings. They were looking for work, they told me, and they rode on early the next morning intending to call on some ranchers I named who might need men.

About half an hour later, as I was leaving camp for the day's trip, three sheriffs rode up, following the trail of my visitors. I pointed out the direction, and they went along the trail over Red Creek Pass. A few hours later as I rode past a little quaking asp grove on the north side of the mountain I noticed a flock of magpies circling over the trees and a coyote slinking through the underbrush. I went into the grove to investigate.

[10] Josh Deane, "The Adventures of Josh Deane, postmaster at Sunshine, Wyoming," a typescript in the files of The Western Range Cattle Industry Study.

Here I found the bodies of three men, dead not more than two hours. Two of them were my companions of the night before; the third was my old mail carrier, Wilson. He had evidently avoided my camp through fear of being recognized, and joined his companions that morning. The three must have been taken unawares by their pursuers, for there was no sign of a battle, and their guns were untouched. The sheriffs had shot them without warning, no doubt, rather than risk their own lives in an attempt to take them alive. The sight sickened me, though I was not unaccustomed to brutalities. Magpies had been picking at the eyes of the men, and a mountain lion had torn one of them to pieces. There was no sign of the sheriffs.

I rode down to the Embar Ranch and borrowed a shovel from Dan Aldrich, the caretaker. Returning to the scene of the murder I dug a deep hole, into which I rolled the bodies. After covering their faces with handkerchiefs to keep the dirt off, I shoveled in some earth, and then piled big rocks on so that the bodies could not be easily dug up by animals. I had no way of marking the grave.

No one paid any attention to the atrocious act, as horse thieves were the most hated criminals in that day and place. I could not feel, however, that there was any excuse for treating these men worse than wild beasts. The time taken in burying the men delayed me so much that I had to spend the night at the Embar, and went on with the mail the next morning. I heard very little about the thieves, and said nothing to anyone as it is always safer to keep still about one's adventures.

COWPUNCHER WEDDING[11]

In his account of a cowboy wedding, Colonel Sliney, pioneer cattleman of northern Wyoming, has presented his own version of romance on the Western range.

The female of the species was the rarest of all the humans at that date. One of those not already preempted was Nancy Apperson, commonly known as "Sagebrush Nance." This lady

[11] Published in the *Sheridan* (Wyoming) *Press*, February, 1936. From a manuscript in the Wyoming State Historical Department.

was so named because of her elusive habits. The presence of a stranger was enough to send the fair Nancy scurrying to cover like a jack rabbit. A robust settler, Charles Lofkin, nicknamed "Big Charlie" on account of his big proportions (he was six feet something, built from the ground up, and had a back on him like a writing desk), finally lured the stampeding **Nancy** into the trap of matrimony.

I was the only justice of the peace in the radius of one hundred miles and preachers were as scarce as snakes in Ireland. So to have the knot tied according to the statutes in such cases made and provided, Nancy and her prospective lord had to make the long trip from their northern home in the wheeled glory of a four-inch prairie schooner. In deference to the conventions in such cases, Nance's father accompanied them as duenna and chaperone. 'Twas thus I met them a few weeks later as I was going up Owl Creek on the roundup, accompanied by a lot of cowboys.

Charlie said, "Hello, Judge. When are you going home?"

"I'm not going home. I am on the roundup."

"Well, when can we get married? I have a license, and here she is," producing the document.

"You can get married right away, and now pile out."

All might have gone well had the cowboy congregation been able to hold down the safety valve; but these rather reckless gentlemen are not wont to place much restraint on their feelings whether these are inspired by pleasure, peace, or war. As Nance disembarked from the wedding chariot, the brooding silence of the desert was shattered by a wild, earsplitting series of whoops and cheers accompanied by the pop, pop, pop of the six-shooters. No herd of wild steers, red-eyed from panic, ever made a more sudden and wilder dash than Nance did. In a flash she jerked her arm loose from her father's and fled for the tall timber. For a moment everybody was stricken dumb. The terror of such a catastrophe as an interruption of the ceremony left the crowd speechless.

In any other country the fleeting Nance might be going yet. The cowboy's mind, trained to the school of the desert, immediately grasped the possibilities of which the surroundings were pregnant. As Nance vanished, someone shouted, "H——boys, catch her." This feature was not on the program, but it lent a new thrill to the affair. In a few seconds five or six of the cowboys were breaking records in the hunt for the stampeding Nance. Anyone who has watched a plainsman stop a wild steer with the flying loop of his saddle rope, can easily forecast the result.

It was only a few moments until the fleeing Nance found her headlong flight stopped by the lariat rope closing on her hind leg. When the good lady somewhat recovered her composure, the words were pronounced which linked together the earthly fortunes of the elusive Nance and "Big Charlie." Thus ended the first wedding in the Big Horn Basin.

WARFARE OF THE RANGES[12]

Between cowmen and sheepmen, trouble started when the first sheep was thrown onto the range. Strangely enough, however, in the end this conflict was decided not by gunfire but by the unpredictable shifts in markets and prices.

Now occasionally in the seventies and eighties sheepmen appropriated a beef or cowboys riddled a trespassing herder, but such incidents in no wise marred the general serenity. There was an abundance of free range, and restless spirits could always slaughter buffalo and Indians. The actual warfare between the sheepmen and the cowmen came with the incoming of the farmers during the nineties. Then, the range contracting, the sheep and cattle kings partitioned it off into sheep land and cow land, invoking the unwritten law of priority in drawing the line of demarkation, a "dead line," fatal to trespassing hoofs.

A middle-aged, foreign-born American, Swanson had gradually acquired a small flock of sheep. Always a hard worker, he was also sober and respected, a stubborn man, tenacious of what he felt to be his rights. Consequently, when he heard that the sheep and cow men, in their respective associations, had selected as a dead line the boundary between Delta and Mesa counties

[12] A. W. North, "The Warfare of the Ranges," *Harper's Weekly,* September 10, 1909, 11–12.

[Colorado], two of the divisions shorn off the western portion of "Old Gunnison," he resolutely decided to disregard such restriction to his grazing rights. Therefore, in the late autumn, some three years ago, he drove his sheep from summer pastures down across the Uncompahgre Valley, westward past the thriving little city of Delta, on toward Kanna Creek and the Whitewater, on across the dead line. A single herder only was with him. Suddenly, with a hoarse shout, a party of masked men rode upon them.

"Swanson, up with your hands. By God! you shan't enter the cow land with that bunch of sheep," cried the leader.

Up went the herder's hands. Like a flash up came Swanson's rifle.

"I'm an American citizen," said he, spiritedly. "This is government land. I'll stand on my rights."

One of the riders raised his carbine. Swanson covered him— his gun snapped. A puff of smoke from the rider's and "Pete" Swanson was dead. The herder was promptly tied and gagged. Then bending low in their saddles, the horsemen dashed in among the sheep, clubbing, clubbing, right and left. In a few minutes the butchery was completed.

A stake now marks the spot. Though locals and Pinkertons have striven for the $10,000 reward offered by the Uncompahgre Valley sheepmen for the apprehension of the murderer, he is still at large. Some say that he might be found near the Uintah Indian Reservation, but whoever would secure that reward must needs be quick on the trigger. . . .

About this same time, however, an entirely different type of man was guarding ten thousand sheep hard by the Blue. Over six feet in height, slender of frame, with a face boyish in repose, stern in time of action, "Tobe" Barnes at thirty had been through a world of adventures. . . .

On the Blue he "took up" his quarter-section and built a log house and corrals. Presently came a rumor, "You'll have to leave." He left—for two days, returning with two hundred rifle cartridges and an equally generous supply for his automatic revolver. Then there was posted near his cabin a written notice, "You gotter leave, or your sheep'll be killed." He left the cabin

—to sleep near his charges. Next came a peremptory warning, "You gotter leave in three days, or you'll get shot." Simultaneously came word from his boss, "No trouble wanted; move the sheep."

"You put me in charge of your sheep here for the season, an' I won't leave here 'less you fire me," was his laconic response to his superior. "Tobe Barnes has four hundred rounds. If you want him to leave, you'll have to move him," was his answer to the cowmen. For the next month he spent his nights on the ground, rods away from a blazing fire, sleeping with "half an eye open," his arms by his side.

Dissatisfaction broke out among the cowpunchers, now commissioned to "extarminate" Barnes. "Oh, Hell!" growled one of the best shots and most rabid of the gang. "I've drunk with Tobe; he'd loan me his last dollar—an' he can shoot like the devil with that Luger of his'n. Let him have the Blue."

Needless to say Barnes still "has the Blue."

THE JIGGERS[13]

This story, it seems, may be applied not only to sheepherders but to many people who, indeed, have never seen a sheep except at night.

Standing on the pebbled strand of Manhattan Beach the other day, was a young man dressed in the rough garb of the Plains. A companion explained his peculiar actions as follows:

"That's Sheepherder Jack, as we call him out in the Bijou Basin. He's got the sheep-jiggers bad. Just watch him a minute. Ye see he's got ten little pebbles or jiggers in his right hand. Now he'll count from one up to a hundred and then he'll put one of them jiggers into his left hand. When he gets all of the jiggers into his left hand, that will make a thousand, and he'll cut a notch in the rim of his hat or his boot heel. Didn't ye ever notice the notches cut in a sheep-buckaroo's hat? That's what it means. When Jack gets a thousand counted, he counts another thousand, and passes the jiggers back to his right hand, and keeps on in that way back and forth all day if we let him. . . .

[13] "Oddities," *Dawson Scrapbooks*, Vol. II, 45. Unidentified newspaper clipping.

"We broughten him over here thinkin' the life and bluster of the city might help him, but it's no use. He just stands like you see him all day long and counts people for sheep, the same as if he was on the Kiowa plains!

"I was out once in the foothills of the Turkey Mountains working for Old Man Pinkerton near Wagon Mound, and I had so much trouble with coyotes and underbrush that I used to count my bunch of sheep three times a day. I didn't have no time for anything else, and it mighty near took me off my base.

"I could see sheep a-jumpin' over the bars night and day, and could hear their eternal bleat ringin' in my head like Boulanger's march on a hand organ."

A QUESTION OF TASTE[14]

It has been aptly stated that every question has two sides. This was true, certainly, in the eyes of a sheepman named Woodruff.

A wholly erroneous impression exists back East—that the Western sheepman is a spiritless and subdued, not so say a cowardly, sort of an individual. We never yet met up with a sheepman who would crawfish in the presence of the devil. During the war between the Wyoming cattlemen and sheepmen a few years ago a scene was pulled off in a little restaurant in Lander one afternoon when a meek-looking sheepman named Woodruff walked in and took a seat at a table.

"Bring me a broiled mutton chop," said Woodruff to the waiter. A big-booted and spurred cowboy, who was munching a steak at a table in the corner of the feed shack, heard the sheepman's order, and he got up from his place and swung clankingly over to Woodruff's table. "Say, look a-here ombrey," said the cowboy, in an insulting manner, to the sheepman, "I take it as an insult f'r any locoed sheep snoozer t' slam into any place where I'm eatin' an' order such silly vittels as a mutton chop—d'ye know that?"

"Is that so?" inquired Woodruff coolly. "Hey, there, you waiter." The waiter hurried from the kitchen and stood at atten-

[14] "Frontier Sketches," *Dawson Scrapbooks*, Vol. I, 67. Unidentified newspaper clipping.

tion before Woodruff's table, over which the cowboy still loomed threateningly. "Waiter," said Woodruff, "make that two mutton chops, instead of one." With that Woodruff's gun was out like a flash and he was drawing a tidy bead on the bullying cowboy's heart. "You, you fathead of a heifer-prodder, are going to eat that other chop," said the sheepman.

The cowboy was fairly struck up, and the edge was on him. He slouched into the other seat at Woodruff's table, taking pains to keep his hands above his waistline, for Woodruff kept him covered. Five minutes later the waiter brought in the two mutton chops. The cowboy ate his and he ate it first.

MORE YARNS ABOUT SHEEP[15]

According to Frank Benton, collector of sidetrack anecdotes, cattlemen somewhat resented the presence of sheepmen on stock trains rolling east to Omaha. Nevertheless, on occasion even the crustiest old spur-jangler could be soft of heart.

We all agreed there was some difference in sheepmen, and that Rambolet Bill and Cottswool Canvasback certainly belonged to the better class, and we all fell to telling stories of the generous, openhanded things that sheepmen of our acquaintance had done.

Packsaddle Jack said he knowed a sheepman once by the name of Black Face, who was so good hearted that he paid twenty dollars towards one of his herder's doctor bill when he lost both feet by their being frozen in the great Wyoming blizzard in '94. The herder stayed with the sheep for seventy-two hours in the Bad Lands and saved all the three thousand sheep except seven that got over the bank of the creek into ice and water and drowned. The herder having got all but these seven head out and getting his feet wet they froze so hard that Black Face said his feet was rattling together like rocks when he found him still herding the sheep. Of course, the sheep might have all perished in the storm if the herder didn't stay with them, and of course, the herder didn't have anything to eat the entire three days in the storm, as he was miles from any habitation, and that way saved Black Face thirty cents in grub. But

[15] Benton, *Cowboy Life*, 70–75.

we all agreed that while Black Face would feel the greatest anguish at the loss of the seven sheep and giving up the twenty dollars, yet the satisfaction of doing a generous deed and the pride he would experience when it was mentioned in the item column of the local county paper would partially alleviate that anguish.

Eatumup Jake said he knew a sheepman by the name of Hatchet Face from Connecticut, who had sheep ranches out there in Utah, and he was so kind-hearted that when one of his herders kept his sheep in a widow neighbor's field till they ate everything in sight, even her lawn and flower garden, he apologized to the widow when she returned from nursing a poor family through a spell of sickness, and told her he would pay her something, and while he never did pay her anything, yet he always seemed sorry, while a lot of sheepmen would have laid awake nights to have studied a way how to eat out the widow again. Eatumup Jake said old Hatchet Face, when he prayed in church Sundays (he being a strict Presbyterian), he always prayed for the poor and widows and orphans, and that showed he had a good heart, to use what influence he had with God Almighty and get Him to do something for widows and orphans and poor people.

Dillbery Ike said he knew a sheepman by the name of Shearclose, and while he never gave his hired help any meat to eat except old broken-mouthed ewes in the winter and dead lambs in the spring and summer, and herded his sheep around homesteaders' little ranches till their milk cows mighty near starved to death, yet old Shearclose gave five dollars for a ticket to a charity ball once when a list of the names of all the people who bought tickets was printed in the county paper.

After we summed all these things up, our hearts got so warm thinking of these acts of generosity by sheepmen that we concluded to make a hunt for Rambolet Bill, Cottswool Canvasback and Jackdo. We now discussed a great many plans how to rescue them. While we were arguing the stock train came, and when we told the conductor, he immediately had the agent wire General Freight Agent C. J. Lane, at Omaha, the following message:

"Two prominent sheepmen swept away by freshet while camping ahead of special train No. 79531. Please wire instructions how to find them."

Lane immediately wired back not to find them, and if there was any trace of them to obliterate it at once.

THE POSTHOLE DIGGER'S GHOST[16]

Fence posts, at the turn of the century, were becoming quite numerous in the West. Looping along on his stock train, Frank Benton had reason, perhaps, to wonder how they all got there.

Years ago Senator Warren, Manager Gleason and some other Massachusetts Yankees started in the sheep business in southern Wyoming and northern Colorado, and as the country was large they thought it would be a good thing to fence in a few hundred thousand acres of government land and save the grass so fenced in case of hard winters and other things and graze their sheep in this enclosure only when there was no more grass around the little homesteads taken here and there by settlers. So hiring a young German from the Old Country, who couldn't speak a word of English, to dig the postholes, they got him a brand new shovel, a post bar about eight feet long, the famous receipt for cooking jack rabbits, and started him digging near the twenty-seventh degree of longitude west from Washington. Pointing toward the setting sun in the west, they went off and left him. The German was never seen alive again, but he left a never-ending line of postholes behind him. The Warren Live Stock Company, it is said, put a great many men setting the posts in these holes and stringing barbed wire on them, and although they kept ever increasing the force that built the fence, yet they never caught up with the German; and time after time the post setters would come to the top of a high hill or a range of mountains and think they would come in sight of the German, only to see a long line of postholes stretching away over hill and valley towards the setting sun.

After a while the Mormons along the line of Utah and Wyoming complained of seeing a ghost about the time they drove

[16] Benton, *Cowboy Life,* 83–87.

their cows home of an evening. They said it was a German with grizzled locks and flowing beard, with a large meerschaum pipe in his mouth and a shovel in one hand from which the blade was worn down to the handle and a post bar no bigger than a drag tooth in the other hand. He was always looking toward the setting sun, shading his eyes with his hand and muttering these words: "*Das sinkende Sonne, ich fange sie nicht.*"

But when they approached close to him, or spoke to him, he immediately vanished. When the ghost wasn't disturbed it seemed to be digging holes. It would go through the motions of digging a hole in the ground, then rising up, take thirteen steps in a westerly direction, look back to see if the line was straight, dig another hole, and go on. Sometimes the ghost seemed to be studying a well-worn piece of paper, which was undoubtedly the receipt for cooking jack rabbits, and would mutter in German, "*O wohene, O wohene ist er gegangen, mit Schwanz so kurz und Ohr so lang? O wohene ist mein Hase gegangen?*"

After a while the ghost began to appear in western Utah and still later on in Nevada, always digging a never-ending imaginary line of postholes. No one ever knew where the actual postholes left off and the imaginary ones commenced.

As the Routt County cattlemen in western Colorado never allowed any sheepmen to encroach on their range, and they always killed all the sheep and sheepmen who dared to intrude, of course, the Warren Live Stock Company had to stop building fence west and turn north before they got there.

Pikes Peak Prevaricator

P IKES PEAK is not one of those mountains which rise dramatically, in a cluster of pinnacles and granite needle spires, above less imposing cordillera heights. Rather, it sits like some white-bearded old-timer, huge, hump-shouldered, and contemplative, at the western edge of the Plains. In seasons when the summer sun becomes too bright, or the winter air too cold, a solitary gray cloud, shaped often like a sombrero, forms over it, providing protection for its bald crown and lending to it an added appearance of serenity and philosophical meditation. Outwardly there is indeed something massive, dignified, and unshakable about Pikes Peak, in the fashion of a solid citizen; inwardly, on the other hand—as those most intimately acquainted with this peak can testify—there is something else again, a hint of roguishness perhaps, or of secret fires and humors which must burst forth, at times, in artistic proof of temperament.

When, for example, Sergeant O'Keefe and Balaam, his mule, enlisted members of the United States Signal Corps, arrived in January, 1876, to take over the Pike weather station, peak moodiness and distempers became manifest. Rumblings and stirrings occurred. Instruments well seated grew erratic; trails once winding peacefully up through forest and meadow revealed new menaces; game showed a fresh and threatening truculence; and on all sides, at the peak crest, the drama of the elements heightened. Off and on for three years, in the face of mounting uncertainties, Sergeant O'Keefe and Balaam, his mule, observed all peak phenomena, combining in their collaborative reports an Irishman's indestructible level-headedness with an American's raucous enthusiasm for the incomprehensible. Only under such prompting did Pikes Peak, so long the silent and enigmatic, give voice to deeper character. Only since then—and old settlers may be pardoned, possibly, for asking what added signs of temperament some day will appear—has this bluff Rocky Mountain resident consented to stand with frontiersman, miner, and cowman, dipping its cloud cap daily, beckoning with an almost waggish lack of propriety to strangers as well as to its nonplussed neighbors below, and, in its unhurried way, making its own contributions to the legends and tall tales of the West.

RATS[1]

When Sergeant O'Keefe's first Pikes Peak story was collected by Judge Eliphalet Price, Colorado Springs correspondent of the Pueblo Chieftain, *it appeared under the heading "Attacked by Rats, Terrible Conflict on the Summit of Pikes Peak," was dated "Colorado Springs, May 25, 1876," and carried the mysterious but highly arresting by-line, "Mucilage." So astonishing did this narrative prove to be that it was reprinted not only in the* Colorado Springs Gazette *and Denver's* Rocky Mountain News *but, appropriately, in alert newspapers scattered throughout the United States.*

The vast number of rats inhabiting the rocky crevices and cavernous passages at the summit of Pikes Peak, Colorado, have recently become formidable and dangerous. These animals are known to feed upon a saccharine gum that percolates through the pores of the rocks, apparently upheaved by that volcanic action which at irregular intervals of a few days gives the mountain crest that vibratory motion which has been detected by the instruments used in the office of the United States Signal Station. Since the establishment of the station, at an altitude of nearly 15,000 feet, these animals have acquired a voracious appetite for raw meat, the scent of which seems to impart to them a ferocity rivaling the starving Siberian wolf. The most singular trait in the character of these animals is that they are never seen in the daytime. When the moon pours down her queenly light upon the summit, they are visible in countless numbers, hopping

[1] Also reprinted in "History of El Paso County," Frank Hall, *History of Colorado*, III (Chicago, 1891), 374–76. According to the *Rocky Mountain News*, September 28, 1877, "A late number of Frank Leslie's *Illustrated Times* reprints this clever hoax, with a cut showing the progress of the battle in the signal office."

among the rocky boulders that crown this barren waste, and during the summer months they may be seen swimming and sporting in the waters of the lake, a short distance below the crest of the Peak, and on a dark, cloudy night their trail in the water exhibits a glowing, sparkling light, giving to the waters of the lake a flickering, silvery appearance.

A few days since, Mr. John O'Keefe, one of the government operators at the signal station, returned to his post from Colorado Springs, taking with him a quarter of beef. It being late in the afternoon, his colleague, Mr. Hobbs, immediately left with the pack animal for the Springs. Soon after dark, while Mr. O'Keefe was engaged in the office, forwarding night dispatches to Washington, he was startled by a loud scream from Mrs. O'Keefe, who had retired for the night in an adjoining bedroom, and who came rushing into the office screaming, "The rats! the rats!" Mr. O'Keefe with great presence of mind, immediately girdled his wife with a scroll of zinc plating, such as had been used in the roofing of the station, which prevented the animals from climbing upon her person, and although his own person was almost literally covered with them, he succeeded in encasing his legs each in a joint of stovepipe, when he commenced a fierce and desperate struggle for his life with a heavy war club preserved at the station among other Indian relics captured at the battle of Sand Creek. Notwithstanding hundreds were destroyed on every side they seemed to pour (with ever increasing numbers) from the bedroom, the door of which had been left open. The entire quarter of beef was eaten in less than five minutes, which seemed only to sharpen their appetite for an attack on Mrs. O'Keefe, whose face, hands and neck were terribly lacerated.

In the midst of the warfare, Mrs. O'Keefe managed to reach a coil of electric wire hanging near the battery, and being a mountain girl, familiar with the throwing of a lariat, she hurled it through the air causing it to encircle her husband, and spring out from its loosened fastening making innumerable spiral traps, along which she poured the electric fluid from the heavily charged battery. In a moment the room was ablaze with electric light and whenever the rats came in contact with the wire they were hurled to an almost instant death. The appearance of daylight, made such by the coruscation of the heavily charged wire, caused them to take refuge among the crevices and caverns of the mountains, by way of the bedroom window, through which they had forced their way. But the saddest part of this night attack upon the Peak is the destroying of their infant child, which Mrs. O'Keefe thought she had made secure by a heavy covering of bed clothing, but the rats had found their way to the infant (only two months old), and had left nothing of it but the peeled and mumbled skull.

Later—Drs. Horn and Anderson have just returned from the Peak. It was at first thought that the left arm of Sergeant O'Keefe would have to be amputated, but they now believe it can be saved.

WEATHER[2]

Following his initial harrowing experience, Sergeant O'Keefe's residence on the Peak was interrupted by assignment to temporary duty at the Philadelphia Centennial Exposition, which opened on May 10, 1876. Returning some four years later, in February, 1880, to become the non-commissioned officer in charge of the Peak weather station, he found himself still the undimmed hero of the day, the Colorado Springs Gazette *welcoming his arrival in the city, expressing the hope that he would have no further trouble with rats, and publishing—in due course —the account of his next difficulty, entitled "Weather Bound— Wonderful Adventures of a Signal Service Officer on his Way to the Peak."*

Sergeant O'Keefe returned last evening from an unsuccessful attempt to ascend the Peak. He says that it is the first time within his experience that he had been thus baffled, and he asks to be excused from ever being subjected to a similar experience. By the reports which he had received from Mr. Sweeney, who is stationed at the Peak, he was led to infer that but little snow had fallen and in consequence he was not prepared to contend with the obstacles which blocked his path.

[2] *Colorado Springs Gazette* (weekly edition), October 16 and November 20, 1880.

The journey for the first few miles of the trail was without any dissatisfactory feature, but while making an abrupt turn in the trail in the vicinity of Mennehaha Falls, the Sergeant was brought to a standstill by an immense herd of black-tailed deer which impeded his further progress. He contends that the herd contained fully seven hundred head and says that it took just one hour and forty minutes for them to pass a given point.

The Sergeant was armed only with a .32 caliber Smith and Wesson revolver and with this poor apology for a firearm he succeeded in killing seventeen of the deer. The only plausible reason that Sergeant O'Keefe can give for the remarkable appearance of this vast herd is that they were driven from South Park by the recent storm. As the Sergeant was compelled to continue his journey to the Peak he gathered the game which he had slaughtered, tied their tails together and slung them over the neck of his faithful mule, Balaam, and continued on his way.

Everything passed off smoothly until timberline was reached when the Sergeant encountered another serious barrier as the fierce northwest wind which accompanied the storm had formed mountains of snow across the trail. With the much trusted veteran mule Balaam, and an unusual amount of perseverance on the part of himself, Sergeant O'Keefe contrived to surmount a tremendous snowdrift twenty-eight feet in depth. When safely upon the other side he paused for a moment and taking his field glass he viewed the prospect o'er and examined the difficulties with which he had to contend. As far as the eye could reach nothing but snowbanks could be seen some of which were at least one hundred (100) feet in height. It required only a brief space of time for the Sergeant to make up his mind that it would be useless for him to risk his life in making another rash attempt so he concluded to return to the Springs, but upon turning to step into the saddle he discovered that the mule had disappeared. The Sergeant was now in a sad plight. Had he only survived the terrible rat raid of 1876 to find death again staring him in the face from starvation? He retraced his steps through the mammoth snowdrift, and after a terrible siege of over one hour he found himself standing upon the other side thoroughly exhausted. After he had somewhat revived he glanced around him in hopes of finding some trace of the lost mule, and what was his chagrin to perceive the much trusted Balaam lying upon his back with feet uplifted in the air at the bottom of a deep ravine. The deer, with which he had been festooned, were scattered from top to bottom of the ravine. The Sergeant secured the game and the mule and again started on his homeward journey.

While passing along a very secluded portion of the trail he was attacked by six ravenous mountain lions and in order to save his own life he was compelled to cast away the game which had required so much exertion to capture. Even the seventeen deer did not replenish their ravenous appetites and still they pursued him, but by the proper manipulation of that mule O'Keefe managed to evade them. He reached the signal office in this city at eight o'clock last night, and it is doubtful whether he ever again attempts to traverse the Pikes Peak trail.

(A Correction—November 20, 1880)

Sergeant O'Keefe is very much worried over the story of his adventures, in trying to ascend the Peak, which appeared in the *Gazette* recently. This story has been copied by almost every paper of prominence in the East and O'Keefe says he wouldn't care so much about the matter but for one or two inaccuracies which crept into the *Gazette* story. He says he would not have it thought by his friends in the East that he had mistold matters. He does not want Peter Cooper, George Washington Childs, Whitelaw Reid, James Gordon Bennett, President Hayes, and Dr. Tanner, all of whom he holds in the highest esteem, to think that he would exaggerate. We therefore cheerfully make the correction that he requests. He says there were only one hundred and twenty-six (126) black-tailed deer and that the 127th deer had a white tail. We are now sure that the story is quite correct.

Sergeant O'Keefe Brings Home the Game

ERUPTION[3]

When volcanic agues and distempers shook Pikes Peak in 1880, both Sergeant O'Keefe and the Colorado Springs Gazette *were prepared. The Sergeant's account portrays, as usual, the admirable clarity, calmness, fortitude, and attention to detail with which he faced all such eventualities.*

The probability of a volcano existing in the Rocky Mountains has never entered the minds of our citizens. Conclusive evidence that such a thing does exist and not very far from Colorado Springs has recently been furnished us by Sergeant O'Keefe of the signal service. The first knowledge that was given us of this peculiar and newly discovered phenomenon was reported last Saturday afternoon and since that time a *Gazette* reporter under the guidance of Sergeant O'Keefe visited the scene of what proved to be one of the most wondrous discoveries ever brought to light in this mountain region.

Nearly all of the citizens of Colorado Springs have seen or read of the crater which is located near the summit and just west of the Peak. It has always been conceded by scientists that this selfsame crater had in time gone by been the scene of a terrible eruption as particles of lava had been discovered in the crevices of the rock adjoining it. Those who have investigated more closely the various formations which are peculiar to a volcanic mountain generally have affirmed that there are plenty of evidences to show plainly that the Pikes Peak crater has in its center a circular or cuplike opening through which lava has certainly been emitted.

It was on the night of the 29th of October that the crater first displayed any signs of volcanic activity; Sergeant O'Keefe was aroused from his slumbers by a dreary, doleful sound which apparently emanated from beneath the signal station. His first convictions were that it was an earthquake but his impression was soon dispelled by the fact that the sound still continued without any signs of a jar. The Sergeant concluded to investi-

---

[3] *Colorado Springs Gazette* (daily edition), November 17 and November 20, 1880. Reprinted in the weekly edition, November 20, 1880, and also in the *Rocky Mountain News*, November 19, 1880.

gate the cause of this mysterious sound and he, in company with his assistant, Mr. F. L. Jones, dressed themselves and started out in search of the cause thereof. They had barely stepped over the doorsill when a bright flash, at first thought to be lightning, surmounted the summit of the Peak. It was only of a second's duration and the Peak was again clothed in darkness. From this time on the sound theretofore described seemed to decrease until the usual quiet of the solemn mountain peak was again restored.

The following day Sergeant O'Keefe visited the crater, feeling confident that the sound heard on the night previous had emanated from that source. What was his surprise on looking down in the crater to discover vapor curling up from the cuplike enclosure. This discovery only prompted him to further continue his researches, and after two hours' laborious climbing he found himself standing within about 22 yards of the crater chimney. The heat even at this distance was very oppressive and the ground about him was covered with pulverized ashes and lava which had been emitted from what he believed to be an incipient volcano.

O'Keefe was lost in astonishment. The snow for a distance of a mile from the crater had entirely disappeared. This was all the more remarkable as it had upon the day previous been several feet in depth. The Sergeant was very much astonished at the remarkable discovery thus brought to light but he was not deceived by the calm. He was convinced that the absolute repose which the volcano then displayed would be of short duration.

Since the 29th of October but one eruption has occurred and that was on the night of November 7th, when another one similar to that which occurred on the 29th, only more violent, occurred. Sergeant O'Keefe happened to be up on the roof of the signal station on this occasion and he portrays the majesty of the scene as the grandest that he has ever witnessed, not excepting that of Vesuvius seen by him in 1822 when he was a lad and before he left his native Italy for America.

The eruption began with a tremendous burst, which shook Pikes Peak to its very foundation, hurling into the air dense clouds of ashes and lava. These explosions succeeded each other with rapidity and increased violence for about one hour, when

235

the volcano seemed to enter into a profound sleep. During the eruption the clouds are strongly illuminated by the reflection of the glowing lava in the crater, giving the scene the appearance of a vast conflagration. This will account for the peculiar light which has been noticed by the sheepherders on the plains east of this city.

Sergeant O'Keefe informs us that the flow of the lava tends towards Ruxtion's Creek, whence the water for the supply of the city is procured and there is no doubt that the hot lava will if it reaches the creek so heat the water that it will be of no earthly use for drinking purposes. It is evident that the eruption has but just begun and should it continue any length of time there is no doubt but that Colorado Springs will meet the same fate as that which destroyed the flourishing cities of Pompeii and Herculaneum. The flow of lava has already extended a distance of three miles from the mouth of the crater and only two eruptions have taken place. Scientists give it as their opinion that the present upheaval will last about three months, after which the volcano will settle down to a state of comparative repose only to burst with renewed vigor in about six years.

The reporter who was sent to investigate this portentous development has not yet returned and fears are entertained for his safety.

SPRING STORM[4]

In the blackness of the Pikes Peak night, it was natural that men should exaggerate and speak of things which were not there. As evidenced by the report of Sergeant C. M. Hobbs, station controller in 1876, actual events occurring in those early years were frightening enough.

May 13, 1876.—Heavy masses of cumulus clouds hung around the Peak in the early afternoon, and snow began at 1:55 P.M. At 3:00 P.M., loud thunder was heard, and flashes of light raced out from the instruments. At the same time began the most violent storm which has prevailed on the Peak this winter, in the midst of which I arrived on the summit with O'Keefe, a Mr. Yates, an

[4] "Annual Report of the Chief Signal-Officer, for 1875," *Report of the Secretary of War to the Forty-Fourth Congress, 1876,* 61–62.

invalid from the Springs, both the mules, and a horse. We left the lake this morning at 8:00 A.M., and I spent all the morning and the afternoon, until 3:00, fixing the line; and just as I concluded to suspend operations on it for the day some heavy, dark clouds that had been hanging over South Peak all of the afternoon moved overhead, and peal after peal of thunder sounded almost at our sides and awoke the echoes in the mountains and valleys around and below us. At the same time snow began to fall and the wind to increase in violence, but I had seen too much bad weather on the Peak to be turned back by this. When we began the last mile, which is the worst of the trail, it was impossible to face the wind with open eyes, and for the last half a mile it was by far the most severe storm that either I, Greenwell, or O'Keefe, who has spent two months here, has ever seen.

O'Keefe fell far behind, and was lost to sight long before I suspected what a nest of trouble we were getting into. After we reached the crater we could not see twenty-five feet ahead of us at times, and I am not exaggerating in the least, and an eighth of a mile from the station I was completely lost, and had to abandon myself to the instincts of Balaam, trusting that we had followed the hidden trail; but we finally went wrong, and, with Yates, myself, and the horse, were completely buried in the snow. We scrambled out, however, with the animals at times sinking to their backs, until we came across a telegraph line, and I knew which way to go. Looking at Yates, I saw that he could not survive such a storm much longer, so I took his horse and told him to follow the line to the house as quickly as possible and send Greenwell out to my assistance. After he left I tied Balaam to a telegraph pole and started forward with the horse. The wind was blowing 46-miles per hour at the time, driving the little pellets of snow like bullets, and time and again I thought I would have to abandon the animals to their fate, even when I knew that I was not more than two hundred feet from the house; but I was determined to keep by them as long as possible. More than once the animal fell on the rocks underneath the snow, cutting her legs in a fearful manner, and it would be impossible to get her started again. Finally, above the noise of the storm I heard Greenwell calling; and when I came out of the darkness, a short

237

distance in front, I gave him the horse and went back for Balaam, whom I found braced up against the driving wind, like the old soldier that she is.

I urged her forward foot by foot, and finally housed her in the woodshed, where Greenwell had arrived with the horse. I sent him out at once to look for O'Keefe, and then began to look to myself and visitor. From the tops of our heads to the soles of our boots there wasn't a single square inch of surface that had been exposed, even to our faces, that wasn't covered with solid ice, quarter of an inch thick, and when Greenwell and O'Keefe arrived, in fifteen or twenty minutes, with Kit, they were in the same condition; animals as well as men were walking pillars of ice and snow. Terrible as was the experience to us residenters, it was doubly so to Mr. Yates, who had never in his life seen anything even suggestive of it, and who honestly believed that his last hour had come.

Had we lost both the mules and the horse and saved only ourselves, we would have considered ourselves fortunate; but with all the animals in good quarters, we could look back to the terrible ordeal through which we had passed only with thankful hearts.

When I left the station the first of the month almost all the snow had disappeared from the Peak; but it is now as much or more than there had been at any time during the past winter; and if the weather had been fair, so that I could have seen the present appearance of the summit, I would have returned to the lake without making a single attempt at finishing the ascent.

O'KEEFE'S GOOD AND FAITHFUL FRIEND[5]

Like Babe, Paul Bunyan's blue ox, and many another famous American character, Sergeant O'Keefe's mule, Balaam, was christened under peculiar circumstances. Pack mule, Rocky Mountain canary, and registered government asset, Balaam attained the Pikes Peak heights in 1873, performed prodigies in line of duty, and continued long after the Sergeant himself had been forced, by storms within the Weather Service, to change his occupation.

[5] *Colorado Springs Gazette* (weekly edition), December 18, 1880.

A small group of people who had gathered in front of the signal office yesterday morning attracted the attention of a *Gazette* reporter, and upon investigation the center of attraction was found to be Sergeant O'Keefe and his ancient government mule Balaam. As the reporter approached Sergeant O'Keefe was heard to remark to the bystanders who had gathered around him, "Gentlemen, you can laugh at that mule as much as you please but he is endowed with better instincts and has got more of a history to back him than any one of you." Whereupon Balaam gave a confirmatory bray. The mule in question was a dapple gray standing about 14 hands high and exhibiting unmistakable signs of having been subjected to many hardships and much exposure. He is a government mule and has been employed ever since the signal station was established on the Peak in transporting the officers to and from the summit.

The Sergeant spoke the truth when he said Balaam had a history, for he was the first mule to traverse the Pikes Peak trail and to breathe the breath of life at an altitude of 14,000 feet above the level of the sea. For seven long years Balaam has climbed and reclimbed that rugged Peak and although he is 32 years old he is to all intents and purposes good for 10 years more of mountain life.

During the seven years of his mountain experience Balaam has made, according to statistics carefully recorded by Sergeant O'Keefe, 1,924 trips from this city to the Peak or an equivalent of 40,960 miles or about twice the circumference of the globe. He has worn out 560 sets of shoes, equal in weight to about a ton of iron. It has cost the department to keep him during that time including forage, shoeing and other necessary expense somewhat over $4,000. From these facts one can realize the value placed upon him by his owners.

There may be those who will wonder at the peculiar name this wonderful mule bears. The name, "Balaam," was given him by an old and much respected citizen of Colorado Springs. The following will explain why the name was given: It was in the summer of 1875 that Sergeant O'Keefe became involved in an argument with Cherokee Charley, a notorious desperado, who will be remembered by many of our citizens. The argument grew out of a dispute between Cherokee Charley and the Sergeant concerning the latter's nativity. The former was bold in his assertions that O'Keefe was an Irishman and not an Italian. The reproach on his nativity O'Keefe could not for a moment tolerate, and the result was a very interesting and protracted argument. Both participants were much bruised and mangled, and were arrested and conducted before the squire of what was then the small town of Colorado Springs. Both were remanded to jail, and, as the customary monthly allowance from headquarters at Washington was not at hand, the Sergeant was compelled to pawn his mule in order to bail 'im. Even since that time the mule has been known to everyone as "Balaam."

BALAAM ON A BENDER[6]

Trails are trails, duty is duty—and too much is too much. So Balaam must have thought, in the year 1881, as he embarked upon his unscheduled Rocky Mountain vacation.

Mr. J. K. Sweeney, of the signal service, is more fully convinced than ever before that the veteran and historic mule, Balaam, is endowed with more instinct than usually falls to the lot of an average human being. Some days ago we stated that Balaam had escaped from the custody of Sergeant O'Keefe, since which time all efforts to recapture the sagacious animal have been to no avail.

"It is nothing more than I expected," said Mr. Sweeney, while in conversation with a *Gazette* reporter, yesterday. "I knew that mule would make a bold, bad break for liberty some day."

"What made you think so?" asked the reporter.

"Well, you see it is only a few days ago that the government cut down that animal's rations and I remarked at the time that there was no economy in cutting down an intelligent mule's rations. From that day to the time that the mule escaped from O'Keefe, there was mutiny in Balaam's eye and I told O'Keefe that Balaam would commit some rash act before many days had passed over his head."

[6] *Colorado Springs Gazette* (weekly edition), February 5, 1881.

From what we could learn, Balaam's escape from O'Keefe was only accomplished through considerable strategy. It seems that the Sergeant had stopped at the lake house for the night. He unsaddled the mule and placed him in the barn near the house without giving him his usual evening's rations. O'Keefe said he hated to do this but he had to obey orders. Some time afterward while the Sergeant was preparing to roll up in his blanket for the night a series of heartrending brays from the mule attracted his attention. Thinking that Balaam had been attacked by some wild animal of the mountains, Sergeant O'-Keefe hurriedly dressed and started for the stable. The moment he opened the stable door Balaam, who was standing in readiness, darted through the stable door, dashed down the mountainside, and disappeared in the darkness. O'Keefe was at once convinced that he had been outwitted by an ignorant, unsophisticated government mule. His indignation knew no bounds and he swore most emphatically that if he ever again came in possession of that mule he would cremate him and send the ashes to the Smithsonian Institution at Washington as a specimen of the ashes thrown out by the Pikes Peak volcano.

The next morning Sergeant O'Keefe clambered over snow banks varying from fifty to one hundred feet in height to the Peak and upon his arrival he telegraphed to Mr. Sweeney the facts relative to the escape of Balaam and instructed him to saddle the other mule, Kit, and put forth his efforts to recapture Balaam.

"Just my luck," exclaimed Mr. Sweeney as he clocked the telegraphic instrument with his forefinger. "If there is any impossible affair to bring about I am the man they look to to perform it."

About fifteen minutes later it was ascertained that the electrical current had ceased to divulge its secrets, in other words communication between the Peak and the central office had been temporarily discontinued by a break in the lines. Mr. Sweeney was again heard to remark in tones not entirely consistent with his usually agreeable and pleasing manner: "I'll bet my month's salary that Balaam realized over a week ago that he would be called upon to assist in repairing the telegraph line and here we are in a fine predicament without a mule that has had an electrical education."

Mr. Sweeney is pluck personified, and the following morning he started out with that poor unintelligent, unintellectual and uneducated mule, Kit, to repair the telegraph line, and if possible to reclaim the prodigal mule, Balaam. After several unsuccessful attempts to find the defective place in the wire, he started for Jones' Park in search of Balaam, thinking that he would easily be caught. Several hours of most diligent search divulged his hiding place, but to catch him was another thing.

There he was with a band of seven wild horses, the manes and tails of which dragged the ground. The horses were of a jet black color and their manes and tails pure white. It was apparent that Balaam had become imbued with the spirit that prevailed among his wild associates and it is averred by Mr. Sweeney, who is like Washington in one respect, that under the example brought to bear upon him, his tail and mane had grown not less than two feet during the two days that he had been at liberty. Even an ear of corn would not tempt him, and Mr. Sweeney says that in no instance did he get within 800 yards of him.

He finally gave up his efforts to recapture the animal and returned to this city with the avowed intention of returning the following day without being thwarted in his purpose.

True to his declarations of the previous day Mr. Sweeney started out yesterday morning and upon his arrival at Jones' Park he was surprised to discover that Balaam had disappeared. After a protracted search among the wild and rocky canyons Mr. Sweeney heard a great uproar and cautiously looking around a rock, saw a sight that made him shiver. There was Balaam with every particular hair standing on end fighting for his life with three full-grown mountain lions. Mr. Sweeney was so provoked at the refractory mule that he didn't care much which whipped but anxious to see the affray out he hid himself behind an adjoining knoll and viewed the situation. Whenever any one of the lions would approach Balaam he would strike at them with his forefeet and thus compel them to retreat, and when they went behind he would kick them in the ribs. In this way he held them at bay, and his vigorous kicks proved very effective. The lions did not give up the conquest until two of their number were laid dead upon the grass at Balaam's feet.

Mr. Sweeney watched the affray with breathless interest and on several occasions when the lions made a bold charge he said to himself, "Balaam is a goner!"

He was much surprised when the remaining lion retreated from the field of battle, but it occurred to him that Balaam was quite exhausted and could be easily caught, but what was his chagrin when the mule dashed off through a deep ravine and soon disappeared from view. Seeing that it was useless to attempt to give him chase Mr. Sweeney turned his attention to the scene of the terrible battle. It was apparent that the savage beasts had first attacked the wild horses for two of them lay dead not far from the carcasses of the lions. Mr. Sweeney was at first nearly overcome with the ghastly spectacle that he beheld, the two dead lions and two dead horses lying at his feet. Realizing that the skins of the lions were of some value he set about skinning the beasts and tied the lion skins to his saddle. Before starting for home he happened to think of the long manes and tails on the wild horses and taking his knife he cut them off and also tied them to the horn of his saddle.

We were shown the trophies above named in the signal office last evening. The hair cut from the wild horses lacks only two inches of being five feet long, while the lion skins are the largest we have ever seen. Mr. Sweeney proposes to keep the hair and skins as remembrances of the exciting adventure and they can be seen at the signal office. When we left, Mr. Sweeney shouted, waving one of the horses's tails over his head, "Hurrah for the United States and Balaam, the government mule." Mr. Sweeney will try to catch Balaam today.

A TRIBUTE TO OLD BALAAM[7]

Balaam was retaken—much to the delight, apparently, of the citizens and newspaper reporters of Colorado Springs. In celebration, the Gazette *edition for May 21 1881, announced the completion of a work of art entitled "Balaam the Beautiful," by*

[7] *Colorado Springs and Manitou* (Colorado Springs, n. d.)

Mr. Charles Craig. Some time later Balaam's adventures were even presented in verse form by an anonymous poet and circulated by the merchants of Colorado Springs and Manitou, whose descriptive booklet was designed especially for the Rocky Mountain tourists of the day.

Where great Pikes Peak his summit rears
   'Mid foot-hills robed in richest brown,
And o'er the Great Plains proudly peers—
   A monarch he with snowy crown,—
There high above the ocean's tides,
A famed, historic mule resides.

Upon the Peak's supremest height,
   Brave men a tireless vigil keep;
'Tis they who, with unerring sight,
   Spy storms afar that onward sweep,
And herald to the world below
When sun shall shine or tempest blow.

From plain to mountain's crest there leads,
   Round cliff and chasm's brink, a trail;
Sure feet, indeed, the creature needs
   Who safe the dizzy heights would scale,
Where one false step the wretch might throw
O'er precipice to death below.

Of all the beasts that climb this trail
   'Tis Balaam (so our mule is named)
Whose history forms the strangest tale,
   Whose exploits are so justly famed—
"Old Prob's" most trusty delegate,
Far Western things to regulate.

For full eight years has Balaam toiled
   This signal service to perform,
His coat with dust of summer soiled,
   His marrow chilled by wintry storm;
And now old age comes on apace,
But find of waning powers no trace.

Pikes Peak Prevaricator

This ancient, grizzled mule I sought,
    If haply he'd be interviewed;
Since sure in Holy Writ 'tis taught,
    How, where the barring angel stood,
A prophet, who was sure no saint,
Had listened to an ass's plaint.

Perhaps long residence on heights,
    Where all know that the air is thin,
May have induced the airy flights
    Of romance this mule reveled in,
Or mighty sweep of range and plain
Have guaged the workings of his brain.

But sure it is no poet's ear
    E'er listened to a stranger tale;
The rocks re-echoed far and near,
    The poet's face grew ashy pale,
As Balaam brayed sonorously
His most astounding history.

He told of high-born ancestry,
    Of noble sire and gentle dam,
Brothers and sisters, gay and free,
    And his young life so bright and calm;
He traced a long, unbroken line
Of proud relations asinine.

Ambitions soon this scion seized
    Which amply proved his pedigree;
He would go West, where parents pleased,
    The Great Plains and the mountains see;
Nor should he e'er in quiet rest
Till he had climbed the Rocky's crest.

That he, this scheme which genius shows,
    Found ways and means to carry out,
No one who mulish methods knows
    Could ever have a lingering doubt.
It may suffice us now to say
That, like all mules, he had his way.

So now, his true vocation found,
   He started on a proud career;
From plain to summit safe and sound,
   He carried hundreds every year—
Ladies who shrieked at steep ascent,
And many a scared but silent gent.

All this and more Old Balaam tells,
   And feels his youth renewed thereby;
But now his bray in anger swells
   And viciously his heels do fly,
While laboring to me to rehearse
His shameful wrongs in halting verse.

"I was a faithful mule," he said,
   "And meant to do the honest thing;
How was I shocked, one night in bed,
   To hear a sharp, resounding ring
That said, by click of telegraph,
My feed must be reduced one-half!

"The civil service, so it said,
   At last has got to be reformed,
A start must somewhere soon be made,
   This citadel corrupt be stormed;
But, since big guns might fire back
They'd try at first a Pikes Peak jack.

All this was too much to be borne;
   My plans with lightning speed were made,
And I was free before the morn.
   Escaped by strategy deep laid,
And guided to the plains below
By the volcano's lurid glow.

"When I was down scarce half the way,
   Three mountain lions gave me chase,
I met them: one yet lives they say,
   The rest in fragments sail through space!
All who seen my backward reach
Will know that solemn truth I teach.

Pikes Peak Prevaricator

"This victory gained, I came to where
   A stream of lava crossed the trail;
The fiery current singed my hair,
   I labored, but without avail
To cross the seething, boiling tide
That must have been full ten yards wide.

"At last I spied a pine-crowned hill,
   O'er topping quiet the highest flame;
Upon its crest I waited till
   A Colorado zephyr came,
Then with my ample ears set sail,
And over sped before the gale!

"So now I'm on my way to see
   The head men of the Narrow Guage;
If they'll but listen to my plea
   And these my burning wrongs assuage,
Between us yet, I have no fears,
We'll take the whole world by the ears.

"I'll ask them to extend their rail
   Clear to the summit of the Peak,
Run opposition to the trail,
   And all that Signal Service clique;
'Old Prob' shall yet bewail the day
When he put Balaam on half-pay.

"The Rio Grande runs, I hear,
   O'er cloud-wrapped summits, 'mid the snow,
Clambers where mountain sheep might fear,
   Or winds through canyons far below.
Success shall yet my efforts crown;
Farewell, I'm off for Denver town!"

With heels and tail aloft in air,
   Old Balaam scampers o'er the plain,
While lifts the poet's conscious hair
   And wildly throbs his swelling brain,
At thoughts of what e'en mules may dare
In this great country of light air!

RESIGNATION[8]

*Windy times, tall tales, doggerel, and publicity for an en-
listed sergeant and his mule, it seems, were not acceptable to
those who supervised the Signal Corps. "Sergeant O'Keefe of
the Pikes Peak signal office," ran the Denver press release, "has
resigned. His rat stories and other myths and legends of that
region caused him to be known as the 'Prevaricator' of Pikes
Peak. Sergeant O'Keefe, with winter snowbound years on the
top of the Pikes Peak, was afforded a rich field for 'fakes' that
made him a national character. The Sergeant was handsomely
banqueted at Colorado Springs before he left that region." For
Denver readers, in that melancholy month of December, 1881,
Mr. Stanley Wood, outstanding Front Range reporter, wrote
in detail of the banquet.*

Sergeant O'Keefe, the well-known prevaricator of Pikes
Peak, has been transferred to another signal station, and yesterday yielded his position to a successor. His friends in this city,
under the leadership of the newspapermen, resolved to give the
Sergeant a farewell banquet, and accordingly the opera house
was secured and the banquet took place here last evening. At
exactly 8 o'clock P.M. the invited guests sat down to four generously provided tables, which were arranged in the form of a
parallelogram in the body of the house, the orchestra chairs
being covered with a temporary floor. The parquet circle, the
balcony, and the gallery of the theater were crowded with spec-
tators who had been attracted there to listen to the speeches and
toasts of the evening, and who testified their enjoyment and
appreciation by frequent bursts of applause.

Lieutenant H. P. Scott, city editor of the *Gazette*, presided,
while Alderman Charles Walker acted as chaplain. After the
dinner had been discussed the tables were cleared and decanters,
generously supplied with water from the various mineral springs
of Manitou (this is a temperance town) were brought out. The
president arose, and with his goblet filled to the brim with Iron
Ute water, proposed the following toast: "O'Keefe, one of the

[8] *Rocky Mountain News*, December 21, 1881. Also *Colorado Springs
Gazette*, (daily edition), December 22, 1881.

greatest prevaricators, equalled by few, excelled by none. True to his record may his life be a romance and in his final resting place may he lie easy." Apropos of this toast Lieutenant Scott said: "The rosy realms of romance are as real to O'Keefe as the stern and sterile steppes of truth are to many. The golden glow which gilds the granite summit of the Peak is but the type of that glamour which surrounds it through the mendacious genius of O'Keefe. This aureole envelopes the mountain and some of O'Keefe's legends—are more stupendous than the Peak itself. In the words of another: 'The microcosm is lost in the macrocosm and the segregation is swept along in the boundless choral aggregation.' (tremendous applause from the gallery). Triumphant tergiversation is productive of more deep and lasting pleasure than parsimonious prevarication, or in the words of the poet the normal condition of affairs is:

> 'Truth forever on the scaffold,
> Wrong forever on the throne.'
> "Gentlemen, here's lookin' at you."

The toast was drunk amid thunderous applause, but when Sergeant O'Keefe arose to reply there was instantaneous and absolute silence. The Sergeant spoke substantially as follows: "Gentlemen. This is the proudest moment av me loif. It is prouder dthan dthe wan whin Oi was a volcano—prouder dthan dthe wan whin Oi vanquished dthe mountain rats—prouder even dthan dthe wan whin I gazed on my completed work av whitewashing dthe Peak.

"It is meself dthat thanks ye for dthis reception and if Oi fail to espriss me gratichoode ye must accept dthe intintion for the deed. Wan is not always aquil to his intintions by dthe same token it is meself that failed signally (no Pun) the other day. It happened dthis way: Balaam, dthe government mule, and meself were descending the Peak, when all at wonst we were attacked by a ravenous mountain lion. Oi threw a bit on him wid me carbine; me intintion was to shoot him in dthe oi. Dthis intintion failed; for Oi missed him altogether. He leaped upon me and dracked me from the mole and we struggled togither on the ground. Oi drew me revolver, me intintion failed, for the pistol missed fire. Balaam was intherested specthator av dthe struggle, and seeing me loik to get dthe worst ov it he opened his capacious mouth and with one snap bit dthe lion's head clean off and swallowed it. Ov coorse afther dthat it made no difference how good me intintion was to shoot him in the oi. Gentlemen, Oi go to seek green fields and pasthures new. Oi shall remimber Pikes Peak with gratichoode and riverence and I desire to express to you me sincere thanks for dthis warm and flattering reception."

When the applause which followed this feeling and characteristic addition had subsided, the president introduced Alderman Ainsworth Brown with the announcement that the Alderman would read an original poem composed for the occasion. A sudden hush fell upon the great audience as the Alderman began in tones trembling with emotion:

> "Assist me now divine poetic fire,
> Come to my aid and help me strike the lyre."

"Hould ther," shouted a clear, determined voice, and the tall slender figure of O'Keefe was seen standing sternly erect, "Hould there! Tergivisator, prevaricator, and mendacious are terrums which may be used in a friendly spirit, but whin you talk about sthrikin' the liar oim here every toim."

Alderman Brown at once resumed his seat and with Spartan firmness refused to proceed with his poem. Speeches were made, however, by General Isaac Bailey and others, and the banquet concluded by all those present rising and singing in a very affecting manner, "Farewell, my own; love of my life, farewell." Thus ended one of the most interesting events of the year in Colorado Springs.

REMINISCENCE[9]

Long after Sergeant O'Keefe had resigned from the Signal Corps, Front Range citizens continued to think of him and of Balaam, his mule. It was inevitable, under the circumstances, that other O'Keefe stories should make their appearance, always adding zest and color to the old days on Pikes Peak.

[9] *Rocky Mountain News*, March 10, 1882.

Pikes Peak Prevaricator

Sergeant O'Keefe, formerly of the signal service on Pikes Peak delivered an eloquent and truthful lecture last evening in the hall of the Young Men's Christian Association. Large crowds of people attended and many were turned away being unable to gain admission. The subject of the lecture was: "My experience on Pikes Peak and What I Know About the Weather."

The Sergeant said he had first heard of the Peak when a very small boy. In the old geographies Pikes Peak was supposed to be located somewhere in the vicinity of Puget's Sound. This was long before the Pikes Peak excitement and the expression "Pikes Peak or Bust," had ever been heard of. When I first heard of the Pikes Peak excitement many years afterward and heard how many were ruining their fortunes and coming out to Colorado, I resolved my motto should be not "Pikes Peak or Bust," but that it would be "bust Pikes Peak." Having made the determination I packed my kit and started for Colorado. One of the first men I met when I struck Denver was Count Murat. I asked him what he thought of Pikes Peak.

"D—— Pikes Peak," says he. (You will excuse my profanity, ladies and gentlemen.) "It's a —— son of a ——— of a place out here. I wish Pikes Peak was thrown down and cast into the sea." I told him that was my idea exactly. We ought to blow up the Peak with dynamite, the thing has caused so much trouble to the pioneers by getting them out here. My professor and I went to the vicinity of Pikes Peak and climbed up to the top. "Faith," said Murat, "This is a fine place up here to be sure. We don't want to tear the blessed thing down." "No," says I. "I think the old Peak is the daisy place and that a man with a 'T.D.' pipe, a pack of cards and an occasional drink of whisky might enjoy life here." "So says I." I said to the Count, "Hurrah for Pikes Peak!" Just as the Count was waving a plug hat a gust of wind came along and blew it down to what is now Colorado Springs. "D—— the Peak," said the Count. "There's a new hat gone to h—l."

The Sergeant then proceded to give some experiences of early days, including his adventures with Professor Goldrick among the Mormons and his final enlistment in the Union army, where he rose to the rank of orderly sergeant. At the close of the war the Sergeant returned to Colorado, where he at one time lived on the Peak and intended to establish himself as a hermit. The War Department intending to establish a signal service station on the Peak, selected him as a proper man to have there. He had served with credit in the army and had been twice wounded. He had picked up a good deal of knowledge of meteorological matters, and General Myer, more commonly known as "Old Probabilities," had expressed a high opinion of him.

The Sergeant here gave an interesting history of the origin and progress of the signal service system and a description of the manner of making up with telegrams and arranging storm signals.

He then proceeded to relate a great number of practical jokes which he had played upon clergymen, newspaper reporters and others who had visited the Peak. These truthful tales are too familiar to most people who know the Sergeant to need any repetition in these columns. The speaker told how he had come through the conspiracy of his enemies to sever his connection with the station. He called attention to the fact that Colorado weather had changed greatly for the worse since he left the Peak, and how the country had seen unparalleled storms and atmospheric disturbances since General Hazen was placed at the head of the Signal Service Bureau.

In speaking of the age of the Peak O'Keefe expressed himself as follows: "Through all these years great changes have taken place. Of all those who saw the original peak before the barnacles struck it, few except the burros and the horses hired to tourists at Manitou now view it. But even the Colorado jackass, old as he is, does not remember the day when over this Centennial State rolled a great inland sea. But elevations occurred and depressions of water, parts of dry land came to the surface, and other more sandy soils sank down far beneath the waves. When through the ages all the water had left the center of North America, the higher elevations became high mountains and the lesser elevations, plains and tablelands. Slowly the Peak gained accretions of rocks and soils till it stands today a little nearer the Kingdom of Heaven than the average Denver alderman.

But what good is it that the land below is poor and unproductive? Why not take down this mass of richer and more varied soils and spread it around loosely? Let the Signal Service Bureau use the electric tower in North Denver. It is good enough for any observations they know how to make. So ladies and gentlemen, I come down to my first expression of the evening. Instead of saying, "Pikes Peak or Bust," let us "bust Pikes Peak." If this can't be done, I will engage to do this: I will engage to take Pikes Peak and run it cheaper than the Weather Bureau does. At the same time I will provide better weather."

At the conclusion of the lecture a petition to Congress asking for Sergeant O'Keefe's reappointment to the Peak was read and received a large number of signatures.

O'KEEFE SPEAKS OUT[10]

Although public opinion proved, from the beginning, to be of no avail, Sergeant O'Keefe, lingering in Denver and other cities near Pikes Peak, at least received the opportunity to speak out—as a private American citizen—upon the subject of his "resignation." That he did, in no uncertain terms.

The Sergeant's name is a household word throughout the country, he being more widely known than General Hazen himself, the chief of the service. To mention Pikes Peak is to recall to the mind of every well-informed person the name of Sergeant O'Keefe, whose wonderful adventures on the historic hill have been the theme of much amazement and amusement to those who have read the veracious accounts of them. It having become known that he had left the service, the reporter found out why. He had been promoted by a disgruntled Lieutenant Dunwoody sent out to inspect the station, who wanted free lunch and the place cleaned up. The Sergeant, who had nothing to hide, "carefully" began his story.

"About the middle of September, 1881, Lieutenant Dunwoody arrived in Colorado Springs and telegraphed me on the Peak the fact of his arrival. I at once saddled up Balaam and started for the base station. Upon arrival . . . we argued about formality and then went back up the Peak and argued there.

[10] *Rocky Mountain News*, February 26, 1882.

253

"After enjoying a free lunch," continued the Sergeant, "the Lieutenant made a hasty inspection of the station, and after due deliberation reported it in dirty condition, and then suggested the propriety of having it thoroughly cleaned, the strictest economy was to be observed, however, and the munificent sum of seventy-five cents per week was to be allowed the party taking this gigantic contract.

"Lieutenant Dunwoody suggested that a woman be employed for this work, as it would be more economical and of great saving to the service.

"Just picture to yourself an old washwoman mounted on Balaam; with a scrubbing brush in one hand and a washtub in the other, and a cake of hard soap in her pocket, going up seventeen miles in the mountains to take this contract.

"When this was told to Balaam, the government mule, he laughed and remarked that there were other jackasses in the employ of the government as well as himself.

"Upon our arrival at Colorado Springs the Lieutenant informed me that he had received orders from General Hazen to promote me for valuable services rendered on the Peak, and consequently I received my diploma in a few days appointing me the chief mule driver, and train dispatcher to Dunwoody's burro train, which was to start at regular intervals from Colorado Springs to the Peak with supplies.

"Now, Mr. Reporter, some men would have felt highly elated at this unexpected promotion, but I am of a retiring disposition, and I declined this sudden elevation in the service with thanks. General Hazen wrote a fatherly letter, and told me distinctly that as he went to a good deal of trouble and arrogance to procure this appointment for me he would consider it an act of the basest ingratitude if I refused to accept it, and would consider such a refusal as this disobedience of orders and liable to court martial. Under such circumstances I could not very well decline to accept my well-merited promotion. After two months arduous service my health began to decline, and the physicians at Colorado Springs recommended that I should seek a lower altitude, as a further stay on Pikes Peak might prove detrimental to me health. Testimonials as regards my ability and character were forwarded to General Hazen, with a recommendation that I should be promoted for valuable services rendered, in which the General concurred, and after being relieved from the Peak station, I reported for duty at Washington, D. C., for assignment as an acting signal officer. Owing to a disagreement with the General as to whether mule cleaning should be classified as a distinct branch from meteorology or be embraced in Hazen's chart book of infantry in the rear, I resigned my position as an acting signal officer to date from December 24, 1881."

During the conversation between the Sergeant and his chief in Washington, as reported by Mr. O'Keefe, General Hazen said that Pikes Peak had been brought into national disrepute by the stories told by the veracious observer regarding the mountain rats, the volcano, the artesian well and the whitewashing of the Peak.

There are a good many people in this part of the country who suspect that O'Keefe was frozen out of the service because he was attracting more attention than any other man in the service, not excepting its ornamental chief.

OBITUARY[11]

The nature of O'Keefe's later experiences is largely a matter of conjecture. Occasional notices in the Denver and Colorado Springs newspapers indicate that he was employed for a time by the Colorado Telegraph Company, of Denver, and afterwards as a railway mail agent. His obituary, although including certain inaccuracies as well as the misspelling of his name, rounds out the story of this Western wanderer who, even in his own time, had become legendary along the Rocky Mountain Front Range.

John T. O'Keefe, stoker of steamer No. 2, of the Denver fire department, stationed at Colfax and Santa Fe avenues, died suddenly yesterday afternoon at his home 1174 Champa Street. O'Keefe resided there with his wife and two children, a boy of fourteen years of age and a babe of a few months. . . .

[11] *Rocky Mountain News*, February 3, 1895. The United States weather station on Pikes Peak was abandoned in 1899, and the grave of "Erin O'Keefe" has long since disappeared.

The dead man was an ordinarily healthy appearing person and weighed fully two hundred and twenty pounds. He was devoted to his family and known by all his fellows as a sterling, upright character. . . .

Born thirty-nine years ago in New York City, of Irish parentage, he early exhibited a thirst for education. When but sixteen years of age he passed successfully through the high school examination and entered the congressional competition for a cadetship at Annapolis. He was successful and was appointed in 1872. For two years he studied like a Trojan and was at the head of his class at the termination of each year. In 1873, however, he entered into the hazing combination in which a colored cadet was put through the process and with eighteen other cadets was dismissed from the Academy.

It was but a short time afterwards that he entered the signal service under Capt. Howgate. . . . He was made a sergeant and assigned to duty at Marquette, Michigan. . . . From Marquette O'Keefe was transferred to Colorado Springs but was detailed to Philadelphia during the Centennial celebration in 1876. After the Centennial was over he was again assigned to Colorado and given charge of Pikes Peak signal station. Here it was that Sergeant O'Keefe made his great reputation.

Isolated away up among the clouds it was but seldom that visitors came to him except in the summer months. And when they did come he told them such stories of the horrors of an altitude of fourteen thousand feet that their blood ran cold. He also wrote for the eastern papers the most bloodcurdling accounts of the terrors of Pikes Peak and for months the papers were full of Sergeant O'Keefe's lucubrations.

For nearly eleven years he was in charge of Pikes Peak signal station and about 1887 he left the signal service and entered the railway mail service, where he served with honor and distinction for a number of years. Leaving the railway mail service he was appointed on May 18, 1894, on the Denver fire department through the influence of old-time friends and was regarded as one of the best men in the service. He was a man of wide information, genial by nature, and well thought of by all his associates.

Unnatural Natural History

FROM the beginning, scientists have manifested intense interest in the natural history of the West. Into their records have gone innumerable descriptions of flora and fauna. Bolstering accuracy, many languages—both dead and alive—have been used. No habitat, no relics or imprints, it would appear, have been overlooked. Yet strangely, the most vital specimens—those rare and mysterious creatures reported even now to be roaming the West—have eluded research, and so, as far as the technical experts can say, do not exist.

On the Plains today, of course, observation and study continue at less formal levels. Every self-respecting rancher has his pack of flea-inhabited greyhounds and his corral-full of snorting, mercurial broomtails, with which he pursues, in scientific mood, the coyotes, prairie dogs, swivel-headed owls, bull-bats, and giant, mule-eared rabbits of the sage. Distance; hunger, thirst, dust, wind, and rain; sprains and dislocations; broken legs, arms, noses, backs, and necks—in the pursuit of Western historical fact, these are but minor distractions, incidentals, like those associated with earthquakes, floods, war, and other national whimsies, which merely add a hint of spice and color to the quest.

In the mountains, research methods and objectives differ but results to the student remain much the same. There mule-eared deer, bull elk buglers, thumping grouse, and unreliable grizzlies; catamounts and kindred caterwaulers; sidehill winders, flint-billed woodpeckers, warbling Rocky Mountain canaries, and slide-rock bolters provide intense action, uncertainty, and, not infrequently, regret. But most memorable of all, to the quick and the crippled who return from a day's work in the field, are those quiet evening hours after strain when true perspective dawns. Then it is that surviving students settle back, bandaged and blissful, with their notes. Then it is that cabin fires burn brightest, talk grows cheerful, fur-bearing trout smell strong and fragrant in the pan, and the latest secrets of canyon and slope are exchanged, without reservation, for the common advancement of mankind.

FUR-BEARING TROUT[1]

The origin and habits of Western fur-bearing trout (salmo con epidermis muskwrattis) *have always been of interest to Rocky Mountain anglers.*

The fur-bearing trout, or beazel, is known to the trout streams of Colorado, Michigan, Pennsylvania, and Maine. The origin of this unusual trout in the Arkansas River of Colorado is a story peculiar in itself and follows thusly:

The town of Leadville [Colorado] was incorporated as a mining town in the year of 1878. It was during the winter of 1877 and 1878 that meat was supplied to the miners in the form of venison by professional game hunters. Now during those winter months the miners ate so much venison and fried potatoes that the venison tallow became caked to the roofs of their mouths to the extent that they were unable to taste their coffee and other beverages. This was indeed distressing and often they eliminated this handicap by wiring a bundle of pitch splinters on the top of their heads and setting fire to it. The result was that the tallow was melted and they again had the sense of taste, but the net result was that nearly ninety-seven per cent of the miners in the camp became bald-headed.

About the middle of the spring a gentleman from Kentucky who had been in the hair tonic business in that state reached camp. He was a Republican and had left his state to avoid trouble with government tax agents who tried to collect the heavy tax on his product.

In time he started to manufacture his hair tonic from potatoes on a small creek south of Leadville and to sell his product to the miners of the camp.

It was on a rainy summer evening that he was coming to town with four jugs of hair tonic, one in each hand and one

[1] *Canon City* (Colorado) *Record*, February 16, 1939.

under each arm. It was necessary for him to cross a trout stream which empties into the Arkansas River on a footlog. In so doing he slipped and had to drop two of the jugs to retain his balance. The result was that the falling jugs struck rocks in the stream and were broken.

Not long after that the trout fishermen of that vicinity changed their methods. Instead of the usual rod and reel, they would go down to the creek on Saturday afternoon, stick a red, white, and blue pole in the bank, put on a white coat, wave a copy of the Police Gazette in one hand, and brandish a pair of scissors in the other, and yell, "Next," until they had the limit of these fine fur-bearing trout with full beards, etc. The trout would leap up onto the bank after these tonsorial lures and were picked up by the fishermen.

This practice continued until the mill tailings from the mills riled the waters so that the trout could no longer see the barber poles.

A FISH DINNER[2]

While hunting at the foot of Long's Peak, in 1871, Joseph Addison Thatcher, Central City banker, added his bit to a visiting cowpuncher's knowledge of Rocky Mountain natural history.

We were telling stories which seemed to interest the cowboy, but he never made a remark—some were pretty highly overdrawn, too. Finally, I said, "Boys, I don't think I ever told you my experience fishing in the North Platte. Well, the fishing was rather poor that summer up there. One morning I took my steel rod, a buttered sandwich in my basket, and set off, expecting to be out all day. About noon I had a half-dozen nice trout in my basket, and a severe rainstorm, with terrible thunder and lightning, came up.

"I left the creek and started across a clear place of ground for a clump of trees to get out of the rain. I was running with my rod held up in my right hand, when a streak of lightning

[2] J. A. T. (Joseph Addison Thatcher), *A Colorado Outing* (Denver, 1905).

struck the steel rod, darting me senseless to the ground. I came to in a short time, found I was not hurt, and looking around I saw that my creel upon the ground was a bed of live coals, and there were my trout lying upon the coals beautifully broiled. My sandwich was ready toasted, and, to show you the eccentricity of electricity, the bones had been taken out of the fish and made into toothpicks and laid beside the fish. A more dainty lunch I never had. What do you think of that?"

The cowboy couldn't stand this last story and turned on his side, laid his hand on his pistol, and said, "I will bet a dollar that's a lie." I turned to him and said, "My friend, I don't want to win your money by betting on a sure thing—but if old Bill Shakespeare was alive, I could prove it by him. Did you know him?" The cowboy said, "No; where did he range his cattle?" There was a silence in the tent; then turning, he said good evening, and went out into the night.

AURIFEROUS TROUT[3]

Like other Westerners, Western fish are great travelers. In the Yellowstone region, old Jim Bridger is said to have identified mountain-climbing trout that had packed over the lofty Pacific Slope by way of Two Ocean Pass. Even more remarkable, however, were the "Auriferous Trout," discovered in the swirling waters of the Grosvent.

The queerest thing I ever saw or heard of was getting gold from the fish in the Grosvent River. The first mess of trout we caught in that river we all noticed, as we began to eat the fish, was filled with grit. None of the boys could assign the cause. I began to meditate, and said to Jo Voshay: "Don't you remember the remark I made to you when I showed you the trout?"

"About their yellow color," asked Jo.

"Exactly," I responded. "I'm a fishologist but never before seen nor heard tell of a yellow trout."

I revolved the matter in my mind a few times, and then

[3] From a newspaper clipping, "Auriferous Trout," which attributed the story to one William Hooton, a prospector near the headwaters of Snake River, "Oddities," *Dawson Scrapbooks*, Vol. II, 43.

dropped onto the cause all at once. So I went and caught a few more, and examined closely. I found gold stowed away all around the gills, and got a good, fair prospect by making a thorough clean-up. But the best prospect was obtained by scraping the trout. Some way or another the gold got under the scales and it was abundant. Gold also clung to the outside of the scales, which is a standing mystery to me. The mystery is, how can gold dust cling to such a slick surface as that of a fish. Is it a property of the fish scales or of the gold that causes it? I haven't the slightest idea, but it's a fact, and that's enough. We made good wages cleaning up the trout, and had more fish than we could eat. The average was about four bits a fish.

There is something more than strange and seemingly unreasonable about these true, genuine gold fish. If every word of what I have said isn't the truth, may I be struck with a realizing sense of the righteousness of veracity, and may I be kicked, belted, and abused generally, figuratively speaking, by the Nemesis of an injured conscience, and be a mark for the truthful who shoot off their mouths at the unreconstructable liars who have not the truth in their "constitution and by-laws," and who can never enter the Kingdom of Heaven, and may I have scales all over my back the rest of my days like a salt water salmon!

A COWPUNCHER LOSES HIS PUP[4]

Tragic indeed was the story of a Colorado cowpuncher and his dog, as reported in Western newspaper columns a generation ago.

Some of the storage reservoirs for irrigation water in southeastern Colorado contain catfish by the thousands, their size varying from the "fry" recently planted to as large, it is reported, as any ever hooked in the Mississippi River.

Ura Lyon, a well-known cowboy of the Bobtail Ranch, located in Otero County, reports the loss of his half-grown Airdale pup, Alkali, who, he says, was swallowed up as bait by a catfish in the Apishapa reservoir, where ten thousand "cat fry"

[4] From an unidentified clipping, "Oddities," *Dawson Scrapbooks*, Vol. II, 41.

were recently placed after the irrigation officials had completed a three-foot crown on the dam retaining the water. (Lyon is truthful.)

"I had been riding all day," said Lyon, "and Alkali was following me. By mid-afternoon the pup was tired out. In order not to leave him behind I took down my lasso, a half-inch, four-strand, closely woven manila, and tied one end to the pup's neck and the other to my saddle horn. When we reached the reservoir the pup was hot and thirsty and before I could stop him had plunged into the water to drink his fill and cool off.

"The rope was still around his neck. He was several feet from the shore, swimming in deep water. I was still in the saddle, "twisting" a smoke, when suddenly I was catapulted over my horse's head to the ground, and my horse, Sagebrush, was slowly being pulled toward the water.

"Sagebrush, one of the best roping horses in the world, who can flip a one-thousand-pound steer and hold him without moving six inches, was straining every muscle in his body, but was slowly being dragged toward the water. Suddenly, however, the rope line grew slack and I caught a glimpse of a long, glistening, blackish body with an extremely large head, that looked like that of a catfish, and a mouth as wide as a door.

"There was a lightning-like plunge. Swish! Snap! The rope had parted and Sagebrush went down on his haunches, but my poor little Alkali and half of my lasso disappeared into their fishy tomb."

GRANDPA TROUT[5]

In Colorado, catches of large, belligerent trout provoke little comment. However, when fishermen are forced to run for their lives, that is news.

Some thirty-odd years ago Tommy Poinsett, a prospector who was working his mining claims close to Blue Lake at the head of the Blue River in the Breckenridge district, got several cans of young rainbow trout and packed them on his burros to stock Blue Lake.

[5] "Oddities," *Dawson Scrapbooks*, Vol. II, 43.

The lake contains lots of fish food and the "rainbows" thrived amazingly, but would only bite for sport, as living was easy. Some of those old-timers evidently have survived the thirty-odd years.

Last summer, while County Commissioner Eli Fletcher was fishing in Blue Lake, he waded out on the sand bar at the upper end of the lake and saw what he first took to be a submerged, big, round stick of cordwood. Looking closer, he saw that it was an immense trout that apparently was sunning himself in the shallow water of the sand bar.

"He was so big he scared me," said Mr. Fletcher, who made several casts at the monster trout that refused to bite. Finally the trout, becoming enraged, made a break for the County Commissioner who was interrupting his siesta, chasing him out of the water and snapping at his rubber wading boots.

Fletcher still has the rubber boots at his home to show any "doubting Thomas."

Asked how long the fish was, he said it was probably a couple of inches or more short of four feet, with teeth nearly an inch long. Commissioner Fletcher believes that the big trout of the Blue Lake should be removed as they probably eat their own weight of smaller fish every week. He is considering making an application for a permit to use a young harpoon with which to kill the big "rainbows."

ANGLING IN WYOMING[6]

Of all accounts of dry-country fishing the world over, perhaps the most valuable are those recorded by Western American ichthyological research experts, who should know what they are talking about.

"Thar's some cur'us things I've seen up our way," earnestly observed the old Wyoming frontiersman, as we watched the piñon boughs snap and crackle one night in camp, in New Mexico, while waiting for the hour of eight and bedtime to come after a hard day's work in the placer diggings on the Rio Hando.

[6] Frank P. Garton, "Around the Camp Fire," *The Great Divide*, Vol. X, No. 2 (October, 1893), 24–25.

"These here desert 'meerages' that look like groves, 'n' cricks, 'n' bunches o' green range set out on the desert sand, where they ain't nothin' o' th' kind in two hundred miles, air th' werst up on the Pizen Crick in our country, I ever seen. That was where I camped, in '84, when I hit that country, 'n' located my band of cattle on the headwaters o' Pizen. Up th' gulch about an hour's ride from my shack, I discovered, ez I thought, ez fine a water hole as y'ever saw, 'n' watered th' stock there fer nearly a week afore I found we'd all bin worked fer suckers. There wuz no water at all. It was only a 'meerage.'

"Well, if I was fooled, you ought of seen a young feller that came up t' my place from Cheyenne onc't t' hev a good fish, ez he called it. He hed a reg'lar dude outfit o' tools fer fishin', an', jest fer th' fun of it, I sent th' feller up t' this here 'meerage' hole, while I jumped my bronk' an' rode up out o' sight behin' th' hogback, and watched 'im. The water looked s'nat'r'l like, 'n' appeared such a likely place fer trout, thet he took off his clo'es, 'n' waded out t' his waist. Then he begun whippin' the stream, 'n' I'm blamed if thet chump didn't ketch sixteen whoppin' fish inside 'f half 'n hour! They was gamey, too, 'n' ud jump like a burned steer, clear out o' the water, t' ketch th' hook. When he hed his basket plum full, he waded ashore 'n' set down t' count 'is fish—'n' then y'ought of seen 'im look! He hedn't no fish, et all—he'd jest been ketchin' 'meerages.' "

A SNAKE IN TIME . . .[7]

Although the rattlesnake tribe has never been popular in the West, individual specimens at times have proved useful. The famous Vanderwalker, of Victor, Colorado, has preserved for the record one such occasion.

Having filled up at the grub layout, we whackers gathered about the chip fire to discuss the day's drive and anything that might stray from the mind of those possessed of a loose tongue. One, a short, thick-set, easy-go-lucky whacker, nicknamed "Dumpy Bob," got the floor first by asking:

[7] "Camp-Fire Tales," by "Vanderwalker of Victor," *The Trail*, Vol. III, No. 3 (August, 1910), 20–22.

"Say fellers, talk about them rattlers we seen today being numerous. They were some bad—sure. But, did you ever whack bulls up around Wallace, in the limestone country, along in July and August? I did, dog my cats if they weren't so thick around there them times we had to put the cattle on stilts, and ride in the wagon to keep from being bit. The snakes were like waves of the ocean coming in shore. Why the pesky—"

"My young friend—," the interruption came from old Pike, the prospector-miner, the ancient mariner of the prairie schooner. He never addressed himself to, or alluded to, another's feeling's or conversation unless to assist his memory or teach a moral. "My young friend," repeated old Pike. "That which seemingly appeared at first notice to be useless and dangerous, and, to our minds uncalled for, may prove at a critical moment our preserver and savior, if you will—to cut a long story short. Well, a few years ago my partner and your humble servant, after a disastrous prospecting trip, found ourselves in a small mining camp. A creek hard by with water as pure and clear as a crystal, after flowing some distance from camp, separated into two streams to meet again a few miles distant at the foot of Leavenworth Mountain. But I digress . . . [They met a kind stranger who entertained them in his cabin.]

"Our new friend had been given our tale of woe. Our preserver, savior, or good angel, as you will, kindly informed us he had several mining claims; that assessment work was required on the same. Would we undertake the job? If satisfactory to all concerned he'd stake us. That was a pudding and we accepted with alacrity.

"In the morning we were directed down the creek. He gave us a map, or drawing, to guide us properly. Having arrived, we looked over the property, discovering a shaft. This we examined. Having a rope for the purpose we intended at least one of us would go below with its aid.

"But, not to let the point of the story get away from us, I am bound to state that there were other features which aided and I am bound to tell 'em. On the way to the claim down the trail, from mere force of habit, I put my hand in my pocket and then wondered if I might not find something that had been overlooked or escaped detection, something that might prove of value.

"In the search I found—you would not guess in a thousand years. But I'll not harrow your feelings. It was—you won't believe me, I know. Well, it was a mouse there. It was such an odd find. I'm a lover of animals, and considering all the circumstances I was justified in attempting to make a pet of this, hoping to train it in the way I should like to have it go. It seemed satisfied with the narrow confines of my pocket, I having replaced the diminutive creature again in the place where I found it.

"Arrived at the shaft, we found a windlass; the rope was properly adjusted, and, being the lighter of the two, it was my province to descend into the depths. Unfortunately the rope was not of sufficient length and the last few windings on the windlass caused it to run and I came to the bottom with great force and very sudden. Instead of the shaft being only twenty feet, it was all of thirty. There I lay senseless from the fall.

"My partner, I found out after, had called me. Getting no answer, he feared I was dead. Realizing that we were strangers in that section and returning to camp frightened him so, he took to the tall uncut.

"After a time I came to my senses. I thought it was strange that I should have been left thus alone. I cried out at the top of my voice. I was pretty desperate. Unless assistance came it would be a case of starvation for me. I prayed for aid, of course—

"My friends, strange are the ways of Providence. While thinking over the desperate situation in which I was placed, something tumbled into the shaft, striking me a glancing blow in its descent. You will be surprised, but it was the biggest rattlesnake that ever came under my notice. It had been stunned by the fall. I stood watching it, having for a time forgotten my predicament in this new and startling visitation. Pretty soon the creature began to wiggle about, the same time I began to feel pretty creepy myself. It was a horrible situation, I assure you. Penned up with a deadly rattler—I acted quickly, I just put my foot on the back of its head, pinning it to the ground.

"As I said, animals of all kinds were a sort of delight to me and, if possible, this snake should work me good and not harm.

I began to stroke it; sort of petting the creature. Then I bethought me of the mouse in my pocket. But his snakeship was in no mood for my endearments. I could have crushed the life out of the thing; but why I did not—well, as I said, Providence works in mysterious ways, and here was one of them.

"Unable to release itself and evidently realizing that I meant it no harm, it began to struggle less. I talked to it in the dead language, which few humans or even reptiles understand properly. The creature seemed to understand somehow that I only meant good and not ill and desired peace between us.

"The mouse again recurred to me. I showed the creature to the snake. Tears came into its eyes as it disappeared down his snakeship's throat. It seemed to be a welcome meal and I explained, in the language of the morgue, how I came to be there and my anxiety to be again among my kind.

"After my talk, the snake remained in a deep study or trance for some time. It seemed an age. It seemingly understood the situation and had made up its mind to act, realizing that it meant freedom for both.

"Soon it began to crawl up my body. Oh! Oh! But I remembered something about 'keen as a serpent,' or something like that. After getting himself coiled in my arms, he began to indicate, with an upward motion of the head, that he desired to reach the collar of the shaft.

"I began the motion of lowering and raising its body, each successive rise being stronger. Bracing myself for his final command or hiss, when all seemed to his liking, with all my strength I flung him toward the opening above, and, with the assistance of his natural spring, he flew toward the mouth of the shaft, just getting a turn about the windlass frame, then after a few efforts successfully gained the surface, disappearing.

"The absence of the snake began to tell on me. The mouse was gone, the snake had its freedom, but poor me was in durance vile. I bethought me that history was about to repeat itself. Once again was a human to be deceived by a serpent.

"After a long and anxious wait for deliverance, I heard a commotion overhead. Some dirt and gravel fell. My gaze was fixed upon a moving object. It appeared to be a rope. Slowly, cautiously, it approached near enough for me to examine it. My surprise was great. It was my old friend, the rattler, and some of his kind.

"Approaching the bottom of my prison, or close enough to where I could just reach him, he motioned me with his head to take hold and climb out. I quickly took advantage of the invitation, so thankful was I for my escape from prison.

"Gentlemen, so sure as I hope to merit your esteem for veracity, I can place my hand on my heart and say, without fear of contradiction, that my friend, the rattler, on gaining the surface had gone among his friends, collected them about the shaft and prevailed upon them to form a rope,—the first one on the surface taking a grip with his tail about the windlass frame. The others slid down the backs of those before them, each taking a grip with his tail about his companion, thus forming a chain or rope to the bottom, and rescuing me from what was likely to be my tomb.

"No, my young friend, one can never tell what favors one may procure, at unexpected times, from a beast, reptile or friend, provided you rope them in properly."

THE TENDERFOOT'S FRIEND[8]

Another touching manifestation of reptilian affection for mankind occurred in Colorado, it appears, some time during the eighties.

A brother from the East came to visit a cowboy working for John Iliff, the cattle king of Colorado in the '80's. One day the tenderfoot came upon a snake pinned down by a boulder which had rolled off a cliff. He released the rattler and won its eternal gratitude. It followed him like a pet dog. Even slept on the foot of his bed at night.

One night he awoke with a start, feeling that something was wrong. The snake was missing from its accustomed place. He went out in the kitchen, feeling a draft from that direction. Sure enough, the window was open and there was the snake with its body tightly wrapped around the burglar, with its tail hanging out the window, rattling for help.

[8] From the files of the Colorado Writers' Program, WPA, 1940.

A PARTICULARLY NARROW ESCAPE[9]

Accidents will happen. Especially is this so when the average Westerner, possessing little fondness for snakes, finds himself face to face with a rattler.

A gentleman who came in from the Tip Top country states that on last Sunday morning a well-known prospector, who stands six feet in his stockings, and wears a No. 13 boot, was enjoying the genial sunshine of a hill when he stepped on the tail of a monster rattlesnake, which was also enjoying a sun bath.

The first intimation the prospector had of the snake's presence was a sharp, angry hiss, quickly followed by a swishing sound, as the great snake threw himself into a whip-like semicircle through the air, dashing its head against the prospector's left top vest pocket, which contained a large square plug of chewing tobacco, into which the snake sunk its fangs and from which it was unable to pull them through the cloth vest, and there the snake hung, with its tail fast under the prospector's boot and its head within a few inches of his mouth, thrashing its body against his overalls with the sound of three hotel chambermaids beating a carpet.

The prospector stood like one mesmerized, inhaling the sickening odor which rose from the mouth of the hissing snake, with his eyes fastened on the beadlike orbs of the enraged reptile. But the snake's struggling grew weaker and weaker as the tobacco-colored venom oozed from the sides of its mouth, the tobacco making it sick. In a short time it hung limp, dangling from the prospector's vest like a great rawhide rope.

The tobacco had made it deathly sick; a film passed over its eyes; the charm was broken. A spasmodic movement of the prospector's arm and the reptile's head was crushed against the plug of tobacco. Then the horrified prospector fell over unconscious, where he was soon afterward found by a companion, all tangled up with the dead snake. He was disentangled and restored to consciousness. He felt for his plug of tobacco, cut out and threw away a bright green piece from the middle of it, took a chew from the corner of the plug and told the above story.

9 "Oddities," *Dawson Scrapbooks*, Vol. II, 37.

NOISY BEDFELLOWS[10]

Snakes and politicians, it has often been claimed, have certain attributes in common.

Eatumup Jake said down on the Republican River in western Kansas the rattlesnakes were awful thick when the country was first settled. He said they had their dens in the Chalk Bluffs along the Republican and Solomon rivers; said these bluffs were full of them. It was nothing for the first settlers in that country to get together on a Sunday afternoon in the fall of the year and kill fifteen thousand rattlesnakes at one bluff as they lay on the shelves of the rock that projected out from its face. He said the snake dens were two or three miles apart, all the way along the river for a hundred miles, and when someone would start in to killing them at one place, why all the snakes at that den would start in to rattling. Then the snakes at the dens on each side of where they were killing them would wake up and hear the neighbors' rattle, and then they'd get mad and begin to rattle and that would wake up the snake dens beyond them and start them to rattling. And in an hour's time all the snakes for a hundred miles along that country would be rattling. When these two hundred million snakes all got to rattling at once you could hear them one hundred miles away and all the settlers in eastern Kansas would go into their cyclone cellars. But after the Populists got so thick in Kansas, if they did get to hear the snakes rattling, they just thought five or six Populists had got together and was talking politics.

Then Packsaddle Jack told about a bull snake family he used to know in southern Kansas. He said the whole family had yellow bodies beautifully marked below the waists; but from their waists up, including their necks and heads, were a shiny coal black. The old man bull snake would beller just like a bull when he was stirred up. The old lady bull snake had sort of an alto voice and the younger master and misses bull snakes went from soprano to tenor down to a hiss. He said this family of bull snakes were very proud of their clothes, as they weren't any other bull

[10] Benton, *Cowboy Life*, 56–60.

snakes dressed like them, all the other bull snakes being just a plain yellow. And old Mrs. Bull Snake used to talk about her ancestors on her father's side, and she called the scrubby willow under which they had their den the family tree, and talked about the family tree half the time.

But with all their glory this aristocratic family of half-black bull snakes came to an untimely end. One day there came along a couple of mangy Kansas hogs and rooted the whole family out, and ate them up as fast as they could; rooted up the family tree also.

The more we told the stories the more snake-bite antidote we imbided, till we got so full of the antidote it's safe to say that it would have been sure death for any poisonous reptile to have bitten any man in the crowd. Some of us wept a good deal over the memory of our dead friends and other things, and altogether this was about the most enjoyable half day of our journey.

VISITOR IN CAMP[11]

Tales of the unexpected guest are always interesting—particularly if the guest is also uninvited.

I remember one event that happened on Stinking Water. I was awakened one night by something crawling over my feet. I brushed at it thinking it was a cricket and got quite a shock when I found that it was a rattler. I jumped out of bed with a yell that woke everyone in camp. My partner crawled out in a hurry, too, believe me. We lit the candles and looked cautiously around for the snake and there he was all coiled up in our bed, just like he intended to spend the night. He was a big, yellow fellow with eleven rattles. We didn't like the idea of his walking in so boldly and running us out of our bed, so of course we got a big club and ended his career right there. The next morning I cut off his rattles and put them in my violin for they are supposed to improve the tone of string instruments.

[11] From an interview with Thomas H. Richardson, an old cattleman of Custer, South Dakota, secured by a Wyoming worker on the Writers' Project of the WPA.

The fellows all razzed me a lot about the snake deal and laughed about how I yelled, so I determined to get even with them. I took a lath and tied some of the rattles on it and sneaked up back of the boss's tent, where a bunch of them were holding a consultation about the work. I had just heard Gillette tell Saulsberg to go to a certain chest in the corner and get some maps from it. I stuck the lath under the tent flap and rattled it by that chest. Saulsberg was sticking his head into the box looking for the maps and say—did he ever come out of there! He nearly jumped through the top of the tent and as he stuttered so badly, it took him quite a while to tell about the snake. They were all excited by that time and a couple of the boys grabbed sledge hammers and started in opposite directions around the tent to find the "snake." I knew they would give me a good "sledding"—drag me about by the feet—if they caught me; so I quickly decided that I would rather meet Malcolm, the smaller of the two. I dodged past him and he fell over the tent ropes; so I got away with the prank.

THE HUNTING TALE OF TRUTHFUL GEORGE[12]

The American West, quite naturally, is full of things besides snakes and fish. Bears, for example, have always exerted a certain influence there.

Jack Ostrander's ranch, a little back from the road connecting Grand Lake camp and Georgetown [Colorado], was very generally regarded by miners, hunters, and sportsmen as a kind of halfway house, where belated travelers passing between these two points might, without fear of intrusion, feel assured of receiving a hearty welcome, generous fare, and a comfortable bunk for the night. A peculiarity of the host was that he absolutely refused to receive any remuneration of a monetary nature in return for his hospitality, which went far toward establishing his popularity.

George Mann and Billy Perrins, hunters and pards of Jack, made his ranch their headquarters, and paid for their lodging

[12] Clarence E. Lower, "The Hunting Tale of Truthful George," *The Trail*, Vol. XVI, No. 4 (September, 1923), 19–20.

by seeing to it that Jack's larder was constantly filled with a fresh supply of various wild game.

One morning a couple of English sportsmen, wearing Stanley sashes and helmets, spike shoes and leggings, struck the ranch just as Billy and George were saddling their ponies preparatory to starting out together for a day's trip, and in the course of a conversation which ensued, the Englishmen inquired what the prospect was regarding the amount of game and sport to be found in that neighborhood.

"Oh, pretty fair," answered George, giving his saddle girth an extra hitch. "There's elk, bear, deer or jack rabbits—jest as ye've a mind to look; good fishing, too, in the creek.

"You see the peak yonder?" he went on, straightening up and indicating a spot in the range some miles distant. "Me and my pard Billy, here, were over at the foot of it not a week ago, and come on a band of nine of the finest elk a man wants to see."

"Kill any?" asked the Englishman, growing interested.

"Oh, yes—five; the rest got away through the timber. We let them go, for we'd bagged enough in the five to give us all the meat we and Ostrander would want for some time; so Billy and me set to work skinning the carcasses. By the time we had finished and cut off the choice parts of the meat, it was coming on night. We only had our riding ponies, and the five elk made more meat than we could pack on them, so we hung what we couldn't carry up in the branches of a tree, out of reach of coyotes, and rode in to Ostrander's with the pelts and part of the meat, meaning to return in the morning and cart the rest of it to the ranch in the wagon."

"Well?" queried the Englishman, as George paused.

"Well," repeated George, "when we went back next morning, blessed if we found a scrap of meat left where we'd hung it the night before—every ounce was clean gone."

"Coyotes?" hazarded the Briton.

"No, bears! When we came to examine the matter, we saw any number of bear tracks in the soft ground, an' diskivered that a family of 'em had come around in the night, climbed the tree and made off with the meat. The tracks were plain and fresh, and led away northwest through the timber. We knew they couldn't be a great distance off, so Billy and me started to trail them up, while Jack drove to the ranch with the wagon.

"Shortly after noon we came on a band of seven bears, lying asleep in a little clearing. They looked as though they were gorged, and we concluded it was with our meat, and we'd make them our meat, too.

"So with that we opened fire on them, laying out four. The others roused up at the shooting and lit out in short order through the woods, saving their hides for the present.

"The four bears that were killed were all of a good size, and would furnish us with fully as much meat as the five elk they'd got away with; so Billy and me set to work skinning them.

"By the time we'd finished, night was coming on again—for it's no quick job to skin a bear. We knew it was too late to go back to the ranch and return that evening with the wagon for the meat, so we packed the four pelts and some of the choice meat on our ponies and hung the rest of the meat up in the branches of a tree, out of reach of the coyotes, same as we had before, and rode back to Ostrander's and reported our luck, meaning to return next morning and pack in the meat to the ranch in the wagon."

"Yes?" said the foreigner, as George paused again.

"Well, sir," said George, "You may or may not believe me, but it's a fact, and no man has ever called me a liar more than once; understand? When we went back next morning, durned if we found any more bear meat left in this tree than we had elk in the other the day before—all mysteriously disappeared—gone as clean as a whistle!"

"Oh, come now, that was hard luck, surely, you know!" said the Englishman. "What was the cause of it, pray?"

"Why when we came to look into the matter, we found a great number of hoof marks in the soft ground surrounding the tree in which we'd hung the bear meat; and we diskivered that the four surviving elk of the band from which we'd killed the five, had, in company with some others, trailed up the bears in the night, from the spot where the elk had been killed, to the spot where Billy and I laid out the bears. You see, the elk imagined the bears had killed their comrades, and trailed them up

274

with the purpose of taking revenge. They came to the tree in which Billy and I had hung the bear meat, and scenting the flesh of their comrades amalgamated with the flesh of the bears, which had eaten them, knew they had struck the right spot, and so got square on the bears, by eating the whole concern, after which they went away.

"Billy and I didn't trail up the elk, though we could easily have done it, for the tracks were fresh enough, but we thought if we did, the three bears we let go the day before might return to get revenge on the elk, and we'd have the same thing over again, and our trouble for nothing, barring the pelts. If you think you care for the sport and don't mind the trip, you gents can go over there and try your luck, if you like. It was just the other day it happened, and likely enough you'll find the tracks still fresh. So long, gentlemen!"

And so saying George swung himself into the saddle and spurred rapidly after his comrade, who by this time was well on his way, leaving the Englishman staring doubtfully after him through his monocle.

TREED[13]

Fortunately for Westerners, spruce and good tall pine trees are still plentiful in the bear country.

During my mail-carrying days I had only one startling experience with a wild animal, although the Big Horn Basin was full of them. One night I was camped on Twenty-One Creek in a drizzling rain. The bell mare, Yellow Gal, was hobbled, but I heard the other horses running through the brush as if startled. It was too dark to see anything; however, I started up through the sagebrush after the horses. A low growl stopped me. I struck a match and saw a she-bear sitting on her haunches five yards in front of me.

My gun was in camp. All my past crimes flashed before me, as they say a man's do when he is drowning. Just then two little

[13] From a manuscript in the files of The Western Cattle Range Industry Study. Josh Deane, who tells the story, was the first mail carrier in the Big Horn Basin, 1880–84, and later postmaster at Sunshine, Wyoming.

cubs darted from behind the bear and started to run, and she came down on all fours and started after them. There were a few trees growing along the stream. I made for the nearest one and started to climb it. In the first crotch there was a magpie's nest as large around as a good sized wash basin, filled with roosting birds. I had to pull the nest to pieces to get up, while the magpies flapped and screeched about my head. After reaching a safe height I lit another match, and saw the bear on her hind feet at the foot of the tree, which was too slender for her to climb. I fastened myself to a branch by my suspenders and prepared to spend the night. I finally slept.

When I awoke the sun was shining and I could hear my mare's bell tinkling in the distance. The old bear was about a hundred yards up the gulch with her back to me, so I got down from my perch and reached camp without attracting her notice.

Once near my gun I was safe enough; so I got some breakfast before settling my account with her. After breakfast I started for my horses, six-shooter in hand. My enemy soon spotted me and came loping up to within fifteen feet of where I had crouched down in the brush. Then she stopped and stood up on her hind legs to look us over.

She was a huge cinnamon bear, weighing perhaps 900 pounds. If the trees had been closer I should have been tempted to make another dash for them. As matters stood, however, there was nothing to do but shoot. I fired twice, hitting her in the neck and under the ear. She growled and fell over. I gave her three more shots to be sure, and then went to look at her. The cubs jumped up and tried to fight me; then stood on their hind legs and started boxing with each other. They were harmless; so I left them alone.

SPORT ON TEN MILE[14]

On Western ranges, the lariat was an essential piece of equipment. Sometimes, however, it proved ineffective.

We were all going up the river one morning on a circle for cattle for the roundup. When we went into a big bottom, Ten Mile Creek, we saw three bears. Two went across and one went up the river. We did not see the bear that went up the river. He just disappeared. The river was a little high, but a bear is a good swimmer. We decided to follow the two that had crossed. Our horses were good swimmers and four of us made the trip nicely. When the bears got across, one went up the river and the other went into the hills. Two of us went after the bear in the hills.

I was riding a pinto horse named "Mule Camp," and he was very much afraid of a rope. But the other man was not a very good roper and he told me I would have to rope him, if he was roped. I told him my horse was shy, but I would try. I had run him a short distance when I caught him. My horse was not only afraid of the rope, but also of the bear; so I was in a jack pot. I could hold the bear all right, but the horse was trying to run. I was like the man who roped the big steer and said: "Someone had better come here that knows something." The horse was about to lose his pack and I was about to lose my rope; so I yelled to the other fellow to shoot the bear. He came up and the first shot he made he shot the bear through the foot. I did not have a six-shooter with me, and if I had I would not have had time to shoot; so the only thing I could do was to turn my rope loose, which I did. I then took the other fellow's gun and finally killed the bear and got my rope.

That night when I went to camp and told of my experience, one of the men told me I was taking a big chance; that he roped a bear one day and the bear sat down and pulled him, horse and all, right up to him. I told him I saw that bear the next day, that he still had the rope, that he was walking on his hind legs swinging a big loop and tried to catch me. He never told me any more bear stories, but he did say he didn't think a bear would do that.

[14] "Life Story of 'Kansas' Wickwire," *Basin* (Wyoming) *Republican Rustler*, September 26, 1935, and succeeding issues.

LUM WILLIAMS PLAYS BEAR[15]

"Kansas" Wickwire unrolls another tale of cowpunchers in the bear country.

One time Lum had killed a bear. He skinned the bear, also skinning out the legs. He put the bear hide on, putting his arms in the front legs of the hide and his legs in the hind legs. Then he started off through the snow. A man saw the tracks and thinking he was on the trail of a bear followed and finally caught up with Lum, who was sitting on a corral talking with another man. He told Lum he had tracked him a long way, thinking he was a bear, and he had a notion to kill him anyway.

LONESOME FROGS[16]

Besides snakes, bears, and gold-bearing trout, myriad other creatures—mythical or actual—inhabit the American West. On occasion even toothaches, as experienced by old-timers, have failed to stifle stories about them.

Andy Garretson of Silverton, Colorado, paid Durango a visit this week on the painful errand of seeing a dentist. In dwelling upon other painful incidents of his long career, he recalled his frog farm venture of the days when San Juan miners were capricious and demanded frog legs and champagne every night for dinner. Andy explained that to gratify this whim he imported a carload of frogs from Arkansas, located them in a marsh just out of town, and was in a fair way to become wealthy beyond the dreams of avarice, when one night a traveler stopped at his cabin and requested shelter for the night. After supper the traveler produced a fiddle and launched into "The Arkansas Traveler." The tune struck Andy's fancy, and was repeated with variations until a late hour. Next morning the traveler departed, and Andy visited his frog ranch, when lo and behold, not a frog was left! The frogs, it seems, had become homesick during the recital of the previous evening, and the last one had departed overland for Arkansas.

---

[15] *Ibid.*
[16] "Oddities," *Dawson Scrapbooks*," Vol. II, 43.

Unnatural Natural History

JACK RABBITS [17]

Conspicuous in the West is the long-eared rabbit, sometimes called the Oregon mule. As one of God's adaptable creatures, the jack rabbit is a match even for auriferous trout.

The tale of the fur-bearing trout at Salida, Colorado, prompted A. S. McIntyre, Walsenburg prospector, to come forward Saturday with a Bunyanesque yarn about the feathered jack rabbits thriving in Huerfano County. "If those boys at Salida think a trout that grows fur to keep warm in winter is something to brag about, let 'em listen to this," McIntyre challenged.

"It all happened about ten years ago when a farmer on the Huerfano River was doing some early spring planting and happened to dig up a nest of little jack rabbits," the prospector recounted.

"Well, sir, he was a kind old fellow and didn't want to see those little jack rabbits die right there; so he put them in his chicken coop.

"When dry summer weather rolled around and feed got kinda scarce, the chickens ate all the fur off those rabbits, yes, sir!

"But even then the bunnies and the hens were real chummy and it wasn't anything to see those naked rabbits sleeping peacefully in a hen's nest," McIntyre spieled on.

"The big surprise came when winter started coming on.

"Those rabbits began to sprout feathers. Yes, sir!

"Now that bunch of rabbits has increased many times and all the offspring are feather-bearing.

"Why," expounded McIntyre, waggling a finger, "I've seen a rabbit perched out on the woodpile flapping his ears and trying to squeeze out a cackle, yes, sir!"

MOSQUITOES[18]

At one time, Coloradans claimed for their state complete freedom from mosquitoes. Eugene Field, famed poet, and others quickly made answer.

[17] *The Denver Post*, February 19, 1939.
[18] Eugene Field, *The Denver Tribune*, August 30, 1881.

279

No, there are no mosquitoes in Colorado. The birds that make their appearance in this locality this time of year are not mosquitoes, but a species of vampire. They build their nest in the lofty pines on the mountain heights and hatch out from ten thousand to twenty thousand little birds apiece. Then they come down to Denver with their families for a protracted holiday. When they strike a man for a meal, they bore a hole in him like an artesian well and pump the gore out of every recess of his body. They can be successfully hunted with shotguns. Their pelts make splendid sole leather, and their beaks can be utilized as pegging awls.—FIELD.

A few years ago some implement men took a large galvanized tank for watering stock to a ranch some distance east of Denver. Since it was too late to make the return trip after they had delivered the tank, they decided to spend the night. The rancher gave them a couple of bedrolls and they pulled the tank upside down over themselves for a roof. During the night they heard a drilling on the iron tank and, from the buzzing also, concluded that a swarm of mosquitoes was after them. When the bills of the giant insects penetrated the metal, the mechanics just bent them over, thus making the attackers prisoners. Secure once more, the men went to sleep. Imagine their surprise, though, when the morning sun awoke them and they realized that sometime during the night the mosquitoes had flown off with the tank.
—UNIDENTIFIED SOURCE.

SHEEP AND GOATS

This tale, too, comes from an unidentified but presumably reliable source.

Snakes and fish are lied about, more or less artistically, everywhere; but even sheep perform wonders in the Rocky Mountain West. It has been reported that the mountain sheep wear their teeth out rapidly due to their habit of close browsing on the rocky slopes. The wisest of them, however, descend to the rich gulches below and there, while grazing, fill their own teeth with gold. These sheep often make long jumps from rock to rock, although not as remarkable, perhaps, as the performance of an Idaho goat reported by an old-timer. According to the story he saw a fine specimen jump from a pinnacle some three hundred feet, then, not finding the place on the opposite side of the crevice suitable for landing, reversed himself and jumped back to safety. Of course, domestic sheep, occasionally called "hoofed locusts," have accomplished no such feats.

HORACE GREELEY AND THE BEDBUG

Again, the original narrator prefers the security of anonymity.

It was in an early-day mining camp in Colorado that Horace Greeley, famed throughout the nation as a writer and traveler, had his experience with the bedbug. While securing a room in the only hotel in town, Greeley saw a bedbug crawl across the ceiling and drop down upon the register before him. Horace remarked: "I have known many types of bedbugs in many different climes, but this is the first time I ever saw one that read the register in order to learn to which room a guest had been assigned."

WILD ANIMALS OF MIDDLE PARK[19]

Ronald L. Ives, it may be readily seen, is well acquainted with certain of the more obscure aspects of Rocky Mountain natural history.

The extensive apocryphal zoology of the [Rocky Mountain] region, containing lengthy and detailed descriptions of several score imaginary and impossible animals, seems to have originated, in large part, with the French fur trappers, many of whom, in the period from about 1790 to about 1830, wintered in Brown's Hole, on the Green River, in extreme northwestern Colorado. During the last two decades, with the coming of college-educated guides and ranger naturalists, many of these fictional creatures, such as the Rockabore, have acquired Mendelian traits.

A few of these creatures are relatively modern inventions, for their structure is similar to that of mechanical devices unknown prior to the first third of the past century. Typical of these is the "Tripodero," imaginary inhabitant of sage flats and chapar-

[19] Ives, "Folklore of Middle Park, Colorado," 27–31.

Horace Greeley and the Enterprising Bedbug

ral thickets. In such an environment, an animal can move with greatest facility when its stature is slight, permitting it to run under the branches, but its chances for survival are greatest if it is tall, and able to see over the brush. By developing legs which telescope like those of a photographer's tripod, the "Tripodero" has increased its chances for survival without sacrificing mobility. Rather obviously, the invention of this creature does not antedate the development of the relatively modern telescoping tripod.

Quite common are descriptions of the "Sand Hill Perch," reputed to inhabit the "Dust Bowl" and other waterless areas. This piscatorial anomaly not only lives without water, but swims backwards through the air to keep dust out of its eyes! This tale was originally thought to have been an importation from Missouri, where, in some areas far from the surface streams, fish may be caught in water wells. Rather recently, however, another possible source has been found. On a painted grave bowl, approximately one thousand years old, from the Mimbres Valley of New Mexico, there is a very clear depiction of the capture of a giant legged fish by a man and a boy. This at least suggests that a tale concerning a fish able to navigate on land was known to some of the pre-Columbia inhabitants of the Southwest.

Where irrigation is practiced, ranchers are humorously angry about the activities of the "Augerino," a malevolent subterranean creature whose sole activity in life is to let the water out of irrigation ditches. This imaginary animal is described as an enormous corkscrew-shaped worm, which drills a helical burrow a few feet under the surface, and lines its hole with silica to prevent cave-ins. According to reports the "Augerino" moves very slowly, is immune to all poisons and weapons, and cannot change its course. No person now living in Middle Park will admit having seen an "Augerino," but the creatures are still supposed to be living, for, "Hell, the ditches still leak, don't they?"

Local "authorities" credit the conception of these creatures to the effects of alcoholic overindulgence, and are prone to cite personal experiences in confirmation. To a limited extent, this may be true, for the hallucinations reported to accompany delirium tremens might lead to the creation of such chimerical fauna, and it is well known in the eastern United States that the frequency of reported encounters with "the Jersey Devil" varies in direct proportion to the amount of applejack locally available.

At least some of the older tales, however, seem to owe their origins to the mental disturbances accompanying long-continued isolation, inadequate diet, vitamin deficiency, anoxaemia, exhaustion or exposure. . . .

In recent years, the apocryphal zoology of the mountain region has undergone numerous extensions and improvements, as the various accounts have been told and retold, with alterations to suit the imagination of the teller. At least a few of the nonexistent animals of this region were deliberately invented for the edification of "flatlanders," whose credulity, at times, appears limitless. Typical of these recent inventions is the "Rachet Owl," a photophobic creature that always faces west, but as the sun follows its daily course, the bird must turn its head, and at sunset it faces due east. To prevent undue strain on its neck muscles, this owl is equipped with a ratchet, which permits easy clockwise rotation of its head, but inhibits counter-clockwise motion. At some time during the night, the owl, in preparation for the coming day, releases the ratchet, making a fearful noise, and allows its head to return to a west-facing position. Actually, the sound of a "ratchet owl" letting loose, is caused by tree limbs rubbing together.

ADDITIONAL WONDERS

Researches into Rocky Mountain apocryphal zoology and allied subjects being never ending, other data have appeared from time to time. Once more in this case, the source—though unquestionably unimpeachable—prefers the shades of anonymity.

As has been remarked, the physical features of the Rocky Mountain West are such that one need not draw upon his imagination for stories of natural wonders. A few years ago a newspaper reporter described Suicide Gulch, southwest of Pueblo [Colorado], which sheepherders carefully avoid, for animals bedded down there had been known to die in great numbers before morning. It was explained that all the plants in that locality absorb selenium, a deadly poison, from the soil, part of which came from a now-extinct volcano.

Miners on the American Eagle property, in Cripple Creek, reported, in 1904, that they found a tree eleven hundred feet underground, in good state of preservation, except as to leaves, and apparently growing, with sap under the bark. In the adjoining property, the Logan, there is a draft which the miners call "the devil's breath." It is a strong current of air which seems to come from the solid rock and extinguishes lighted candles.

Many are the stories of dry creeks, "rising nowhere, running nowhere, and carrying their beds on their back," for in dry weather they often sink into the sands of one place and come to the surface unexpectedly somewhere much further along. Railroaders, also, tell yarns of engines having bridges go out from under them while crossing what had been a few hours before a dry creek bed, but what had suddenly become a foaming torrent that sucked the engine out of sight with no more than a perfunctory warning to the train crew.

TREACHEROUS DUNES[20]

Sand dunes, forever shifting, are dangerous at all times. Especially is this true of the mysterious San Luis formations, in southern Colorado.

One of the strangest legends about the dunes is that of the web-footed horses. On bright moonlight nights, or just before sunrise, so it is said, large horses can be seen against the horizon, manes blowing in the wind, heads uplifted in challenge. In place of hoofs, they have great webbed feet that enable them to race over the sands with ease. There is some truth in this, for bands of wild horses do roam the edges of the dunes. They have developed broad hoofs and usually are able to outdistance ordinary steeds in racing across the sands. The only other animals that frequent the dunes are coyotes, foxes, and an occasional skunk.

Other stories concern the mysterious disappearance of sheepherders and their flocks, presumably in the trackless wastes of the ever-shifting hills. Many of these disappearances can be explained by the fact that sheepherders formerly used Mosca Pass,

[20] *Colorado Guide*, 357–58.

which crossed the high Sangre de Cristos above the dunes, in taking their flocks to summer pasture. No doubt many flocks were sold or kept permanently on the other side of the mountains, and thus "were never seen again." One spring, Peter Hansen, an early rancher in the San Luis Valley, ordered his herders to different parts of the range. The most difficult assignment, that of moving sheep past the dunes, was given to an old Mexican herder who set out with 1,000 sheep and a pack train. Two men accompanied him to the foot of Mosca Pass, from which point he went alone. When weeks had passed with no word of him, Hansen instituted a search. As far as could be determined, the Mexican never reached the other side of the pass, and nothing was ever heard of him.

At the time the San Luis Valley was being settled, rough and dangerous Mosca Pass was much used as a freight route. A long wagon train reached the bottom of the pass one night and halted at the edge of the dunes. The River of the Dunes, apparently shallow, was smoothly flowing across the waste, and the wagons were drawn up together beside it, the mules hobbled and turned out to graze, and the teamsters rolled up in their blankets a short distance away. Next morning both mules and wagons had vanished, and were never found. It is probable that the train dropped into quicksands that occasionally form here, but many persons still credit the disappearance to the supernatural.

Told and retold around campfires is the story of the Mystery Family of the Dunes. Years ago the Martinez family—father, mother, and a small son—lived on a homestead near the sands. They were not friendly with their neighbors, and little was known of them until one day the boy, dazed and unable to speak, stumbled into a ranch house some miles from his home. Neighbors found the mother and father dead in their cabin, but the cause of their death could not be ascertained. The boy refused to say a word about the tragedy. A farmer provided a home for the lad, who took a hand tending sheep. When he was out one day, a dust storm arose. When he did not return, the farmer and his men went in search of him. They tracked the boy and his flock to the edge of the dunes, where the trail was lost. The last member of the Mystery Family had vanished.

286

THE GREAT SALT LAKE PHENOMENON[21]

Lakes without outlets are always of intense interest to the curious.

As is generally known, the Great Salt Lake, though fed by the Bear, Jordan, and possibly other rivers, has no outlet, and it was a common belief that the great lake had a subterranean outlet, otherwise the vast quantity of water poured into it by the two considerable rivers would cause it to overflow its banks. Down in southern Colorado there was, at the time I am writing of, and it may yet be there, a good sized lake that had neither inlet nor outlet, so far as surface indications showed, and it was the general belief that the lake was kept supplied by a subterranean inlet.

According to one, a certain man ventured out on the Utah lake in a small boat. The boat was caught in a whirlpool and, when some distance from the shore, sucked beneath the surface. Clinging to the sides of the boat, with desperation born of despair, the man found himself plunging almost straight downward, with water roaring over and all around him. Suddenly the boat, riding on an even keel, shot forward through a wonderful tunnel-like cavern, the roof and walls covered with varicolored stalactites, presenting a scene surpassing description. Just how long he floated in the underground channel the man could not tell, but an end came to his trip eventually when he found his boat shooting upward, with its occupant holding on for dear life. As perhaps the reader has guessed, the boat and its owner reached the surface of the Colorado lake, but little the worse for the underground voyage, and the great mystery of the outlet and inlet of the two lakes had been solved.

CLIMATE[22]

No account of Western conditions would be complete, of course, without reference to the wonderful weather.

[21] S. T. Sopris, "Early Day Reminiscences," 18–19.

[22] Edgar McMechen, a member of the staff of the State Historical Society of Colorado, vouches for this story.

An ingenious hunter, caught out on the Plains in a blizzard, was glad to find one old stray buffalo bull, for it saved his life. At dusk, with the storm raging so fiercely that it threatened to freeze him to death before morning, he managed to kill the lone buffalo, cut it open and, after disemboweling it, to crawl inside. He pulled the parts together and spent a fairly comfortable night, only to discover at dawn that the opening had frozen and that he himself was now a prisoner threatened with starvation. Fortunately, he was able to solve all of his troubles at one and the same time—he "et his way out."

HOTTER TIMES IN THE FAR WEST[23]

The account of Western weather conditions, continued.

The campfire burned briskly and brightly. We sat around it after supper smoking and talking. . . . Someone had remarked casually that it had been a very hot [Colorado] day and we had all granted our acquiescence.

"Hot! Hot? Did any one say hot?" commanded the colonel in a contradictory sort of way. "Well, if you fellows call today hot, you would die in some places I have been. Why, I remember once being in Death Valley and it was 130 degrees in the shade, or would have been only there was no shade, so I suppose it must have been 150 degrees in the sun. In some places the rocks were cracking with the heat. That is a fact. There was a gentle breeze from the south. It just came along easily, and as we were traveling west, it touched us on our left sides. I have been touched several times, but never as peculiarly as that. Why, do you know each one of us who had whiskers or a beard had the hair singed off on the left side. We did not dare to stop or turn from fear it would do the same on the right side. That was the hottest time I ever had. We had a dog with us, a fine nervy Scotch terrier, when we entered the Valley, and when we came out he was a Mexican hairless dog."

[23] H. B. Stephens, "Around the Camp Fire," *The Great Divide*, Vol. IX, No. 2 (July, 1893), 95.

CANON CITY'S BIG BREEZE[24]

*In any treatise setting forth the results of scientific research,
it is well, experts say, to lighten the heaviest tones with occasional reference to some recognizably human character or incident.
Thus the present volume, in rounding to its close, ends upon a
windy but somehow quite natural note.*

From all outward appearances he was unmistakably a tenderfoot of the first water. He had held down one of the chairs in
front of the Victoria, and displayed his clocked socks to the ad-
miring gaze of the [Canon City] public every evening for a
whole week without getting acquainted with anybody but
"Rinklet Jack," the Adonis of the hardwood arena, but his
dream of fancied security was doomed to be rudely broken in a
manner little expected.

It was Saturday evening when one of the "mossbacks" named
Briggs, more familiarly known as "Old Brig" came ambling
down the street with the easy, yet-get-there grace of a two-
humped camel.

As soon as the boys caught the direction of the old man's
gaze they knew there was some monkey business ahead, so each
and every one of the gang settled himself down in as easy a
position as possible to await for the show to open.

The old man steadily approached without taking his eye off
the victim, and when he reached the near contiguous vicinity
of the young man, he stopped and appeared to be sizing him up
in his own mind. After having apparently satisfied himself of
the gillie's calibre, he sat down with the remark:

"Great Pueblo rolling mills, ain't this hot weather, stranger."

The stranger being positive of the fact that it was rather
warm, merely squirmed in his chair without vouchsafing any
answer.

But Brig, not to be bluffed on a lone hand, continued: "Yes,
stranger, it's hot, but this is nothing to what it was here in June,
1860, when the water in the Grand Canyon [of the Arkansas]
was so much cooler than the atmosphere that it froze over solid,

---

[24] "Oddities," *Dawson Scrapbooks,* Vol. II, 71.

and we had to blast out a tunnel under the ice to let the surplus water through to keep the river from changing its course around by way of Colorado Springs; and Rube Frazier, who had a herd of cattle in Eight Mile Park that summer, made a fortune manufacturing ice cream up there and floating it down the river on rafts, supplying all the towns on the route, and trading what he had left over to a band of Arapahoe Indians, who were camped at Rocky Ford, for buckskins."

The tenderfoot said nothing. . . . But the old man apparently not noticing the silence, continued, after taking a chew of plug tobacco as large as a South Canon brick: "Yes, I struck this state in '58. I've heard the Injuns yell, the bars roar, and the grasshoppers chirp."

The young man now seemed to wake out of his seeming lethargic state, and said: "You don't say so."

"That's what I said, young feller, and you can gamble on its being the straight tip and good goods. Yes, sir, we lived all winter on prickly pears and fresh air; slept in a tree and drank soda water in the summer, and walked over to Denver many a time to buck a dozen grubby coyote pelts against a brace game of rondo and culo."

"You must be proficient in the art of gambling by this time," remarked the tenderfoot.

"Gamble! By the great Manitou of El Paso County, you're right there, stranger, and I should stack up to lose if I wasn't. Why, how in Hel-m's garden and the two tailed comet could I have kept up if I hadn't had a little sport once in awhile? Say, did you ever live on a ranch one hundred and sixty miles from nowhere, with an Injun camping behind every bunch of sagebrush all 'round you?"

"Never."

"Ever track a deer for thirty miles, and when you got in shooting distance take the buck ager; shake yourself down onto a healthy cactus and get up feeling like a cross-eyed squaw's pincushion with the pins stuck in every way but straight, and your pants riveted to the end of your system, like the outside coat of a forty-horse boiler?"

"No sir."

"Darn your salmon colored phiz; of course you never did. What did you ever do for your country or yourself, anyway?"

"I've played an organ in church, and sang in the choir at home."

"Played h——l and shot your mouth off. How many bars do you spose I've killed?"

"Two or three."

"Two or three! Why, you ornery one-lunged graveyard defaulter, my old pard has killed at least seventy-five, and he has only one eye at that, and it's got a catamount in it as thick as a boardinghouse beefsteak. I'll gamble a soprano voiced burro against the bones of your mother-in-law, that I've slaughtered and put the mortal cinch on more'n two hundred of the worst old man-eating, pigeon-toed grizzlies that ever left a grape seed to track 'em by. Why, you white-livered spawn of a pond lily, you never dreamt of what us old-timers had to endure, and wiggle through, and still keep on grindin'. How much flour do you spose we had on hand when we struck camp up there near the Soda Spring in '58?"

"Ten sacks."

"Ten hurrahs!" shouted Old Brig, as he gazed on his unconscious victim with wide-open eyes. "We had just twenty-five pounds and no more, understand?"

"Couldn't you come down town and get some more?"

"Come down town! Why, you fever and ague stricken seidlitz powder, wasn't we a hundred and sixty good big miles from the nearest town? That's what I told you before. How much do you spose our layout cost us?"

"Perhaps a thousand dollars; but of course that depends upon whether or not your wagon, horses, harness, and breech-loading guns were of the best quality."

This seemed to paralyze the old man, for he fell back in his chair and his left leg stuck straight out into the twilight like a large nose on a small man's face, and for about a minute the boys thought he was a goner, but he came to presently and fairly yelled:

"You taffy sucking, cigarette smoking, liver padded, clothes prop, do you spose we come to this country with Maud S.

dressed in silver plated harness, riding in a gold-bespattered chariot drawn by two 60-pound burros, that couldn't travel faster than a foundered army worm and carrying centre-fire, shell-extracting, breech-loading rifles? Why, if we'd had an extra tin plate and enough old cotton to wad our Springfield muskets with, instead of havin' to use leaves and grass, we'd bin way up in the picters and gloriously happy. None of you bottle-raised tenderfeet know what the old-timers that blazed the trail across the howling wilderness had to start life with."

"I should imagine not."

The old man's eyes stuck out like errors in a shorthand reporter's copy. He expectorated about a pint of unadulterated nicotine out into the middle of the street with a sound like a ripe tomato striking a board fence, jammed his hat down tight on his head, and walked off muttering, "Them clammed pampered scums of luxury don't know anything anyway."

We gathered ourself directly after the old man left, and sauntered off up the street looking for Rinklet Jack to inquire into the tenderfoot's pedigree. After a search of about three hours we met him coming from the northwest corner of the city. We asked him for more light, and he said:

"Why, don't you know that rooster? That is Touch-Me-Light-Tom, one of the best free-for-all fakirs in the United States and part of Salt Lake, and was one of the first white men to cross the Great American Desert."

That settled it, and although it was only the shank of the evening, we went right home and retired in a secluded alcove for the night.

Index

Index

Index

Crows, death of Jim Beckwourth, 82–84; Little-Gun and Jim Bridger, 26; medicine man's curse, 11; Chief Bold's band, capture of Joe Meek, 24–26

Plains tribes, attack on supply train, 95–98; habits of greeting, 94–95; prairie massacre, 204–207

Pun-nak tribe, pony raid, 29–30

Sioux, Walking Bull, capture of Jim Bridger, 20–23; encounter with Kit Carson, 80–81; Indian-white council, 26–29; Jim Bridger escapade, 17–23; Jim Bridger exploit, 30–31

Snake tribe, Bald Eagle's band, 16–17; Indian-white council, 26–29; Walkee, friend of Jim Bridger, 17–23

Utes, Mount Shavano legend, 58; raid on Mexicans, 50–53

White (Munchies), legend of, 87–89

"Indians Intercept a Supply Train": 95–98

Inman, Henry, *The Great Salt Lake Trail*: 140–44

"Intriguing Claim Contests": 149–52

"Iron Pins and a Silver Spike": 117–18

Ives, Roland L., "Folklore of Middle Park, Colorado": 116–17, 281–84

"Jack Rabbits": 279

"Jiggers, The": 221–22

"Jim Baker Tames a Drunkard": 74–76

"Jim Bridger and Gold": 36–38

"Jim Bridger's Eyesight": 34–35

"John Morrissey's Wonderful Watch": 165–67

Julesburg, Old: Alfred Slade's revenge, 112–13

Kanakache, Chief: Ute-white battle, 49–50

Kellogg, Daniel, "Across the Plains in '58": 93–95

"Kit Carson Fofarraw": 80–82

Langford, Nathaniel Pitt, *Diary of the Washburn Expedition to the Yellowstone and Firehole Rivers in the Year 1870*: 8, 10

Leadville, Colorado: fishing yarn, 258–59; Tom Walsh, prospector, 128–29

Legends: burro markings, 57–58

"Legend of the Lost Train": 116–17

"Legends of the Purgatoire": 61–62

"Legends of the White Indians": 87–89

Legends, Place: Lost Cabin lode, Wyoming, 138–40; lost mine, Cache la Poudre, 152–53; lost train of Middle Park, 116–17; Mountain of the Holy Cross, 58; "Phantom Wrecker" (Colorado Front Range), 117; pony express (Wyoming), phantom rider, 101–103; Purgatoire River, 61–62; San Luis Valley, Mosca Pass tragedy, 53–56, Saquache Lake tragedy, 50–53; Mount Shavano, 58; Spanish Peaks, old mines, 64–67; white Indians (Munchies), Sonora Province, Mexico, 87–89

"Life and Death of Jim Beckwourth, The": 82–84

Little-Gun: Crow chief, scene with Jim Bridger, 26

"Lonesome Frogs": 278

"Lost Cabin Lode, The": 138–40

"Lost Fortune in Molasses, The": 160–61

"Lost Mine of the Cache la Poudre, The": 152–53

"Lost Steer, The": 212–13

Lowe Corporal: Indian-white council, 26–29

Lowe, Percival, *Five Years a Dragoon*: 26–29

Lower, Clarence E., "The Hunting Tale of Truthful George": 272–75

"Lucky Strike in Montana": 144–46

"Lum Williams Plays Bear": 278

Lyle, Eugene P., Jr., "The Lure of Gold": 128–29, 129–33

Index

Rocky Mountain Tales

HAS BEEN SET IN

TEN POINT LINOTYPE JANSON

AND PRINTED

ON WOVE ANTIQUE PAPER

BY THE

UNIVERSITY OF OKLAHOMA PRESS

2989